AFRICAN NIGHTS

AFRICAN NIGHTS

Black Erotic Folk Tales

EDITED BY LEO FROBENIUS

HERDER AND HERDER

1971
HERDER AND HERDER NEW YORK
232 Madison Avenue, New York 10016

This translation was made by Peter Ross

CONTENTS

GLOSSARY

AGELLID   Aristocratic caste of landowners (Kabyle).

AHUN   A clever tortoise in African fable.

ANGAREB   Couch (Arabic).

BAUDI   The Fulbe saga. One of the greatest bardic epics of Sahel. It is sung by the Mabo.

DIALLI   Caste of singers and story-tellers in the Sahel country.

DIMADIO   Caste of serfs (among the Fulbe).

DUGUTIGI   Village headman (among the Mande).

FULBE   An old pastoral people famous for their aristocratic build and for their intelligence. Migrated very early from Senegal across West Africa to Lake Chad.

KABYLE   Light-skinned Berbers (Morocco).

KORDOFAN   Mohammedan kingdom lying between Khartoum, Darfur and the White Nile.

MABO   Caste of singers and weavers (among the Fulbe), responsible for preserving the oral tradition.

MANDE   Tribe living on the northern slopes of the Futa Jallon mountains, formerly part of the kingdom of Mali.

MARABOUT   A dervish in North Africa; an itinerant preacher.

MUEZZIN   A Muslim cryer who calls the hour of daily prayers.

MUNSHI   Jungle dwellers living beside the Benue River (Cameroons) and regarded by their Sudanese neighbours as thieves and barbarians.

7

NOUMU	Caste of blacksmiths (among the Mande).
NUPE	A highly developed people of Central Sudan, who resisted the cultural onslaught of Islam. This people lives on the left bank of the Niger between the Yoruba in the West and the Hausa in the North.
PUI	The Soninké saga recalling the heroic deeds of the men of Kalla—the most famous and popular work in the whole of Senegambia.
SAHEL	A grass plain between the Sahara and the Sudan, once the Kingdom of Ghana. The heroic deeds of this area are recorded in the epics known as the Baudi, the Pui, and the Dausi.
SERIBA	Settlement, compound, encampments (Arabic).
SUFA	Servant(of the house=su); retainer (among the Fulbe).
YORUBA	An ancient urban people, living on the right bank of the Lower Niger. Ibadan was the first major indigenous city in the continent. Here we may find Frobenius's "Atlantis".

INTRODUCTION *Charles H. Nichols*

Now that recent scholars have increased our knowledge of African history and culture, the modern reader is better prepared for the pleasures to be found in reading these folk tales. The stories collected in this volume reveal the humor, wit, cruelty, anguish, and fascination which fill our most private and passionate emotions: those involving sex. The African author unmasks the familiar and time-worn wars between the sexes with a naturalness, a freshness, an immediacy, and a subtle range of emotion which capture and hold a reader. No nymphomaniac was ever more effectively cured than the wife of Kordofan; no cuckold more resourceful than he who pretended to be blind. All the women know how to employ the lovedealer. But the uninhibited and delightful treatment of sex is but one aspect of the treasures to be found in this collection. Here is humor based on clever turns of phrase, on incongruous and ironic situations, on trickery and absurdity. The knaves and the fools compete for the center of the stage. Fables, heroic sagas, and fanciful tales appear, but most of these stories reflect the realities of the daily lives of vital and resourceful people. We get insights into the African personality, into diverse communities, and a revelation of the African's outlook and attitude towards the baffling, larger meaning of life. Here is the human comedy played out against the African background. Here is the African in his essential being.

African Nights includes a small part of a large collection of African tales assembled by the German ethnologist, Leo Frobenius (1873–1938), entitled *Das Schwarze Dekameron: Belege und Aktenstücke Uber Liebe, Witz und Heldentum in Innerafrika* and published in Berlin in 1910. Between 1921 and 1928 Frobenius brought out twelve volumes of such African writings in Munich (*Atlantis, Folk Tales and Folk Poetry of Africa*), translated from the original languages into German. A creative thinker and a dedicated scholar, Frobenius made twelve

9

expeditions to several parts of Africa between 1904 and 1935 and returned with artifacts, utensils, weapons, pictures, art objects, and other materials, most of which are deposited in the Municipal Museum of Ethnology in Frankfurt am Main. His various trips took him to West Africa, East Africa, North Africa, as well as Central and South Africa. These tales in *African Nights* have reached us from widely separated peoples from Arabs and Berbers, from the Sudanese, from Hausas, from the Sahel and the Kassai. His painstaking and wide-ranging observations have appeared in several books. In 1894 he published a detailed account of African secret societies. Later he was intrigued by the fact that some of the cave drawing in southern France and Spain are identical to those found in Africa. Most of the pictures represent animals, and one motif recurs again and again among the Arabs and Berbers, that representing a man standing with upraised hands before a buffalo or a ram. Kabyl folklore often deals with the buffalo and the ram, for the buffalo was regarded as the king of all game animals and the ram as the god of agriculture and guide for the calendar year. In attempting to explain similar forms of culture and art in widely separated parts of the world, ethnologists have assumed that (1) either all cultures go through certain similar stages or (2) that some contact between the cultures has taken place, that is, that individuals or groups have migrated. Frobenius insisted that environment explained the various manifestations of culture, and he attributed the fact of identical elements in distant regions to direct culture contact. But he was not satisfied merely to assemble data. He sought to understand the essential nature of culture and the relation of disparate elements within a culture to each other. He worked out methods of organizing data in space and time with his conception of the *Kulturkreis* (cultural circle). This led him to formulate a theory of the structure and development of human groups, a morphology of culture. In such works as *Der Westafrikanische Kulturkreis* (1897), *The Origin of African Civilizations* (1898), and *Probleme der Kultur* (4 volumes, 1899–1901) he formulated his theory of the nature and development of cultures.

For Frobenius a culture is a living organism which, like man himself, passes through the stages of youth, maturity, and old age. In the early stage in the formation of a culture, man, responsive to the phenomena in his environment, is emotionally and creatively involved in fashioning the emerging society, its forms and mores. This stage Frobenius called *Ergriffenheit* or emotional involvement. In the second stage, marked by maturity and stability, man has mastered his environment. He expresses this in religious ritual, social order, art, and economy. This stage Frobenius called *Ausdruck* (expression). In the final stage of a culture there is greater concern with usefulness, with technique. The meaningful substance of religion, literature, and art fades. Ritual and expression become routine. This phase Frobenius referred to as *Anwendung* or application. Although for him cultures experience an organic development which proceeds inexorably and cannot be stopped, each culture has "a soul of its own." Frobenius tried to get to the spiritual center of the cultures he studied.

Hence the German ethnologist sought to understand the diverse elements in African cultures. He was indefatigable in gathering data and sympathetc in observing patiently customs foreign to his own. In comparison to the thinkers and ethnologists of his time, he was surprisingly open-minded and brought considerable scientific objectivity to his task. While the modern reader will find him, at times, patronizing and occasionally given to questionable conclusions, (as in *The Childhood of Man*), his work is still considered essentially sound by modern authorities. Frobenius insisted, for example, in *Der Ursprung der Afrikanischen Kulturen* that at the turn of the century one could no longer speak of "primitive" peoples since all known groups had man-made shelter, weapons, and fire. He clearly saw the richness and vitality of the normal differences between groups. Ultimately he tried to understand man through his culture. These attitudes are the more remarkable in view of the ideas of racial superiority that flourished then among Europeans who at the end of the nineteenth century were scrambling for dominance, resources, and markets in Africa.

Indeed, Frobenius' perception of the relationship ot African art and literature to their religion, life-style, and philosophy is remarkable evidence of his respect for the cultures he investigated. Even so short a collection of

African writings as we present here is a valuable introduction to civilizations which have been too long ignored. Europeans and Americans have regarded Africans as "primitive", "childlike", and "uncivilized", not only because they wished to rationalize their shocking inhumanity in enslaving and exploiting the Africans, but because they knew and still know so little of the African past. Until the discoveries of modern archeologists and the studies of anthropologists, it was assumed that Africans never had developed an architecture, a written language, or a literature. Even today many otherwise informed people think Africa's development stopped in the Iron Age. Recent scholars like Basil Davidson in such works as *The Lost Cities of Africa* and *The African Past* and J. D. Fage in *A History of West Africa* have presented proof of the great cities, the architecture and empires of sub-Saharan Africa. The great period of American history reaches from about 600 A.D. to 1600 A.D., when the empires of Ghana, Mali, Songhay, the Hausa States, Benin, and others flourished. Arabic, Chinese, and African records have established the early existence of highly developed civilizations in Africa. West Sudanese writing goes back at least 850 years. Indeed, Egypt was one of the first nations to invent a script. Nubia and Ethiopia used script before the tenth century and in the thirteenth century Ethiopia boasted a literary rennaissance. There are now at least 41 written African languages. Yet long before this written literature Africa had had an extraordinary oral tradition of folk tales, sagas, fables, as well as heroic and domestic stories. One West African king had a living library of storytellers and historians whose memories kept the past alive (see P. Bohannon *Africa and the Africans*). The stories here collected were told and dramatized by word of mouth. It is very likely that they were transmitted from generation to generation over a long period of time. Many give evidence that they ante-date the coming of Europeans to Africa, though some show the influence of Islam. Now that we in the West have, at last, opened a dialogue with Africa, a continent resurgent, articulate, and growing in world influence, this book is especially welcome and timely.

Essentially *African Nights* contains four kinds of stories: heroic tales or sagas, fables or fairy tales, erotic stories and domestic, realistic narratives. They are in the oral tradition conversational, spontaneous, alive. They are told unhurriedly, with relish, often suspenseful, stark or humorous, employing a wide range of literary devices. Heroic tales like "The Hero Gossi" or "Surro Sanke" are stories of love and honor in which the hero tests his manhood, where bold men acting on a simplistic moral code seem to enhance a feudal, hierarchical society. Sometimes such tales have a dream quality—a kind of wish fulfillment—the bold, the clever, or the despised hero sleeps with a beautiful princess, acquires gold and herds of cattle, and destroys the enemies of his people. The "Amazon Legends" in which the sexes discover each other and the delights of love are like ancient myths. But most of these tales are erotic ones giving us fascinating glimpses of bizarre customs and an inside view of domestic life.

In spite of the fact that this literature comes to us in translation and grows out of cultures which we have only begun to investigate, it is a literature with a highly developed sense of style, exploring the possibilities of figurative language, irony, suspense, and humor. The African capacity for subtleties of form is obvious in African sculpture which so powerfully influenced such European artists as Picasso, Matisse, and Bracque. Here the authors communicate in an even wider range of feelings, moods, and ideas. Frobenius's versions were in German, and he depended upon translators, yet it is clear that he attempted faithfully to reproduce the quality of the originals. He never injects interpretations of his own and each tale is a self-contained entity-unified, dramatic, unique. Such stories as "The Love Dealer" or "The Agellid's Daughters" or "Ainichthem" present protagonists who in their cleverness and understanding of human nature achieve unexpected success—not in love but in worldly goods. Like Bocaccio's tales in *The Decameron* or *Arabian Nights* their appeal is in their human interest: the marriage of the believable and the unexpected in a style marked by wit, economy, and the structural use of detail. Yet unlike such familiar tales in *Arabian Nights* as "Aladdin and the Wonderful Lamp" or "The Magic Carpet", the African tales here rarely introduce "magic" or elements inconsistent with our everyday human experience. None of them is sentimental. The amazing deeds of some of the heroes have a logical explanation. Thus Surro

13

Sanke drives off 97 men with bow and arrow by using cunning and surprise attack, and we quickly recognize how cowardly and craven they are. This and other such stories as "Mussa's Gratitude," though full of gory details, are tests of manhood involving not only the virtues of physical courage but also honesty, intelligence, and a sense of justice.

It is clear that this literature grows out of complex civilizations, for the technique of the tales is sophisticated —showing a spectrum of feeling, tone, and intention. Humor, irony, incongruity, and absurdity appear in the accidental good luck of the village idiot or the apparent acceptance by a group of "The Sister With a Penis"—a disguised male seducer. Human folly, knavery, and stupidity are attacked. Dialogue is used not only to reveal character or emphasize the discrepancy between reality and pretense but as an important structural element in dramatic action, as in "The Coffee-House Owner's Wife." The depth and complexity of human motives emerges in the trickery and pretense, the disguises and protean roles which cuckolded husbands adopt. The ostensible non-chalance of the story teller, his use of improvisation, sponteneity and repetition of detail does not obscure the skillful use of vigorous dialogue, the functional use of language and detail and the complex and symbolic use of imagery. The variety and originality of phallic symbols is remarkable. The lover "puts a thorn in the canek's hair." The nymphomaniac urges her seducer to "leap once more into the trench." Animal imaginery has a similarly striking effect—as when the clever, patient spider, or the seductive and deceptive snake or the imperial lion is introduced. As in some of the fables, the African story-teller is fond of lessons of compact wisdom. Thus maxims and proverbs frequently appear as when the brother whose business is love-making says, "The blacksmith and the love dealer accomplish nothing if they reveal their trade secrets." All in all, as Frobenius himself characterized the style of the African tale, it is "functional, austere, astringent, architectonic."

Characteristically, African tales reflect the joy of life, the sense of community, the sensitivity and symbiotic harmony with nature which make most of the stories in African Nights so delightful. But this kind of affirmation

14

is not the whole picture, for the African mind is keenly conscious of the deviousness and brutishness of some men, of the folly and knavery of which human beings are capable, of the fear and loneliness of puny man in a vast and perilous universe. A tale like "Sidi Baba" leaves the reader transfixed by its horror and brutal ity-like Euripides' *Medea* or the plays of Aeschylus. The husband who murders and roasts his mother- and father-in-law and whose wife then serves him food cooked in the flesh and fat of *his* own mother is an allegorical figure, a paradigm of evil in man. These crimes against the old people are vicious indeed in a society where ancestor worship and respect for the elders of the tribe were vital tenets of their religion. Mythic, too, in its symbolic intention is the account of the incestuous son of Nupe who unknowingly cohabits with his mother and sister-daughter. Cast out and despised everywhere for transgressing a strict taboo, he is at last appointed Imam (the holy man of his tribe), for he more than any other has been sanctioned through suffering.

Since "art is the meaning of life," we find in these stories, too, glimpses of the African life style, insights into cultures little understood in the United States. Collected around the turn of the century these tales were probably passed on by many generations of Africans. It is certain that they show no evidence of contact with european conquerors. The societies depicted, though varied, show certain broad similarities. They are usually agricultural, have a division of labor among artisans, a governmental structure and complex moral and social ideas designed to regulate family and group life. Some stories from the Sudan and central Africa refer to the Moslem religion. Although some groups represented appear to be living in an hierarchical or feudal society they suggest stability and order. It is a world not yet shaken by the conflict, fear, and alienation of colonial Africa where the individual's self-esteem and self-image are badly damaged. Hunting, fishing, planting, reaping, making his tools, trading, performing his religious rites he seems to be functioning in a world he can cope with. This is not to say that he does not suffer the uncertainties of weather, the fear of death, and the threat of destruction by wild animals or hostile tribes. But his self-contained world has reasonably well ordered human relations and ideas of value which transcend merely material well-being. The African personality reflected in this book looks out upon the world with a certain zest and dignity. It is characterized by a reverence for life, a respect for loyalty, courage, strength and justice and a realistic acceptance of the inevitable tragedy of human experience. The pleasures of sex are expected and sought with unabashed eagerness. But even a polygamous community expects wives to be faithful, yet the unfaithful are not ostracized. The Africans are tough-minded enough to accept human failure, and sophisticated about man's possibilities and the possibilities of literary art.

The conquest of Africa by Europeans not only destroyed the structure of several African cultures, but cut many of their living links to the past. The traditional hospitality of Africans to foreigners made their subjugation easy. But the conflicts of personality wrought by European ideas of the Africans' inferiority and by their necessary adjustment to two widely divergent worlds can scarcely be imagined. By the turn of the century virtually all of black Africa was profoundly disrupted by exploitative and insensitive Europeans. Aimé Cesaire could speak of "millions of men who have been skillfully injected with fear, inferiority complexes, trepidation, servility, despair, abasement" quoted by Fanon, *Black Skin White Masks*, p.7. Franz Fanon points out the cultural and moral implications of the conquest of Africa: "Under the colonial regime, gratitude, sincerity, and honor are empty words. From the moment that you and your like are liquidated like so many dogs, you have no other resource but to use all and every means to regain your importance as a man. You must therefore weigh as heavily as you can upon the body of your torturer in order that his soul, lost in some byway, may finally find once more its universal dimensions" (Fanon, *The Wretched of the Earth*, p.295). The recent writers of Africa—like Senghor, Hutchinson, Mphahlele, Abrahams, Tutola—dramatize the anguish and conflict of the African who is still not master in his own homeland. Yet they manage to establish spiritual bonds with the spirit of the African past—to revive the African identity.

The vital center of that African identity and of African culture is, of course, spiritual. African nations are considered "under-developed" because our standards of human achievement are so often material things, technology, and military power. Far more fundamental ultimately are the values of a culture. When we look at Africa in the light of its attitudes toward work, play, love, children, responses to nature and death, laughter, poetry, wonder, worship, there is much to reconcile and heal this violent and frenetic world of ours. Frobenius perceived that African literature rested on concepts of reality and the fate of men which are anchored in religion and its applications to the African life style. The tales in *African Nights* even in their wit and laughter or cruelty and cynicism rest on assumptions which are humane, ethical and timeless. For at the heart of African religion there is a transcendent faith: there is a spiritual power beyond the physical world, emanating from nature which embodies all the elemental forces of life and maintains the order and meaning of the universe. This "manism" or "animism" gives dignity and sensitivity to man, for he, too, has this guiding spirit within him, and he must respect its presence in the natural world around him. As a man he was sent into the visible world with a mission to fulfill—a mission which links him with those sacred spirits of ancestors who have gone before and returned, having served their people, to their God. Such a philosophy seeks a harmonious relation to nature, strong family ties, hospitality to strangers, reasonableness in times of stress, patience in suffering and serenity in the face of the inevitability of death. Art and song, story-telling and dance are an integral part of their lives and function in all aspects of their work, their celebration and their ritual. Anchored in this world and facing the unknown without illusions, the African is nevertheless conscious of the possibilities of human aspiration.

The tellers of these tales, then, like those in *The Decameron* or *Arabian Nights*, entertained the tribe, reminded them of their past and enlarged their sympathies. But we who hold this book in our hands have many pleasurable hours of laughter, suspense and vicarious experience ahead of us. For it is very likely that the American or English reader has never read anything in his life before like *African Nights*.

A long, long time ago women lived in a land of their own and men lived in a land of their own. The men's town was very, very big. The women's town was very, very big.

One day a hunter went out. He went a long way, right across the country. He came into the women's country. The women saw the man. The women fell upon the man and the women beat the man. The man ran quickly away. The man fled into his town. The man hurried to his King and said: "I went far, far away. I came to another land. In the other land the people fell on me and beat me. I ran away from there as fast as I could." The King asked the hunter, "What kind of people were they who drove you away?" The hunter said: "The people were different from us. They had a piece of flesh here (indicating one side of his chest) and a piece of flesh here (indicating the other). And the people had long hair. They were very beautiful."

The King said to the hunter: "I should like to see this tribe. How can I see them?" The hunter said: "No one can see these people. Any man, as soon as he sets foot there, will be beaten and driven out by that tribe." The King said: "Then go catch some and bring them here." The hunter said: "O King, it cannot be done! It cannot be done!" The King said: "Then fight them, or do what you want. Only I have to see these people." The hunter said: "We will not be able to fight them, for this tribe is stronger than we are. If you let me go now, I will think about this thing until tomorrow and then come back."

The King said: "Very well," and the hunter went home.

The next day the hunter came back to the King and said: "Do you want to see some of these people?" The King said: "Yes, I want to see some of these people." The hunter said: "If you can provide good honey and sugar-cane I will do what I can to bring you these people, or some of them." The King said: "You shall have the honey and the sugarcane. I will send for some at once." The King sent two men into the bush to look for honey. The two men went into the bush. The men found the honey. They brought a big gourd full of honey to the King. The King sent honey to the hunter. The hunter boiled the honey in water. He also took a honeycomb with honey still in it and put it in his shoulder-bag. But he gave the honey-water to the King. Then the hunter went out and cut a piece of sweet sugarcane. He cut the cane into little pieces and put them into his straw shoulder-bag. The hunter set out once more.

The hunter went the same way as he had gone the first time. The hunter again came to the women's country. The women saw the hunter. They ran towards him. They wanted to catch him and beat him. The hunter called out: "Don't beat me! I have got something very special. I have got something very, very sweet that I will give to your King. I have been sent by another King." The women said: "The other King counts for nothing But show us what is very, very sweet. If we take you to our Queen and this thing is not as sweet as you say, then our Queen will kill you and she will be angry with us." The hunter said: "I will gladly give you a little, for I have brought plenty with me." The hunter broke off a piece of the honeycomb filled with honey and gave it to the women. The women took it. The women tasted it. The women said: "You spoke the truth. It is very good!" The women tasted it again and asked: "What is it?" The hunter said: "That is the dirt from my King's eba[1]. I am to take it to your Queen." The women asked: "Have you also brought your King's eba?" The hunter said: "Yes, I have brought my King's eba. It is up here in my shoulder-bag where it is making its cherki.[2] It makes the dirt that you have been eating." The women said to one another: "Then we will take this man to our Queen. For what he brings from his King is so good that our Queen must taste it." The women said to one another: "Yes, our Queen must taste the King's eba and its dirt."

[1] Penis.
[2] Dirt.

The women said: "Come with us." The women placed the hunter in their midst and took him to their Queen. The Queen said: "What sort of person is this? What do you want?" The hunter said: "I am from another country. My King has sent me. My King has sent you, O Queen, a present. I bring the present. The present is very sweet." The Queen said: "What is it?" The women who had brought the hunter said: "Do not kill him, for his present is very sweet. He has brought his King's eba. He has an eba in his bag. In the bag the eba is making its dirt. We have only tasted the dirt, but even the dirt is more sweet than anything we have to eat. Do not kill the man!" The Queen looked at the hunter.

The Queen said to the hunter: "Then give me some of the sweetness your King has sent. I will taste it." The hunter said: "O Queen, let us go into the house. You women can stay in the catamba."[1] The other women stayed in the catamba. The Queen went into her house with the hunter. The Queen sat down on her bed. The hunter sat down beside her on the bed. The Queen said: "Now give it to me!" The hunter said: "Now taste the cherki-ba!" The hunter broke off a big piece of honeycomb and gave it to the Queen. The Queen put it into her mouth. The Queen said: "It is sweet." The Queen chewed it. The Queen said: "It is very good. Give me some more!" The hunter gave the Queen the rest of the comb. The Queen ate the whole of the comb. The Queen said: "It is very good! It is eba dirt? How can I get an eba?"

The hunter said: "Do you want an eba? I have one with me. In my country everyone has an eba. I also have the eba of my dead dako[2] with me. First eat my dako's eba." The Queen said: "I will. Give me some!" The hunter put his hand into his bag and brought out a piece of sugarcane. The hunter gave the Queen a piece of sugarcane and said: "Chew this my dako's eba." The Queen took the sugarcane and chewed it. The Queen said: "It is good. It is very good. Give me some more!" The hunter gave the Queen all of the sugarcane that he had with him. The Queen ate it all. The Queen chewed all of the sugarcane. She said: "Give me some more of your dako's eba." The hunter said: "I no longer have any more of my

1 Forecourt.
2 Grandfather.

21

dako's eba. For each of my dakos had only one eba. Each man in our country also has only one eba."

The Queen said: "Every man in your country has one eba that can be eaten?" The hunter said: "Yes, every man in my country has one eba that can be eaten. But a person's eba is not eaten once and for all. An eba can be eaten every day, once or even twice." The Queen asked the hunter: "Have you then got an eba?" The hunter said: "Yes, I too have an eba." The Queen said: "Is it possible for me to eat your eba?" The hunter said: "It is possible for you to eat my eba. But a living person's eba is eaten differently." The Queen asked: "How is a living person's eba eaten?" The hunter said: "Shall I show you?" The Queen said: "Yes, show me." The hunter said: "Then lie down on the bed." The Queen lay down on the bed. The Queen's bed was a very fine bed. The hunter lay down with the Queen. He lay down alongside the Queen. The hunter said: "Put your legs around me!" The Queen put one of her legs over the hunter. The hunter said: "Feel here!" The Queen took hold of the hunter's eba. The Queen put the hunter's eba into her vagina. The hunter had intercourse with the Queen. The Queen said: "It is very good! It is very good!" The Queen said: "It is sweeter than the sweetness of the dako's eba! Let me eat your eba again!" Then the hunter had intercourse with the Queen for a second time.

The Queen said: "In your country everyone has an eba like this? An eba that can be enjoyed over and over again?" The hunter said: "Yes, in my country every man has an eba like this. But my King has an eba that is sweeter by far than mine." The Queen said: "I would like to try eating your King's eba." The hunter said: "If you want to eat my King's eba, why not come to him? To-morrow I will go straight back and tell him that you are coming." The Queen said: "Yes, you can go to your King and tell him that I will come to him with my women to try out his eba. But stay with me a little longer so that I can eat your eba again." The hunter remained two more nights with the Queen, and slept with her each night.

The hunter said: "Now I will go back to my King." The Queen said: "Stay with me another two nights so that I can again eat your eba." The hunter said: "I cannot stay any longer. If I do my King will be angry with me. Then my King will punish me. Do you want my King to punish me? Did I not bring you something sweet?" The Queen said: "You brought me something sweeter than I have ever tasted. I do not want your King to punish you. But you must stay with me." The hunter said: "Is it not easy for you to come to us? Then you will get something sweeter than you have had from me." The Queen said: "Yes. Go back to your King. I will go with you." The hunter said: "Let me go on ahead and tell the King that you are coming." The Queen said: "Yes, go on ahead and tell your King that I am coming. Tell me that I am coming with my people. I want all of my women to be given an eba, since everyone in your country has one." The hunter said: "Each of your women will have an eba. There will be no problem. We have enough." The Queen went out to her women and said: "I have tasted the eba. It is much sweeter than anything else. The hunter is going to see his King. The hunter will tell the King that I am coming and that I am bringing you with me. The hunter will have an eba for each one of you when we get there." The women cried out: "Each one of us will have a sweet eba! Each of us will have an eba!" The hunter went.

The hunter crossed the countryside and came back into his town. The hunter went to his King. The hunter said to his King: "I have again been to those people." The King said: "Will I be able to see those people?" The hunter said: "I have made friends with those people. The Queen is coming with her people. The Queen wants to eat your eba. The other women also want to eat ebas. When these people arrive, each women should be given one man to sleep with, away from everyone else. Then you will see what will happen. It is very good." The King said: "You have done it? It is not bad?" The hunter said: "It is very good. It is much better than anything else." The King said: "Then I will call all the people together and tell them what you have told me. When are these people coming?" The hunter said: "I can go now and bring them." The King said: "Yes. Go as quickly as you can!" The hunter went back again.

The hunter came back to the women. The hunter said to the Queen and her women: "My King asks you to come to him now. Each of you will be given not only eba

23

dirt but an eba!" The Queen said: "That is good. Let us go there now." The women said: "Each of us will have a sweet eba! Each of us will have a sweet eba!" The Queen said: "We will stay with the men for two months, then we will go home again." The women packed their gourds and put them on their heads. The hunter went with the women.

The hunter arrived in the King's town with the Queen and her women. The King received the Queen. All the men were with their King. The King led the Queen into his house. The King slept with the Queen. Every man slept with a woman. The women said: "That is sweeter by far than anything else." The Queen said to the King: "I will stay with you for two months. Then I will leave with my women."

The Queen and her women stayed for two months in the men's town. When the two months were over the Queen said: "We will stay another two months in this country. Then I and my women will return." The Queen and her women stayed two more months in the men's town. When the two months were over the Queen said: "We will stay two months longer." The women stayed on in the men's country.

The women became pregnant. The women bore children. The children slept with each other and bore children. Men and women did not separate ever again. The women did not ever again go away from the men.

MYTH OF THE AMAZONS—II   *Kabyle*

In the beginning men and women did not live above ground. There was only one man and one woman and they lived underground. These were the only people and they did not know that they were not the same. One day, when they were beside their spring, both wanted a drink of water. The man said: "Let me drink." The woman said: "No, I will drink the water first. I came first." The man tried to push the woman aside. But the woman hit

24

him. They both hit each other. The man hit the woman so that she fell down. Her clothes fell apart. Her thighs were bared.

The man saw the woman lying naked in front of him. He saw that she was different. He saw that she had an achatschoon.[1] He felt that he had an abbush.[2] He pushed a finger into it and the woman said: "That is good." The man felt his abbush grow big. He had intercourse with the woman. He lay beside her for eight days. Not until then did he get up.

At the end of nine months the woman gave birth to four daughters. At the end of another nine months the woman gave birth to four sons. At the end of another nine months the woman gave birth to four daughters. At the end of another nine months the woman gave birth to four sons. Finally the man and the woman had fifty daughters and fifty sons. But the father and mother did not know what to do with the children. They sent their children away.

Together the fifty girls set off towards the North. Together the fifty boys set off towards the East. For several years the girls made their way underground towards the North, until they saw light above their heads. In that place there was a hole in the ground. The girls saw the sky above their heads. The girls asked: "Why should we stay here under the ground? Let us climb out. Then we can see the sky." Thereupon the girls climbed up through the hole until they were all above ground.

For several years the fifty boys also made their way underground until they came to another place where there was a hole in the ground and they could see the sky above their heads. The boys looked at the sky and said: "Why should we stay underground when there is a place where we can see the sky?" The boys climbed through the hole until they were above ground.

The fifty girls then went on their way above the ground and the fifty boys went on their way above the ground. But they knew nothing about each other.

Every tree and plant could then talk. The fifty girls looked at the plants and asked them: "Who made you?" The plants said: "The earth made us." The girls asked

[1] Vagina.
[2] Penis.

the earth: "Who made you?" The earth said: "Like you, I exist." At night the girls saw the moon and the stars and called out: "Who made you, so far above us and above all the trees? Is it you who gives us light? And who are you, big stars and little stars? Who made you, big stars and little stars? Or did you who make everything else?" All the girls were calling out and shouting. But the moon and stars were so high up they could not answer. All the fifty girls were shouting and calling.

The boys had arrived near the place where the fifty girls were shouting. They said to each other: "There are some people who talk just like us." We will go there. We will see what they are like." The fifty boys began walking. They walked towards the shouting. When they were almost there they came to the bank of a great river. The river lay between the fifty girls and the fifty boys. But the boys had never seen a river before. They called out. The boys called out. The girls heard the shouting and went towards the boys. The girls came to the far bank of the river. On the other side they saw the boys and called out: "Who are you? Why are you shouting? Are you people?" The fifty boys called out: "We are people. We came up out of the ground. Why were you shouting?" The fifty girls said: "We are people too. We also came up out of the ground. We were shouting to the moon and the stars. We asked them who made them. We asked if they made everything else."

The fifty boys said to the river: "You are not like us, you are not like the earth. We cannot walk on you or pick you up. What are you? How can we cross you to the other side?" The river said: "I am water. You can wash yourselves in me. You can drink me. If you want to reach my other bank go further up where I am not deep. Then you can walk across me." The fifty boys went upstream. They found a place that was shallow. They crossed to the other bank of the river.

Now the fifty boys wanted to join the fifty girls. The fifty girls said: "Do not come close. Stand over there. We will stay here. We will put a strip of ground between us."

The fifty girls and the fifty boys started walking. They did not come together. The ground stayed between them.

One day the fifty boys came upon a spring. The

fifty girls also came upon a spring. The boys said: "The river said that we should wash with water. Let us wash outselves." The fifty boys took their clothes off and went into the water. The fifty girls sat around the other spring and looked at the boys. One girl said: "Come with me. Let us see what the other people are doing." Two other girls said: "We will come with you." All of the others said: "No, we will not come with you."

The three girls crawled through the high grass towards the boys. Two of them stayed back. Only the first girl went closer. The girl looked through some bushes at the boys. The boys had taken off their clothes. The boys were naked. The girl looked at all the boys. The girl saw that the boys were different. They were not the same as girls. When the boys put on their clothes again the girl crawled away. The boys did not see her.

The girl went back to the other girls. The other girls crowded around her. They asked her what she had seen. The first girl said: "Let us wash ourselves in the water. Then I will tell you." The fifty girls took their clothes off. They went into the water of their spring. The inquisitive girl said: "The people over there are different from us. Where we have breasts they have nothing. Where we have an achatshoon, they have something else. The hair on their heads is not long like ours, but short. When you see them naked your heart beats fast. You want to touch them. You cannot forget what they look like." The other girls said: "You are lying!" The first girl said: "Go and look. Your heart will beat fast." The other girls said: "We want to keep walking."

The fifty girls began walking again. The fifty boys also began walking. The boys walked slowly. The girls walked quickly. Their path crossed the boys' path. Their camps at night were close together.

On the day when the fifty boys camped close to the fifty girls the boys said: "Let us no longer sleep under the stars. Let us build houses." Some of the boys began to make holes in the ground. They slept in the earth-holes. Others made tunnels and caves in the ground, and slept there. But some of the boys said: "Stones can be put on top of other stones. Our houses should be made out of stones."

The boys put stones on top of other stones. They left

one hole in the walls for going in and coming out. When they had built the walls one of the boys went to a tree and began to chop it down. But the tree cried out. The tree said: "Why are you cutting me down? What are you doing? Are you older than I am?" The boy said: "I am not older than you are. I want to cut down fifty trees. I will lay your trunks on my house as a roof. I will put your branches inside my house. Your branches will not get wet again." The tree said: "Then I agree." The boy cut down fifty trees. He laid the trunks over his house and covered them with mud and rushes. He broke the branches and stored them in the house. He got some of the bigger trunks in the middle to hold up the roof. When the others saw what a fine house he had made they copied it. But among the boys there was a wild one, and among the girls there was a wild one. The wild boy did not want to live in a house. He did not build himself a house like the rest but crawled about among the others' houses. He was looking always for someone to eat. He was wild and wanted only to kill people and eat them.

The fifty girls were camped not far away. The girls watched as the fifty boys began digging their holes. They watched as the fifty boys built houses. The fifty girls said: "What are the other people doing? What are they doing with the stones? What are they doing with the trees?" The first girl said: "I will go there. I will crawl there and see what the other people are doing. I want to see them naked again."

The girl crawled through the bushes towards the boys' houses. The girl got very close to the houses. The girl slipped into a house. There was no one inside. The girl saw what a good house it was. She looked at everything inside. The wild boy was crawling by. He smelled the girl. He roared. The girl was frightened. She screamed. The girl ran out of the house. She ran towards the camp of the girls.

All of the boys heard the girl scream. All of the boys jumped up and ran after the girl. The girl ran screaming through the bush. The other girls heard her screaming. The girls jumped up and ran towards the girl. The fifty girls and fifty boys ran into each other. Each girl ran into a boy and each boy ran into a girl. The boys and girls fought. Each time it was a boy and a girl that fought. The wild girl and the wild boy also fought each other.

Each boy and girl fighting in the bush could not see any other boy and girl fighting in the bush. The fifty girls were very strong. Each girl threw the boy that she was fighting to the ground. Each girl lay on top of the boy that she was fighting. Each girl said to herself. "Now I will see if the first girl was lying or not." Each girl put her hand between the thighs of the boy that she was fighting. Each girl felt the boy's abbush. When the girl touched them, each boy's abbush began to swell. The boys lay very still. When each girl touched a boy's abbush her heart began to swell. The girls took off their clothes and pushed the abbush of the boy into their achatschum. The boys lay very still. The fifty girls had intercourse with the fifty boys. Then the fifty boys became more excited than the fifty girls.

Each boy took a girl and went with her into his house. They married each other. In their houses each boy said: "It is not right that the woman should lie on top of the man. The man will put his abbush into the girl's achatschun. He will be on top of her. We will be masters." After that they had intercourse in the same way that the men and women of Kaylia do today.

The boys became more excited than the girls. They all lived very contentedly together. Only the wild boy and the wild girl, who had no house, wandered about among them. They were looking for people to eat. The others were always chasing them away. They beat the wild girl and the wild boy whenever they saw them. At last the wild boy and the wild girl said to each other: We are different from the other people. They are always hitting us. We must go away. We must go to the forest. The wild boy and the wild girl went away. They went into the forest. When they were hungry they would come out of the forest and steal children to eat. The wild girl became the first teriel.[1] The wild man became the first lion.

The other men and women were glad to be free of the man-eaters. They lived very happily together. They ate the plants that they had gathered.

[1] Witch.

A father had three sons. The first son was a wood-worker. The second son was a mason. The third was a nsäni.[1] One day the father of the three young men died. Soon after the mother of the three young men died. The three young men were now all alone. None of them was married.

After their parents had died, the three youths were all alone in the house. The usäni was the cleverest of the three youths. The nsäni said to his brothers: "Oh brothers, our father and our mother are dead. There is no one left in the house to prepare our food for us. It is no longer good for us here. Let us therefore take up our shoulder bags, leave this house, and seek our fortunes elsewhere." His two brothers agreed. All three brothers packed their shoulder-bags and set forth.

After a while the three brothers came to another place where there was an Agellid. The nsäni went to the Agellid and said: "We are three brothers. Our father and mother are dead. We have nothing to eat. Give us work so that we can have something to eat." The Agellid said: "What kind of work can you do?" The nsäni said: "One of my brothers is a mason, the other is a wood-worker and I am a nsäni." The Agellid said: "I have use for a mason. I have use for a wood-worker. But I have no use for a nsäni. But I will think about it. Then I will send word to you and let you know whether I have any use for a nsäni. Then I can employ all three of you." But in fact the Agellid did not know what a nsäni was. The Agellid went into his house.

The Agellid was an old man and he had a young wife. The Agellid went to his young wife and said: "Three men have come to me asking for work, a mason, a wood-worker and a nsäni. I do not know what a nsäni does and whether I have any use for him." The young wife knew

---

[1] A Love dealer.

what a nsäni was. She said: "A nsäni asked you for work?
That is very good. A nsäni who can use his tool well can
be of the greatest use. Spend no more time thinking about
it, but take all three into your service. The wood-worker
and the mason can work for you and I will give the nsäni
many things to do. Hurry. Send for these people." The
Agellid said: "Of what use is the nsäni?" The young wife
replied: "A nsäni earns his gold while he sleeps. You
must therefore prepare a good bed for him. I will look
after everything else." The Agellid went away.

The Agellid sent for the three brothers. He gave work
to the mason and the wood-worker. To the nsäni he said:
"I have had a room prepared for you with a good bed in
it. There you can work." The nsäni was led into the room
where the fine bed was. When the Agellid's young wife
heard that the nsäni was in the house she at once had a
good meal prepared for him and sent a maidservant across
with it.

The maidservant took the meal into the nsäni's chamber
and set down the dishes, saying: "This has been sent you
by the Agellid's young wife. Enjoy it." The nsäni did not
look at the maidservant but only shrugged his shoulders.
The maidservant said: "Why do you not want to eat?"
The nsäni said nothing but only wriggled his shoulders.
The maidservant gathered up the dishes and took the
food back to the Agellid's young wife. The maidservant
said: "The man will not eat. He did not even look at me
out of the corners of his eyes."

The Agellid's young wife took the dishes from the maid-
servant, saying: "I will take the food to the man myself."
"The Agellid's young wife went into the nsäni's chamber.
When the nsäni saw the Agellid's young wife he laughed
and greeted her. The Agellid's young wife said: "Why
will you not touch any of the food? If you are to be a
lusty nsäni you must eat plenty, otherwise your work will
not be any good." The nsäni said: "I will eat and enjoy
what I feel like. But I am not used to being served by a
maidservant. In my calling food alone is not enough."
The Agellid's young wife said: "So you are a nsäni?"
The nsäni replied: "Certainly I am a nsäni!" The
Agellid's young wife said: "And how good is your work?
Could I entrust a valuable jewel to you?" The nsäni replied: "Only try it and your astonishment at discovering

31

what a treasure you possess will be such that you will not recover your senses for a week or more."

The Agellid's young wife said: "In that case, O nsäni, show me at once what you can do." The nsäni said: "Lie down and take a deep breath." The Agellid's young wife lay down on the couch. The nsäni lay down beside her. After a while the Agellid's young wife fell into a swoon. When she recovered her senses she said: "O nsäni, stay long with my husband, for he is old and infirm." The nsäni replied: "That cannot be, for there are further tasks awaiting me elsewhere." The Agellid's young wife said: "I have a golden hen that lays golden eggs. I will give it you if you go on working at my jewel for another month. On top of that I will give you three hundred duro in gold. But I beg you to stay one more month with me."

The nsäni agreed. He remained a whole month with the Agellid's young wife. For most of the time during that month the Agellid's young wife was in a swoon. When the month had gone by she gave the nsäni the golden hen and the three hundred duro in gold. The nsäni took leave of her and went to find his brothers. The two brothers said to the nsäni: "Let us not stay here any longer. We have been well-fed, but the Agellid gives us no money." Thensäni said: "I, too, have finished my work here. We can now go on our way."

The three brothers set out and, after wandering for many days, came to another Agellid's village. The nsäni went to the Agellid and said: "We are three brothers who, have lost our father and mother. We are looking for a house where we will be fed. We therefore beg you to give us work." The Agellid said: "What sort of work can you do?" The nsäni said: "One of my brothers is a woodworker, the other is a mason, and I am a nsäni. I am as good at my work as my two brothers are at theirs." The Agellid said: "I have good use for a mason and a woodworker. But I am not sure what use I have of a nsäni." But in fact the Agellid did not know what a nsani was. The nsäni laughed and said: "You do not know what use you have of a nsäni? Have you not got a wife?" The Agellid replied: "I have a wife, but she is old and never gives me any peace."

The nsäni said: "Then I have come at the right time, even if you do not know it. Only ask your wife if she has

32

any work for a nsäni. If you give me a hundred duros in gold I will see to it that your wife leaves you in peace until the day you die. But do not tell her this, or she will pester you twice as much as before." The Agellid said: "Wait here. I will see if I can give you work."

The Agellid went to his wife and said: "Three young men are here looking for work. The first brother is a mason. The second brother is a wood-worker." The wife said: "What can we do with these people? Nothing needs to be done." The Agellid said: "That is my opinion also. The third brother is a nsäni." The woman said: "What did you say? A nsäni? By my father's gullet, I have long wished to have a nsäni who is skilled at his work. He will have plenty of work. Let the mason and wood-worker stay as well. There is much in your house that they can do. But watch them closely so that they do not steal. But send the nsäni to me. I will give him plenty of work and see that he does it well. But you must have a good bed prepared in the room next to mine." The Agellid said: "Are you not afraid of the nsäni?" Laughing, the woman replied: "It is evident that you are old. A nsäni must always do his work in a room near a woman. If he cannot have such a room he cannot work."

The Agellid returned to the nsäni and said. "I will employ all three of you. You yourself must go to my wife. She will give you work. And do not forget your promise. If you keep your promise I will reward you." The nsäni said: "Is your wife very old?" The Agellid replied: "She is at the age when women are at their worst. You will find it difficult to carry out your work to her satisfaction." The nsäni said: "I will see what I can do."

The nsäni went to the wife. The wife was no longer young. The wife greeted the nsäni saying: "So you are a nsäni?" The nsäni replied: "Yes, I am a nsäni." The wife said: "I am reaching the age when a woman once more rejoices in her body and longs to taste again, while yet there is time, the pleasures she has enjoyed earlier in her life. Will you be my nsäni? If you make me live again the joys I have experienced I will give you something of great value. I have a golden horse with a golden saddle and golden bridle. This is what I would give you." The nsäni said: "See if you have enough food in the house to last a month. If you have, lock the door and come to me."

When a month had gone by the woman opened the door of her house. The woman gave him the golden horse with the golden saddle and the golden bridle, saying: "I thank you. During this month you have made me relive all the pleasures I have enjoyed in this life. You have made me so tired that I want to go on sleeping until the end of my life. My husband must not come near me again. You have more than earned your reward. Accept my thanks." The nsäni took his leave of her saying: "I will go, but it will not be easy. You asked more of me than most men would be able to perform. But now I know that I can meet with nothing in my calling that will lies my powers."

The nsäni went to the Agellid. He said to the Agellid: "Give me the present that you promised me." The Agellid said: "You have earned it. For a full month my wife has not troubled me." The nsäni said: "Your wife will not trouble you in the future." The Agellid asked: "How did you do this?" The nsäni replied: "A blacksmith or a nsäni who speaks of his craft is not worth anything." The Agellid gave the nsäni two hundred duro in gold and let him go.

The nsäni went to his brothers. His brothers said to him: "Let us not stay here any longer. Though the Agellid gives us our keep he gives us nothing else." The nsäni said: "I have finished my work. We should go on to another place. But let us not walk fast, for my work has tired me." The three brothers set forth.

When they had been travelling for a long time they came to a place where an Agellid lived. He was very, very rich and he had a daughter whom he refused to give away in marriage. There was no man whose wealth and power were equal to his own. The Agellid wanted to build a big house for his daughter. But the Agellid could not find any masons or woodworkers. He was offering much money.

The nsäni went to the Agellid and said: "We are three brothers whose father and mother have died. Now we are looking for work and a house where we can eat." The Agellid asked: "What kind of work can you do?" The nsäni said: "My first brother is a mason, my second brother is a woodworker, and I am a nsäni." The Agellid said: "Your brothers can begin work at once. I will pay them much money. But you are a nsäni. What can I give a

34

nsäni to do?" The Agellid did not know what a nsäni was. The nsäni said: "Only women know what use to make of a nsäni's work. Ask your daughter whether she has anything for me to do."

The Agellid went to his daughter. His daughter lived in a house that was locked with seven doors. The Agellid said to his daughter: "My daughter, a nsäni is here. Have you work for him to do?" The daughter cried: "What! A nsäni is here? Do you ask if I have work for him to do? Yes, I have work. I will give him as much work as he can manage. Since you will not allow me to marry, I must enjoy myself some other way. Send me the nsäni. I will give him work, food, and lodging in my house." The Agellid went away. He sent the nsäni to his daughter.

The Agellid's daughter greeted the nsäni, saying: "What can you do?" The nsäni answered. "I am a nsäni and know how to do my work." The Agellid's daughter said: "Let's us see who will work best at your skill by the end of the week. If your strength gives out, I will have you put to death. If I tire first, I will give you a golden doll and a box full of gold. Do you agree?" The nsäni said: "Yes, I agree. Show me the bed."

The Agellid's daughter prepared a good bed for the nsäni in a room next to her own. Then the Agellid's daughter said: "Now teach me your craft. I must start at the beginning." The nsäni said: "The first thing to be done is to put the threat into the eye of the needle. We will practice that. The thread is fourteen knots long. On the first day we will take one knot, on the second two, on the third three. If I were to put all fourteen knots at once through the eye of the needle you would die. Now lie down."

On the first day the Agellid's daughter fell into a swoon. On the second day the Agellid's daughter groaned aloud. On the third day the Agellid's daughter said: "Just one knot more!" On the eighth day the Agellid's daughter cried: "All the knots! All the knots!" The nsäni said: "Not so; it would kill you." On the ninth day the Agellid came to see how his daughter was faring. When he opened the second door his daughter heard him coming. She sprang up and said: "Quick, get into his chest!" The Agellid's daughter made the nsäni climb into the chest.

35

She shut the lid over him. The Agellid came in and talked to his daughter.

But the nsäni was overcome with fear and began to pee. His water ran out from under the chest into the middle of the room. The Agellid asked: "What is this liquid?" The Agellid's daughter said: "A bottle of scent has broken and is leaking." The Agellid bent down, dipped his finger in the wat, and smelled it. When he had smelled the liquid the Agellid said: "It is true: this scent smells very fine." Then the Agellid went.

The Agellid's daughter opened the chest and let the nsäni out. The Agellid's daughter said: "I have saved your life." The nsäni said: "Now come. I will save your life too." The Agellid's daughter said: "Yes, do so, and if you do not put me into a swoon I will have you put to death." After a while the Agellid's daughter fell into a swoon. When she came to her senses again she felt so dizzy that she could not walk. The Agellid's daughter said: "You have won. Take the golden doll and the box of gold. I thank you. Even if my father never gives me in marriage, there will be something for me to look back on with pleasure. Accept my thanks."

The nsäni took the doll and the box full of gold. He took his leave of the Agellid's daughter and went to his brothers. He said: "O brothers, we have all earned well in this place. Let us now go on our way and see if we can put our money to good use."

The brothers agreed. They packed their belongings. They set forth again on their travels. They journeyed until they came to a crossroads. At the crossroads they took leave of one another. Each went his own way.

After many wanderings the nsäni came to a big town ruled over by a Tagellit.[1] The Tagellit was still very young. She had just married an Agellid, but he had died on his wedding night. Now the young Tagellit was living as a widow. The people told the näsni much about the Tagellit's youth and beauty.

Hearing all this, the nsäni said to himself: "This is the best place for me. This is where I shall stay." The nsäni rented a house backing onto the house of the Tagellit. When evening came the nsäni began to hammer. He went

[1] Princess: female counterpart of an Agellid.

on hammering all through the night. All the while he was hammering on the wall behind which the young Tagellit had her bed. The young Tagellit was unable to sleep that night.

The next morning the Tagellit called for her old negress and said to her: "Go at once to the house on the other side of this wall and find out who has dared to hammer all through the night. I could not sleep. Now I want to strike the man." The negress went at once. She came to the nsäni. On going in to the nsäni's house she immediately caught sight of the golden hen that could lay golden eggs. The old negress put her hand to her mouth. She could not talk.

The nsäni greeted the negress, saying: "Well mother, what brings you to my house?" The old negress said: "The young Tagellit sent me to find out who had been hammering during the night. She could not sleep." The nsäni said: "I hammered. During the night I made the golden hen that can lay golden eggs. Such work cannot be done during the day. I have to do it at night."

The old negress went back to the young Tagellit and told her her everything. The old negress said: "In the whole world there is nothing so beautiful as this golden hen that can lay golden eggs. The only proper place for the golden hen is your house. But it will be difficult to buy it from the man, for he is richer than you are." The young Tagellit wanted to own the golden hen that could lay golden eggs. She said to the old negress: "Go back and ask the man if he will sell the golden hen that can lay golden eggs. I will buy it from him." The old negress went back to the nsäni. The old negress said to the nsäni: "The young Tagellit wants to buy the golden hen that can lay golden eggs. How much will you sell it for?" The nsäni said: "No money will buy the golden hen that can lay golden eggs. But I will give it to her if she will allow me to look at her legs, from her toes up to above her knees. That is all. If she lets me do that, I will give her the golden hen than can lay golden eggs."

The old negress went back to the young Tagellit and said: "The man will give you the golden hen that can lay golden eggs. But you must let him look at your legs from your toes to your knees." The young Tagellit flew into a rage and cried: "What boldness! I will have him put to death at once." The old negress said: "If you had seen the golden hen than can lay golden eggs, you would not dream of putting him to death. Instead you would show him your legs. It would not hurt you or cost you anything. No one would see you. And the golden hen that can lay golden eggs is the most beautiful thing in the world." The young Tagellit said: "Very well. Tell the man to come here with the golden hen that can lay golden eggs and show it me. But I will not buy it."

The old negress ran back and told the nsäni. The nsäni took the golden hen that could lay golden eggs and went to the young Tagellit's house. The young Tagellit saw the golden hen that could lay golden eggs and said: "So you want to sell the hen?" The nsäni said: "Yes. You know the price." Then the young Tagellit bared her legs to beyond the knee. The nsäni contemplated the young Tagellit's legs, expressed his thanks, and went back to his house without the hen that could lay golden eggs.

When evening came once more the nsäni again began hammering on the wall behind the young Tagellit's bed. He hammered until morning, and the young Tagellit spent another night without any sleep. The following morning she sent the old negress to find out what was causing the noise. One going into the nsäni's house the old negress saw the golden doll. The old negress put her hand to her mouth. She stood there speechless. Then she left without saying a word.

The old negress went back to the young Tagellit and said: "The golden hen that can lay golden eggs is very beautiful. But the golden doll made by the man last night is more beautiful. You must have this golden doll." The young Tagellit said: "Very well. Go to the man's house and ask his price. Perhaps he will only want to see my legs again. I will show them to him for a second time."

The old negress returned to the nsäni and said: "The young Tagellit wants to buy the golden doll. What do you want for it?" The nsäni said: "The golden doll cannot be bought for gold. But if the young Tagellit will show me the upper part of her body down to below her breasts I will gladly give her the golden doll." The old negress hurried back to the young Tagellit and said: "The man will give you the golden doll if you will bare the upper part of your body down to below your breasts." The young

Tagellit said: "This man is truly greedy. Will it be wrong for me to show him the upper part of my body bared down to below the breasts? For I have already shown him my legs naked to the knee, and above?" The old negress said: 'It would not be worse, for the golden doll is even more beautiful than the golden hen that can lay golden eggs." The young Tagellit said: "Then call the man so that I can see the golden doll."

The old negress hurried back to the nsäni and said: "Come with me and show the young Tagellit your golden doll." The young nsäni took his golden doll and went to the house of the young Tagellit. When the young Tagellit saw the golden doll, she at once bared the upper part of her body down to below her breasts. The nsäni looked at the upper part of the young Tagellit's body down to below her breasts, expressed his thanks, and, leaving the doll behind, went back to his house.

When evening came once more the nsäni again began to hammer on the wall behind which lay the young Tagellit's bed, and he went on hammering all night long so that the young Tagellit could not sleep. When morning came the young Tagellit called the old negress and said: "Quick, run out and find what the man has been hammering at this time. And aks him what he wants to see in exchange for it."

The old negress hurried to the nsäni's house. In the doorway she stood still. The nsäni had set up the golden horse with the golden saddle and the golden bridle. The old negress was about to run away again when she remembered what the young Tagellit had told her. The old negress said: "What do you want to see in exchange for the golden horse with the golden saddle and the golden bridle?" The nsäni said: "Her parted legs."

The old negress hurried back to the young Tagellit and said: "It is a golden horse with a golden saddle and golden bridle. The golden hen that can lay golden eggs and the golden doll are like dung beside them. All he wants is to see your parted legs.' The young Tagellit said: "Quick! Run back and tell the man to bring me the golden horse with the golden saddle and golden bridle." The old negress ran back to the nsäni and said: "Take the golden horse with the golden saddle and the golden bridle and come with me to the young Tagellit."

The nsäni took the golden horse with the golden saddle and the golden bridle and went with the old negress to the young Tagellit. The young Tagellit saw the golden horse with the golden saddle and golden bridle and said: "You can look at anything you want." The nsäni looked between the young Tagellit's parted legs, shook his head, and said: "Alas!" The young Tagellit asked: "Why do you say alas!" The nsäni said: "I am sad to see that youor ishenfeer[1] is not straight. It ought to be fixed. Look for yourself in a mirror." The nsäni then expressed his thanks He left the golden horse with the golden saddle and golden bridle for the young Tagellit, and went back to his house.

The young Tagellit jumped up and found a mirror. She put it on the ground and stood over it with her legs wide apart. What she saw gave her such a shock that she threw herself sobbing onto the bed. The old negress came in and asked: What are you crying about?" The young Tagellit said: "My ishenfeer is crooked. The clever man saw it too and said that my ishenfeer should be fixed. But is there anyone who can fix my ishenfeer?"

The old negress said: "Who should be able to do it if not the man clever enough to make the golden hen that can lay golden eggs, the golden doll, and the golden horse with the golden saddle and the golden bridle? Surely he would be able to fix your ishenfeer." The young Tagellit said: 'You are right. Go to the clever man's house and ask him if he will do it."

The old negress came to the nsäni and said to him: "The young Tagellit has sent me to ask if you can fix her crooked ishenfeer." The nsäni said: 'I can. But I will need eight days to do the work. Ask the young Tagellit if that is too long. None could do it in less time." The old negress said: "Come with me and talk to my mistress."

The nsäni went to the young Tagellit. The young Tagellit wept and said: "Tell me quickly whether you are willing to fix my crooked ishenfeer. If so, then begin at once." The nsäni said: "I can fix it" The nsäni began to stroke and rub the young Tagellit. The young Tagellit said: "That feels very good." Then the young Tagellit fell into a swoon, saying only: "More! More!" For eight

---

[1] Vulva.

days the nsäni lay with the young Tagellit. Then she awoke and said: "Is my ishenfeer now straight?" The nsäni said: "You can find out by trying the lid on the basket to see if it fits." The young Tagellit said: "Quick, then! Try the lid on the basket again!" The young Tagellit moaned and said: "Ah, how well the lid fits the basket!"

The young Tagellit married the nsäni. The nsäni became Agellid of the town. The young wife loved her husband above everything. She said: "I have a golden hen that can lay golden eggs. I have a golden doll. I have a golden horse with a golden saddle and a golden bridle. But I also have a cover for my basket, and that is best of all."

Having become Agellid, the nsäni often sat in judgment. One day, two men were brought in who were poor and ragged because they had not succeeded in their calling. They were his two brothers, the mason and the woodworker. The nsäni took them into the town and gave of them each a good wife.

THE CURE OF A MAN-CRAZY WOMAN *Kordofan*

A man married a woman who was very beautiful. The woman was very beautiful and very clever. But the woman's desires exceeded all measure. Since the husband who had married her was unable to satisfy her, she seized every opportunity that her cleverness could devise to sleep with a friend or a handsome stranger. When the woman met a friend on her way to the market, she would have her joy of him. In the market she would search out a handsome stranger and was always able to find a hidden corner where she could take her pleasure with him. On the way back she would visit a woman friend whose husband would be sure to oblige her and, on reaching home, her appetite would without fail persuade her husband to join her on the angareb. But in view of the condition of his wife's sexual parts the husband invariably knew that he

41

was not the first man to make her happy that morning. And whereas the woman was always ready to demand more of the husband than he was able to give, he for his part was by no means pleased that the woman whom he had married should rely on other men for the greater part of her marriage pleasures.

Yet the husband had no proof of his wife's passion except for the excited condition of her body, which was always warm and moist and always yearning for more. The woman was far too clever to be caught out by her husband during her secret meetings with other men. She always managed to avoid her husband. It even happened that the husband would spy on her, hiding behind a straw fence and looking down the path that she had taken seeking adventure, and all the while the clever one, separated from her husband only by the straw fence would be enjoying the delights of her encounter to the full.

When matters had been going in this way for some time, the husband said to himself: "There can no longer be any doubt about it. My wife is not only more avid for pleasure than I am, but she is also cleverer. I shall therefore discuss the matter with a friend." So the husband went to one of his friends and told him everything. He said: "My friend, I beg you to be a true friend to me and to help me in a certain matter. You know that I am married to a woman who is not only beautiful but clever. She can also enjoy the sexual powers of many men without lessening her own capacity for pleasure. All my friends no doubt already know about all of this from their own experience. But I do not want to reproach them for having taken advantage of the delights that happened to come their way. I know that my wife cannot go out to pee without putting her crotch to some other use. I know that she is always able to find a man to share her pleasure, and that she can share it without my knowing when and how. I assume that you know this and blush to tell you that not only do I not condone my wife's excesses, but that I am not clever enough to expose them. What is even worse is that, having first been aroused by another man she demands the same exercise of me. She drains my resources in proportion to the number of friends and partners she has found to share that pleasure which ought to be my right alone. So foresee the time when every man who lives in this town, by participating in my marital bliss, will impose upon me exertions which—since I as an individual will have to perform as much as all the rest put together—must soon bring me to the brink of the grave. I therefore beg, you, my friend, to advise me how best to withdraw my wife from this masculine consortium so that I can obtain the rest and recuperation I so urgently need."

The friend said: "Since you are clearly able to discuss this matter with calm and in dignified fashion, I shall not attempt to deny that your wife's cleverness and insatiable appetitie are common knowledge in this town. It is indeed true that your powers will soon be exhausted, since a lone individual could never succeed in doing by himself what can only be accomplished by the communal efforts of all the town's male inhabitants. Hence, unless you do something to remedy matters, you will quickly succumb to such unequal odds, and to avoid this you must move to another town. I will accompany you, remain there a day, and come away again. You will find that circumstances will change. I also hope that if your wife spends several hours a day sitting in the cold water peculiar to that town, there will be a marked change for the better. But there is one concession you will have to make. On the day we arrive in the town I must come together with your wife for the last time. This will be necessary in order to introduce her to her new way of life and to teach her the lessons that have to be taught. Since she has shared your bliss with so many others, you will not object to this one last time of friendly participation, especially since your sole possession will be ensured there after."

The husband gave his assent. He arranged for all of his goods to be packed, set off on the journey to the strange town with his friend and his wife, and one afternoon arrived outside its gates. The friend had arranged for the journey to be undertaken in long stages, and had further stipulated that the woman must go the whole way on foot. Thus every evening her exhaustion was such that her usual requirement gave way to her excessive weariness. But on the last day, before they arrived outside the gates of the strange town, not only had the march been a very short one, but the woman had grown accustomed to this novel use of her legs so that her former urge returned with new vigor.

Thus the woman, having gone behind the seriba of the camp to pee was able to lure forth her husband's friend, who showed himself eager to accept her challenge and rapidly engaged with her in exercise. When the performance was over he said: "It will do you good, if we insert another thorn into the camel's hair." The woman consented with alacrity and when this, too, had been accomplished, she attempted to get up, but the man said: "Unfortunate woman, a joyless future lies ahead of you, and it would be well for me to saddle you once more." The woman, whose delight in the exercise had grown with its repetition, said: "Come quickly, for I can easily carry another rider. "When it was over she asked: "Why did you call me an unfortunate woman and say that a joyless future lay ahead of me?" The friend said: "All of the men in the town where you and your husband will be living have not one, but two male organs which, moreover, are made of iron so that the wretched women who yield to them feel no pleasure but the most terrible pain." In alarm the woman said: "Come, my friend. See if you can manage one more leap into the ditch." The friend complied with her request. Then he said to the woman: "Now you must go in to your husband who is certainly waiting like a wild beast to leap on his prey. Let him ravish the lambs that are left!" With that they separated and the woman went into the tent and took from her husband all that he had to give her that day. But as he entered his wife's hospitable doorway the husband said to himself: "Truly my friend has made full use of his opportunities and has diligently instructed my wife. But if it has done any good, I will not complain."

The husband entered the town with his friend and his wife and took lodgings in a respectable house with a friendly landlord. As he was settling in with his wife, his friend went to a coffee house together with the amiable landlord and other respectable men. Since he had been to the town before and was therefore acquainted with its inhabitants, his companions asked him about the married man whom as yet they did not know. To this the friend replied: "This man is greatly to be pitied, for in every town to which he goes with his wife he meets with serious trouble. You must know that this beautiful woman has one passion. After having lured a man onto her couch,

44

she cuts off his male organ with a pair of scissors. And since the woman's charms are exceptional and men are always taken in by her, the husband has been compelled, after violent disputes, to depart suddenly from each town in turn, leaving behind a trail of emasculated youths." The tale created a great sensation among his audience. After much conversation the men took leave of each other.

The following day the friend said: 'It would be dishonorable of me if I were to stay any longer with you and your wife. I am leaving. Do not forget the cold hip-baths, and believe me when I say that in the future all will go well."

Now every day the woman gazed after the men of the town and they seemed to her well-built and strong and most desirable. She thought to herself: "This business of two iron members is very strange." Everywhere the woman went, the men of the town looked after her, admiring her beauty and saying to themselves: "This passion for using scissors is very strange." But the man who desired most ardently to lie with this beautiful woman was the friendly landlord in whose house the husband had taken up lodgings. And as he was the immediate recipient of her signals, she being most adept in signs and promptings, they were able to make a secret assignment for a time when the husband had business in the town. Now the friendly man thought to himself: 'It would be well for me to arm myself with a knife against a possible attack with a pair of scissors." He therefore hid a knife under his clothes, went in to the woman, and lay down on the angareb beside her. But the beautiful woman thought: "It might be safer to find out if there is any truth in the story of the two iron members." So when the man moved closer to her on the angareb, she began with the greatest possible caution to run her hand along under his garments. She had nearly attained the object both of her investigation and her desire when the silver rings on her fingers knocked against the dagger which the friendly but cautious man was wearing under his garments. Then by accident she touched the blade of the knife, and scratched her hand on it.

On hearing the clink made by the rings, the man gave a yell. The woman, when she felt the dagger, also gave a

45

yell. In terror, the woman leapt up and, trembling, took refuge in a corner of the room. Pulling his robe together, the man made off. The woman saw the blood running down her hand and said to herself: "What a dreadful danger I exposed myself to! So it is true after all! How terrible if this man's hard iron members had ravaged the tender soil of my pleasure garden. The men of this town are fearsome indeed!"

Soon afterwards her husband came home and said: "Come, now, wife, take a bath in this town's most excellent water."

That evening the friendly man went to the coffee house and sat down among the other men. He had a stricken air and his expression was not friendly. The other men looked at him. They moved closer. At last an older man said: "Tell us, my friend. You seem so exhausted! What happened? Was it cut off?" The friendly man said: "No, things did not go so far as that. Her scissors clinked. I heard them and was able to leap away at the very last moment!"

THE HUSBAND'S REVENGE *Kordofan*

A man having married a young wife was soon afterwards visited in a dream by his father, who told him he must make a pilgrimage to Mecca. The next morning the man got his baggage ready, went to his wife, and said: "Young wife, my father has appeared before me in a dream and begged me to go to Mecca. I am now leaving. But it may well be in the few days that we have been married, that you have conceived. I hope to return before you bear the child, so that I shall be near you when it is born. However, as soon as you become aware of the first signs of pregnancy you must consult an old woman whom I shall appoint to look after you." Thereupon the young husband took leave of his young wife and set out on his pilgrimage.

Now in the same town there lived a muezzin who daily carried out his professional duties from the minaret of the great mosque. This muezzin had seen the young wife and he had also heard from the lips of her husband that the latter was leaving on pilgrimage to Mecca. The muezzin said to himself: "This young wife will now be leading a very quiet life—a state she will find the more painful for having had only a few days in which to experience the joys of matrimony. But this young wife is so beautiful and cultivated that, it seems to me, I could find no more agreeable occupation than to carry on the work begun by the pilgrim to Mecca. I shall therefore make friends with the old woman who has access to the young wife. Perhaps she can help me to satisfy the urge I have to console the young beauty in her solitude."

So one day the muezzin spoke to the old woman, asking her to come to see him, as he had something to discuss with her. Soon afterwards the old woman came as he had asked and, finding himself alone with her, the muezzin said: "Woman, I have no doubt that out of your great experience you will know that people's needs and desires vary considerably." The old woman said: "Certainly I know this, and could tell you a great deal on the matter." The muezzin said: "Then you will know that, while some men may take it into their heads that there is an absolute necessity for them to journey to Mecca, others may feel an equally intense urge, though in a less lofty part of their anatomy, for objects that are closer to hand. This you will know." The old woman said: "There you are undoubtedly right. However, I do not suppose that you have asked me to come here in order to question me about the best road to Mecca." The muezzin said: "That is true. I have no intention whatever of making a pilgrimage to Mecca." The old woman said: "Then perhaps your urge is situated lower down inasmuch as the object of your desire is closer at hand." The muezzin said: "I could not have put it better myself. Indeed, for half the day my calling keeps me so close to the affairs of the Prophet that I could not think of inclining the upper part of my body any further in the direction of Mecca than is prescribed by prayer. Moreover, a few days ago I watched yet another of my acquaintances set off on a pilgrimage to Mecca where he promised to pray for me. Thus the upper part of my body is well provided for." The old woman said: "Since you hold that your loftier needs are accounted for by your friend in Mecca, no doubt you feel yourself able to carry out such duties as the pilgrim to Mecca is neglecting meanwhile here in the town?" The muezzin said: "I can see that you are a clever woman. In no circumstances will you find me wanting in gratitude, either towards you or towards anyone else."

The old woman said: "That being so, I will gladly do what I can to help you attain the goals that you desire, nor do I think it should be very difficult if what you have in mind is to resume the activity so abruptly broken off by the newly married pilgrim to Mecca." The muezzin then thanked the old woman, who went hurrying back to the plgrim's young wife. The old woman said to the younger one: "I have been thinking that your husband has treated you very badly and that you are greatly to be pitied." The young woman asked: "Why are you speaking ill of my husband?" The old woman said: "I am not speaking ill of your husband. But I must say that he has treated you badly with this unfinished baby. He should have finished making his wife's baby instead of being in such a hurry to carry out his father's wishes." The young woman said: "What do you mean, an unfinished baby?" The old woman said: "Well, he never finished making the baby. It was only its body he completed. If the baby is born as it now is it will have neither head nor limbs. He went away leaving his work undone, and it is you who will have to bear the humiliation of giving birth to a cripple." The young woman was very frightened. She asked: "Are you sure that this is so?"

The old woman said: "I am sure that it is so! Ask anyone who knows anything about it. Only a few days ago I was talking in much the same terms to the meuzzin of the great minaret who is renowned for the excellence of his work on babies." The young woman said: "How wicked my husband is! How wicked my husband is! But tell me, could not the muezzin who is renowned for the excellence of his work on babies not help me to complete the child?" The old woman said: "Yes, he can. You only have to ask." The young woman said: "Friend, I beg you, go quickly to the clever muezzin. Tell him to come here as soon as possible, before it is too late." The old woman said: "I will got at once. When shall I tell the muezzin to come?" The young woman said: "Tell him to come as soon as he has the time." The old woman went.

The old woman came to the muezzin and said: "Go to her now, my friend. The pilgrim's young wife wants to see you as soon as possible!" Thanking the old woman, the muezzin set out immediately. He came to the wife of the pilgrim to Mecca. The young woman greeted him, saying: "I thank you for coming. My husband has left me with an unfinished baby and has gone on pilgrimage to Mecca without waiting to make a start on its limbs. I have asked you to come here so that you can complete the work in which you are said to be most skilled." The muezzin said: "I shall be happy to help you." The young woman said: "How long will it take you?" The muezzin said: "It cannot be done all at one go. This is work I want to do well, the more so since your husband is saying prayers for me in Mecca." The young woman said: "That is good. But make a start at once so that no time is lost." The muezzin said: "Then lie down on the angareb. I will put all my strength into the work at once."

The young woman lay down on the angareb as she had been told. As for the muezzin, in following his urge he also fulfilled his promise that he would put all his strength into his work, doing so to such good purpose that the young woman said satisfied beyond all expectation. On getting up from the angareb she said: "It is true. You are really much better at such work than my husband. Come back often and continue the business as you have begun it." The muezzin said: "I promise you that I will. And I trust that I shall give you as much cause for satisfaction as I have this time. But you must let me know beforehand if you have any particular desires so that I can act accordingly at the appropriate moment." The young woman said: "Seeing that you have kindly expressed the wish to forestall my desires, perhaps you could see to it, if the child is a boy, that he is given as excellent a tool for the business as you yourself possess. It would be a pity for the boy to have one that was as small and feeble as his father's." The muezzin said: "All this I can promise you, for I flatter myself that it is precisely in detailed work such as this that I excel beyond all other, baby-makers in this town." The young woman said: "Must you go already, or could you perhaps go on working for a little while longer?" The muezzin said: "Just now I formed the baby's mouth. If you are not tired, lie down again and I will put its nose into position." The young woman said: "I am certainly very far from being so tired that I would object to your putting the nose into position. Indeed, it seems to me that your vigorous method of work suits me much better than my husband's softer ways." With these words the young woman again lay down on the angareb and the muezzin put the nose so firmly into position that the prospective mother, under the influence of his skilled attentions, began to moan with pleasure.

Thereafter the muezzin went as often as he wished to visit the pilgrim's young wife, and she for her part was delighted beyond measure with his diligent labors. But in order to devote himself wholly and entirely to his work on the young woman, the muezzin sent his own wife, herself still young but more familiar and therefore less interesting, to visit her parents for several months. Then he devoted himself with redoubled energy to the young wife of the pilgrim to Mecca.

Meanwhile the pilgrim, having duly said his prayers in Mecca, one day unexpectedly returned home. When his wife saw him coming she could not bring herself to welcome him joyfully. Indeed, she turned her back on him as he entered, paying no further attention to him, and, upon his speaking kindly to her, she would not answer but sullenly left the room. Then the pilgrim to Mecca said to himself: "Something has been happening here. I must find out what it is." At the first opportunity he again spoke kindly to his wife. But this time also she turned sullenly away, and began to leave the room.

But the pilgrim said to his young wife: "Do not go! Stay here and tell me why you will not answer me, and why you look at me with hostile eyes." The young wife turned to face her husband. Looked at him very angrily, she said: "You ask why I am hostile towards you? Well, it is because you are a bad husband, a very bad husband! To please your dead father you went running off to Mecca, leaving me, your live young wife with an unfinished baby. And just because you had broken off your work like that, I should have had to bear the humiliation of giving birth to a cripple! Now you can give thanks to the hard-working muezzin of the greatest minaret who so excellently

took up the labor you had failed to complete and tire-
lessly went on adding limbs to the torso—nose, big toe,
and all!"

On hearing this the pilgrim to Mecca said to himself:
"So that is what has happened!" But to his wife the pilgrim said nothing. That same day he went to see the
muezzin, with whom he had already long been
acquainted, him that he had prayed for him in Mecca as
promised. The two became close friends, and the pilgrim
carefully nurtured this friendship, visiting the muezzin
every day. Hence it was not long before he learned that
his new friend had sent his wife to a town a few days'
journey away on a visit of several months to her parents.
The pilgrim took careful note of this information and,
moreover, visited his friend the muezzin so frequently that
the latter could undertake nothing without his knowledge.

For several days the muezzin felt pleasantly relieved of
the part-time occupation that he had been accustomed to
practice. For the young wife of the pilgrim to Mecca had
shown herself exceptionally active of late while the big
toes were in the process of being made and she had, moreover, given evidence of greater perseverance and recep-
tivity that he was able in the long run to satisfy. Having
enjoyed several pleasant and restful days in the company
of his new friend, however, the muezzin once again began
to wish for a renewal of his activities. He said to himself:
Of course, in the long run the kind of woman that I
should want would not be like the wife of this pilgrim
to Mecca, a woman who is more active and with greater
endurance than many a man. It would indeed be very
pleasant if my own wife were to return to me, for in the
long run her gentle ways are more enjoyable and less
exacting than the abandon of the other woman."

Now when the pilgrim to Mecca had been back in the
town for a certain time, much of the time had been spent
in the company of the muezzin, he one day said to his
friend: "Tomorrow I shall again be going away for a few
days, and I shall visit such and such a town," naming the
town where the muezzin's wife was staying with his
parents-in-law. When the muezzin heard he thought to
himself: "Clearly this man is going away only in order
to escape from his wife and so recuperate for a few days.

Now since his own wife will have made considerable demands upon him, it would seem to me that for some time he will constitute little danger to other women." But out loud the muezzin said to the pilgrim to Mecca: "Do you know anyone you can stay with in that town?" The pilgrim replied: "No, I do not know anyone in that town." The muezzin said: "Listen, my friend, by a happy coincidence that town is the home of my parents-in-law with whom my wife is at present staying. I will therefore give you a letter to my father-in-law enabling you to stay with him. But when you return I would beg you to do me the favour of bringing my wife back under your care and making sure that nothing happens to her on your way across the desert." The pilgrim to Mecca said: "I did indeed have another lodging in mind, but if such is your intention, my friend, I will gladly do as you wish."

The following day the pilgrim to Mecca set off with the letter, and eventually arrived at the house of the muezzin's parents-in-law. Having stayed with them for a few days he prepared to leave for home and his host requested him, in accordance with the contents of his son-in-law's letter, to take custody of his daughter and accompany her back to her husband, the muezzin. So the pilgrim to Mecca set off with the muezzin's wife, covering only a short distance and not undertaking a full day's march until the second day of their journey, when they entered the desert. Though not long by ordinary standards, the march was arduous enough, entailing as it did a night in the solitude of the wilderness with only a few trees for shelter.

Thus, when the pilgrim to Meca and the muezzin's wife camped that evening in the lonely spot beneath the trees, they were very weary. The pilgrim to Mecca said to the muezzin's wife: "Listen, we are now in a very isolated spot and it would be well if one of us were to keep watch so that we are not taken unawares by the approach of thieves or wild beasts. Let me sleep for the first few hours so that I am quite refreshed. Then wake me and I will watch for the rest of the night so that you can go on sleeping, without care or disturbance until the morning." The muezzin's wife said: "That suits me very well." The pilgrim to Mecca said: "Wake me then, when two hours have gone by."

Then the pilgrim to Mecca lay down and at once fell asleep. But though the muezzin's wife was determined to remain awake, she was tired after the hardships of the days march, and thus it happened that after a time she too fell asleep. A little while later the pilgrim to Mecca awoke. After making absolutely sure that the young woman was fast asleep, he went across to her and removed from throat, wrists, and hands all of the gold ornaments that she was wearing, hiding them in his long robe. Then he lay down again where he had been before and slept until the following morning.

When morning came the muezzin's wife was the first to wake. She at once noticed the loss of all her ornaments. In great alarm she woke the pilgrim to Mecca. Starting out of his sleep the latter said: "Why did you not wake me during the night? Something evil might easily have happened." The muezzin's wife said: "Something evil did happen. I was so tired that I fell asleep and a thief came up and robbed me of all my gold ornaments." The pilgrim to Mecca leapt up, saying: "What? A thief has robbed you? Come, we must look for his tracks in the sand so that we know what direction he has taken. Look about on all sides and I too will see what I can find." The muezzin's wife looked about her. She looked on every side. The woman said: "All I can see are the tracks we made ourselves while piling up our baggage yesterday evening." Shaking his head, the pilgrim to Mecca said: "This is a very serious matter; I too can see nothing else. However can it have happened?"

The pilgrim to Mecca sat down and considered. The muezzin's wife sat down next to him and considered. After a while the muezzin's wife said: "Can you not think of anything?" The pilgrim to Mecca said: "I have thought of something, yes, but it is a difficult matter." The muezzin's wife said: "Tell me what it is, for the loss of my jewelry is for me a great misfortune!" The pilgrim to Mecca said: "Then hear, O wife of my friend! You know that as between men and woman there is a difference." The woman said: "I do indeed know it!" The pilgrim to Mecca said: "Well, now, in many women the difference is thievish and much given to stealing. Theft is a natural characteristic of the female difference. Generally, however, a woman's difference steals only from men. But if

53

for any length of time it has not been able to steal from men, it may well steal something from its own mistress. Since there appear to be no strange footprints round about, I can only suppose that your own difference, having for some time had no opportunity of robbing its husband, has now robbed you instead, and concealed the booty within itself." The muezzin's young wife said: "That my difference likes to steal from men I have since my marriage often had occasion to notice. Moreover, recently it has had no opportunity to steal. But tell me, I pray, how can the ornaments be recovered from the difference?"

Wagging his head, the pilgrim to Mecca replied: "It cannot be accomplished by a woman alone. A man has to introduce his own difference slowly and carefully into hers in order to search it. It must be done however, soon after the theft and in addition, slowly and with care, for otherwise the booty will disappear further and further inside and, as you know, it can then only come out again in the form of a child. Otherwise, your difference will turn the jewelry into a stone baby." The muezzin's wife cried out in terror. The muezzin's wife said: "What? I shall give birth to a stone baby?" It would kill me!" The pilgrim to Mecca said: "Yes, it does kill women." Throwing herself on the ground at the pilgrim's feet, the muezzin's wife said: "I implore you! I implore you! Try at once to see if you can retrieve the stolen objects from my difference. I implore you!" The pilgrim to Mecca said: "Lie down! I promise you that I will do my best to make your difference give up its booty."

The woman lay down. With the utmost caution the pilgrim from Mecca began the search with his difference and, having continued it for some time in such a manner that the woman could not fail to sense his care and forethought, he reached down into his robe and brought out a bracelet. The muezzin's wife said: "Yes, that is the first another!" After a short respite, therefore, the pilgrim to one! Thank you! Thank you! Quick, now, look for Mecca resumed his search, this time producing the second bracelet. The young woman was so delighted that she would have liked him to continue his search without delay. But the pilgrim to Mecca insisted that they should first have their breakfast and a drink of wine from the bottle they had brought, which he thought, would restore calm to their differences.

But as a result of drinking the wine, the young woman became even more insistent that the search of her thieving difference be continued. She said: "My difference does not at all object to your searching its every nook and cranny for the stolen jewelry, and it even seems to me to be more than willing than ever to restore the stolen objects. Indeed, each search appears to make it more avid for another!" The pilgrim to Mecca said: "That is easily explained. For your difference stole your gold and precious stones only because it had for so long been unable to steal from a man." The muezzin's wife said: "Hasten! Look for my necklace!" Once again the pilgrim to Mecca complied with her request, this time handing the young woman her necklace.

Thus the young woman had recovered all her jewelry and there was nothing to prevent the pilgrim to Mecca from resuming his journey in her company. But when they had both somewhat restored their strength with food and wine, the muezzin's wife said: "Listen, O friendly man! A little while since a ring was lost in my father's house. Now I think it very possible that my difference was responsible for the theft of that object. I would therefore be much obliged to you if you would search for it far back in my difference." The pilgrim to Mecca, in whom the wine had induced a further desire for the agreeable pursuit, replied: "Certainly, O friendly mistress of a thievish difference! I will do so at once."

The pilgrim to Mecca therefore began his search for the fourth time, conducting it with such thoroughness and energy that finally the muezzin's wife could not help letting wind. The pilgrim to Mecca, who in any case, had reached the end of his strength, now remarked: "Did you hear? Just now your difference swore quite plainly that no more stolen gold or precious stones are hidden away inside it." With these words he rose. The young woman also got up saying: "Indeed I heard it. Moreover, I can now feel my difference. I thank you!"

The pilgrim to Mecca and the woman, after resting for a little while, set off once more and duly arrived in the town, the pilgrim to Mecca at once going off to find his wife and his companion going off to find her husband, the muezzin.

The muezzin welcomed his wife with great joy and, since he had for some time led an extremely retired life, he manifested his pleasure with much assiduity. But his wife fended him off, saying: "On the way here I met with a cruel misadventure for which you are responsible. As you know, women's differences are very thievish and, as you also know, they usually steal only from men. But since you left me so long with my parents, thus depriving my difference of all opportunity of satisfying its natural desire to steal, it robbed me during the night of all my precious stones and gold and silver jewelry in order to turn all this into a stone baby whose birth would, of course, have killed me. Now you can thank the friendly pilgrim to Mecca, who so promptly and conscientiously recovered the jewelry piece by piece from the thief, finally extracting from it the oath that it had stolen nothing further of that kind. If it had not been for the efforts of his difference I would now, thanks to your neglect, be faced with certain death!"

On hearing this the muezzin went out, saying to himself: "This man appears to have managed the business of barter so thoroughly that it seems improbable that my wife will respond kindly to my advances for several days." As the muezzin went on his way he met the pilgrim to Mecca and said: "You have brought back my wife so safely that I can hardly thank you adequately for your unremitting care." The pilgrim to Mecca said: "How else could I have repaid you for the way you came to my assistance on an earlier occasion?"

THE BOY   *Kabyle*

1. ANI-APPRENTICESHIP

There was once two youths who were very great friends though they did not live in the same village but in two different ones at some distance from each other. One day one of them, Ahmar, said to the other: "It is senseless to have to walk such a long way each time one of us wants to talk to the other. Let us move into the same village." His friend agreed. When the two youths got married Ahmar said: "If one of us has a daughter and the other a son, then our children shall marry each other." His friend agreed. When they had been living in the same village for a few months, Ahmar began to regret the agreement he had made with the other, and soon after that a daughter was born to himself, he said: "My wife has given birth. Her child is to be called Aini. Aini is not a girl, but a boy." Thereafter the father always made Aini wear boy's clothing, so that everyone thought the child was a boy.

The other's son and Aini became friends from childhood on. Aini and the boy spent all their days together from morning until night. They played together. They ate together. The boy always knew where Aini was and Aini always knew where the boy was. And so it went on until they both began to grow up.

Aini was quite a big girl. One day as they were playing, grabbing at one another, the boy seized Aini by the shoulders, and caught hold of her breast. The boy said: "Aini, why does your chest stick out like that? Look, Aini, my chest is quite flat!" Aini said: "I do not know. Leave it alone!" Just then an old woman was passing by. She laughed and said to the boy: "It is because your friend is a girl." Aini went off. The boy followed her. Aini went into the forest. Aini wept. Aini sat down on a tree trunk. The boy sat down next to Aini. They talked together. They swore that one day, that they would get married. From that day on Aini and the boy no longer played with each other. Aini and the boy avoided each other when other people were about. People noticed this.

People went to Aini's father and said: "Listen your son Aini is not as merry as he used to be. Aini is always skulking about in corners with his friend. It is as though the two friends were boy and girl and were courting each other." Ahmar said to himself: "Hooo! So it is that kind of friendship. I shall have to do something about it." And Ahmar shut Aini into a room and gave Aini work to do in the room and no longer allowed Aini to leave the farm. So now Aini always stayed at home and when the boy,

Aini's friend, knocked at the farmhouse door to ask if he could see or speak to Aini, he was always told: "Aini is too busy.'

But at night the boy went about the farmhouse listening at the walls to find out in what room Aini was living. He soon found out where Aini lived and, when everyone was asleep, he threw pebbles in through the window. Aini was hit by one of the pebbles. Aini got up, looked out of the window, and recognized the boy. Aini spoke to the boy. Every evening the boy came to the window so that he and Aini could talk to each other without Aini's parents knowing. But the boy saw that this was not the way to get Aini for his wife.

One evening the boy again came to Aini's window. He threw little pebbles and Aini came to the window. The boy said: "Aini, today I will say goodbye. I am going away to another place to see if I can do anything there that will help me to get you for my wife. If I can bring back something big (meaning a high bride-price), then your father will give you to me." Aini said: "Yes, do that." The boy said: "But I swear that if you die, then I too will die, and now you must swear to me that if I die, then you too will die. We only want to live with each other. Will you swear that?" Aini swore it. Aini and the boy took leave of one another.

The next day the boy left the village. On his way he met with an old man. The old man asked the boy: "Where are you going?" The boy said: "I have set out to earn my bread." The old man said: "Then come with me. I will be your father. Be you my son." The boy agreed. He stayed with the old man. The old man was very kind to him. He talked to him, ate with him, and looked after him. But one day the old man arrived when the boy was at play with other boys in the village. He heard the boy call out the name Aini. Now a few years before the old man had married again and his young wife was called Aini. When the old man heard the boy shouting "Aini" he thought it was his own young wife the boy had meant.

The old man grew distrustful. He was no longer friendly to the boy and did not talk to him any more. He let the boy do what he liked. The boy said to himself: "Things are not as they used to be here. I will set out again and try my luck elsewhere. But first I will go back to my father's village and see how Aini is."

The boy went to the old man and said: "Tomorrow I want to go to my father's village and see how things are there." The old man said: "I will go with you, for I want to buy oil there." So they set out together. Not far from the boy's village they crossed a graveyard. There they saw a fresh grave. In the graveyard there was a shepherd who was tending his flock. The old man asked him: "Who has been buried here?" The shepherd said: "They have just buried the girl Aini, who died yesterday.

The boy said to himself: "So Aini is dead and buried. Now I will die." The boy said to the old man: "In our country we do not bury our dead as you do. Let me show. Come, help me lift these stone slabs." Having lifted the stone slabs the boy saw Aini lying dead in the grave. The boy said: "Now you are dead, Aini. But I am coming to be with you." The boy lay down beside Aini's body in the grave and said to the old man: "Now put the stone slabs back over the grave. Then go to buy your oil and then go home to your Aini. But as for me, I shall stay here with my Aini." Then the old man covered over the grave and went into the village to buy oil.

On the day after Aini's burial, Asrain (the avenging angel) came to pronounce judgment over the dead Aini. But on arriving at Aini's grave he found the living boy beside the corpse of Aini. The Asrain asked the boy: "What are you doing beside Aini's corpse? You are alive! I have no business with you. You must leave Ani's corpse and get out of this grave!" The boy said: "Nothing matters to me. Aini is dead and now I too want to die. I shall stay here in the grave with Aini."

Asrain turned about and went back to God. Asrain said: "Such a thing has never happened to me before. I went to find Aini's corpse and beside it I found a living boy. The boy said that since Aini was dead he wanted to die as well. The boy refuses to leave the grave." Having heard what Asrain had to say, God said to Asrain and the boy: "This boy still has forty years of life left. If he is willing to give Aini half of that number, he will only live another twenty years, but Aini will also live another twenty years." The boy laughed in the grave Aini opened her eyes. Aini saw the boy beside her. Aini said: "I thank you!"

On the following day the old man came back from buying oil. As he approached the graveyard he said. "I should like to know whether the boy, who lay down in Aini's grave beside her corpse, is still alive or whether he has died." He went up to the grave, put his ear to the stone slabs, and listened. Then he heard the boy's voice speaking to Aini. The old man said: "They are both alive." The old man took up the stone slabs. Aini and the boy laughed. Aini and the boy climbed out of the grave, thanked the old man, and said goodbye to him. Aini and the boy went away from that place.

The boy said: "Aini, we will build a house in the depths of the forest, far away from all other people. Then we will spend the twenty years still left for us to live." Aini agreed. In the forest the boy built a house. It was strong and solid and had seven doors, so that when it was locked up no one could get in from the outside. During the day when the boy was out hunting he kept the seven doors locked. Then Aini could not get out of the house and no one, except the boy who had the key, could get into the house. But Aini sat at the window, looking out over the forest or up at the sky.

One day two hunters, who were sent out hunting every day by the Agellid of the neighbouring village, came upon the house where Aini lived. The hunters looked up at the window and saw Aini. And there they remained, looking at Aini. Aini was so beautiful that the hunters could not take their eyes off her. They did not go on with their hunting but remained there looking at Aini until the evening. Not until evening had come did they return to the Agellid's village. The Agellid asked the hunters: "Why have you come back today without any game?" The hunters replied: "In the forest we came upon a house. A woman was looking out of the window. She was so beautiful that we could not tear outselves away but had to say there looking up at her. Neither of us could have believed that there was anything so lovely on this earth. And you, too, O Agellid, have never seen anything so beautiful." The Agellid said: "Tomorrow I will go with you and see if what you say is true. If so, I will forgive you for your indolence today."

60

The following day the two hunters showed the Agellid the way to Aini's house. The Agellid came to Aini's house. Aini was looking out of the window. Aini saw that the Agellid was very handsome. The Agellid looked at Aini without a word. He looked at Aini and could find nothing to say. He remained standing there until evening. When evening came Aini said: "Any moment now my husband will come home from hunting. If he finds you here he will kill you." The Agellid said: "Could I not visit you some time?" Aini said: "Every day my husband turns the key in the seven locks of the seven doors. No one therefore can get in." The Agellid went away.

The following day the Agellid called all the men of his village together and said: "Dig a hole and a tunnel in that direction." The Agellid had a passageway dug that led from the floor of his own room to the floor of Aini's room in her house in the forest. One morning when the boy had gone out hunting, after fastening the seven locks on the seven doors behind him, the Agellid came through the tunnel right into Aini's room. Aini was startled. She asked: "Why have you come?" The Agellid said: "I was drawn here by your beauty." Aini said no more. Again Aini noticed how strong and handsome the Agellid was. The Agellid led her to her couch. The Agellid laid her down. Aini said nothing. The Agellid made love with Aini. Aini said nothing. The Agellid made love with her several times. Aini said: 'Now go, for my husband will soon be home. Make friends with my husband." The Agellid went away.

The next day the Agellid went out hunting. The Agellid met the boy and watched him for a while. Then he said: "You seem to be a very skillful hunter." The boy said: "I know a little about it." The Agellid said: "Teach me how to hunt. Everything I kill will be yours." The whole day the boy went hunting with the Agellid. They killed much game. The Agellid gave his share to the boy. The boy went home laden with game. Seeing her husband come home with more game than usual, Aini asked: 'How is it that you have been so successful today?" The boy said: "On my way I met an Agellid and went hunting with him. I showed him what to do. He gave me his share of the game." Aini said: "That is good company for you. You must become his friend."

The next day the boy again met the Agellid in the forest. The Agellid said: "Today we will not go hunting. Come to my house in my village. We will play jammat[1] together." The boy agreed. The Agellid took the boy to his room and played jammat with the boy. The boy was very attentive and the Agellid lost the first game. The Agellid went on losing. The Agellid lost all that he had. The Agellid had nothing left. The boy went home again.

When the boy went out hunting the following day the Agellid came through the underground tunnel to Aini and said: "Yesterday, when playing draughts with your husband, I lost all that I had." Aini said: "Leave everything to me."

The next morning the Agellid again met the boy in the forest. The Agellid said: "Come to my house again. I still have something that I can stake." The boy said: "Wait. Let me take my weapons home, and then I will come." The boy went home opened the doors, went inside, hung up his weapons on a hook on the wall, and went out again. He locked the seven doors, returned to the place in the forest where he had left the Agellid and said: "I am ready. We can go to your house again and play jammat." The Agellid and the boy set off for the village.

When the boy had finished locking the seven doors from the outside so as to rejoin the Agellid in the forest, Aini took the weapons her husband had hung on the wall, lifted them down, and hurried through the tunnel with them to the Agellid's room. There she hung them on the wall at a spot exactly opposite the place where the visiter would be sitting, and directly behind the Agellid's back. Then Aini returned home.

When Aini had been gone some time, the Agellid and the boy came out of the forest into the village. The Agellid led the boy into his room, sayig: "Sit down. I will fetch the draughts." The boy sat down. He looked up. He looked at the wall opposite him. He said to himself: "Those are my weapons!" He said to himself: "Those cannot be my weapons, for I hung my weapons up on the wall at home, and then locked the seven doors behind me. I have the key here in my pocket. Those cannot be my weapons!" The Agellid returned.

[1] Draughts or checkers.

The Agellid said: "Here is the jammat. Now we will play." The Agellid played. The boy played. The boy thought: "Those are my weapons. Those cannot be my weapons." The boy played badly. The boy looked at the wall. He looked at the weapons. The boy lost more and more. He kept thinking: "Those are my weapons. They cannot be my weapons." The boy lost all that he had won from the Agellid the day before. The boy got up and went. He set off for home through the forest.

When the boy had left, Aini came through the tunnel. She took the weapons down from the wall and carried them back to her house, which was closed with seven locks and seven doors. Inside the house Aini hung up the weapons on the wall just as the boy had hung them before going to the Agellid's house. After a while the boy arrived home. He unlocked the seven locks on the seven doors and went inside. He looked at the place where he had hung his weapons on the wall that morning. He saw them hanging there as he had left them. The boy slapped himself on the forehead, saying: "What a fool I was! What a fool I was!" Aini asked: "What is the matter, what is wrong with you?" Where have you been?" The boy said: "I have been with the Agellid, playing jammat with him. I saw weapons hanging on the wall that looked exactly like my own. All the time I was thinking about the weapons and not about the play. In this way the Agellid won back everything that he lost to me in play yesterday."

Aini said: "Then tomorrow you must play the Agellid again and see if you can win back what you have lost today. But tomorrow you must not think about your weapons or about me. Think only about the game. Then you will win." The boy said: "You are right. I will try again." The following morning he went into the forest where he met the Agellid, and said: "Shall we hunt or shall we play?" The Agellid replied: "As you wish." The boy said: "In that case let us play again today. Wait while I take my weapons home. I will come back here."

The boy ran home, hung his weapons on the wall, said goodbye to Aini and went out again, locking each door in turn behind him. Then returned to the place in the forest where he had left his friend the Agellid. He went back with him to his village. They entered the Agellid's room. The Agellid said: "Sit down and I will fetch the draughts." The Agellid went. The boy examined the room. He saw nothing there to disturb him. The boy said: "Today I will not think of anything except the game. Today I will win from the Agellid everything that he possesses."

The Agellid returned with the jammat. He sat down. They began to play. The boy thought only of the game. The boy won. He had already won part of what the Agellid owned when Aini came into the house through the passageway. She walked into the room in which the Agellid was at play with her husband. Without speaking she set down between the two men the tea that she had brought, and then she went out again. She hurried back along the passage to her own house, which was locked with seven locks and seven doors. Now as Aini had bent over to set down the tea, her shadow had fallen on the boy's hands. He had looked up and seen Aini. He had said to himself: "It is not possible!" He said to himself: "It must have been Aini." He looked up. Aini had disappeared again. The boy thought: "It must have been Aini. But I have kept her shut up in the house with the seven doors and seven locks. No, it cannot have been Aini." The boy was no longer thinking about the game. The Agellid began to win back more and more. He began to win what belonged to the boy. But the boy was no longer thinking about the game. His only thought was whether or not he had seen Aini. The boy lost everything that belonged to him. He had absolutely nothing left, and now the Agellid had not only recovered his own possessions but in addition had won everything that the boy possessed. The boy left. The boy hurried out of the village and went home. The boy examined the locks on the seven doors. They were all properly fastened. The boy went into the house. He saw Aini who was lying on her couch. He slapped his forehead, exclaiming: "Fool, fool, fool!"

Aini asked: "What is the matter? Have you won back the Agellid's possessions?" The boy said: "No, I have not won them back. I imagined that I saw you in the Agellid's house and I could think of nothing except whether or not you could have been there, and so I lost not only what I had already won back from the Agellid but everything I possessed as well." Aini said: "Then the Agellid now owns your possessions in addition to his own?" The boy said: "That is so." Aini said: "Then you have lost!"

The following day the boy went out hunting. Scarcely had he gone out, locking the doors behind him, than the Agellid came through the tunnel to Aini. Aini said: "Now that you have won everything from my husband you must be even richer than you were before." The Agellid replied: "That is so." The Agellid said to Aini: "Come with me. Your husband no longer has anything. Come to my house and be my wife." Aini went with the Agellid. The Agellid took her with him to his house.

That evening the boy came in from hunting. He opened all of the doors and called out: "Aini did not answer. The boy searched the whole house. He did not find Aini. He sat down on Aini's couch and said: "This is the Agellid's doing. Aini has gone to him." The boy thought for a while. The boy said: "I have given her twenty years of my life. I shall take them back again."

The boy shut himself in. He remained shut inside the house for forty days. For forty days he did not go out of the house. For forty days he did not see the sun. For forty days he ate nothing and drank nothing. At the end of those forty days no one could have recognized him. He was very thin. His eyes were hollow. He walked with a stoop. He looked like a corpse. He no longer looked like a living man. But when forty days had gone by the boy came out of the house. He unlocked the seven doors, stepped out of his house, and said: "I will get back those twenty years, and not a year will go by without my eating my fill of the best fare provided by God on this earth. For God reserves the best fare, not for the upright, but for the clever. And since God has made me clever rather than stupid, I can dip my ladle into the best fare as well as any other."

So wretched did the boy look that no one recognized him. The boy came to the Agellid. The Agellid, too, failed to recognize him. The boy said: "Can I work for you?" The Agellid said: "You would not have the strength to work." The boy said: "It is only that I have been ill. If you let me work for a time and give me enough to eat, my condition will improve." The Agellid hired the boy. The boy worked and the boy ate. After a while he began to look better.

For a whole month the boy worked for the Agellid. At the end of that time he looked fresher and stronger and more handsome than ever before. All of the women and girls followed him with their eyes. Then he worked for yet another month and ate his fill and became so handsome and strong that he was the handsomest and strongest young man the world had ever seen.

The Agellid's mother came to the boy as he worked in the field and said: "O boy, come to visit me when I am on my couch this evening!" The boy said: 'I will gladly do so, but I am afraid of the Agellid. Your son would see me and then he would kill me. If only your son were dead, then I could even marry you." The Agellid's mother said: "Then you would be mine for ever." The boy said: "Yes, then I would be yours for ever." The Agellid's mother said: 'This very evening I will give my son poison with his supper. Take care not to eat any of the porridge."

In the evening the boy was sitting with the Agellid. The food was brought in. The Agellid took a spoon and dipped it in the porridge. He was about to lift the spoon to his mouth when the boy laid a hand on his arm, saying: "Wait! Before touching it call your dog and feed him some of the porridge." This the Agellid did. The dog ate the porridge and at once fell dead. In great alarm the Agellid exclaimed: "What is this? My mother cooks my food herself!" The boy said: "Wait! I was the first to be taught a lesson and now it is your turn. Do you know who I am?" The Agellid exclaimed: "What? You are my laborer." The boy shook his head.

The boy said: "You are wrong. I am not your laborer but your teacher, and moreover I am Aini's husband." The Agellid wanted to jump up and get his weapons. The boy said: "There is no need. If I had wished to take my revenge on you for stealing Aini from me all I had to do was to let you eat the poisoned food prepared for you by your mother, who wished to kill you in order to marry me. But I did not let you. I do not wish to take my revenge on you. Nor do I wish to marry your mother. All I want is to be given back the years which I once gave to Aini. I demand Aini of you. But I will not kill you, for you have now had the same experience with your mother that I had with Aini. Give me both of these women. I am going to burn them alive."

66

The Agellid gave Aini to the boy. He gave him his mother. The boy lit a big fire. The boy said to Aini: "When you are dead, I gave you half my life, I gave you twenty years. In return you ran away from me to a man who was rich and an Agellid, whereas I was only a poor hunter. You did nt use the twenty years I gave you as we had once both sworn to do. Therefore today I demand the twenty years back again. That is all." The boy burned Aini and the Agellid's mother alive.

Then the boy went away to another country.

2. THE AGELLID'S DAUGHTERS—JOURNEYMAN

The boy was very strong and clever and handsome. All men were anxious to secure his services. He came to a district whose Agellid was everywhere famous for his wisdom as a judge. The boy had been with the Agellid for a few days when the latter said: "I often have to make journeys to settle disputes. At such times there is no one here to take my place. I would ask you whether you would be prepared to stay here in my house as my representative, for I have never found anyone clever enough to fill that office. Think about this matter until tomorrow." When he had said this, the Agellid went away and the boy stayed behind on the farm.

He walked up and down in the yard thinking over what the Agellid had said. He said out loud: "Shall I stay or shall I not stay?" Behind him two voices replied: "Unless you are a fool you will stay." The boy turned around. He saw two beautiful full-grown girls. The girls went into the house. They were the Agellid's daughters. Inside the house they began to laugh. The boy said to himself: "That would make a very nice double helping for a clever man." In the evening the Agellid returned. The boy said: "I do not need to think it over any more. I have made up my mind to accept your proposal that I should stay here as your representative."

The next morning the Agellid had to go away. As soon as he had ridden out of the yard his two beautiful daughters came to the boy, laughed, and said: "Boy, will you make a wager with us? You are so fine and strong a man that it is a pleasure for women to have dealings with you. Tell us now whether you are willing to make a wager with us." The boy said: "I am willing. Tell me what the wager is." The two beautiful girls laughed and said: "We will give you fifty gold pieces if you can swive us twenty times in succession. You will give us fifty gold pieces if you fail to do so." The handsome boy laughed and said: "Let us lose no time. We will begin at once." The boy lay with the two girls twenty times. He also swived them twenty times. But the twentieth time he could not finish. The two beautiful girls said: "You are a strong and handsome man but you will not get the fifty gold pieces. It is you who must pay us fifty gold pieces. For you swived us twenty times, but the twentieth time you grew weak." The boy said: "The matter is a complicated one and can only be decided by a judge. I suggest we put this matter before your father, the Agellid, and leave the decision to him."

The two beautiful girls gave a shriek. They said: "How can you suggest such a thing? Our father would kill us if he heard what we had done! He would hack us to pieces if he heard that we had made such a wager to you. You must not speak to our father about it. We would sooner give you the fifty gold pieces." The boy said: "You need not be afraid. I have no intention of speaking to your father about the dealings we have had together. I will not discuss anything of the kind with him. But since this is a dispute and my office in this house is that of judge, I will have to ask him for a decision."

The two beautiful girls were so frightened that, when their father came home, they went to hide in the stable next to the living room. The Agellid had not been back very long when the boy came in, greeted him, and after sitting down beside him, said: "Yesterday two men came to see me. They had made a wager together and were arguing about who had won it. One was a horse dealer, the owner of a strong horse. He had wagered fifty gold pieces that his horse could take twenty measures of corn. The other was a corn merchant and he had wagered fifty gold pieces that the horse could not take twenty measures of corn. They then put it to the test. The horse ate nineteen measures of corn one after the other. Taking the twentieth measure into its mouth it chewed it and then spat it out again. Holding that the horse had not taken the twentieth measure of corn, the corn merchant demanded fifty gold pieces of its owner. The owner of the horse declared that the horse had taken all twenty measures of corn, thus fulfilling its task. For if the horse had chosen to spit out the twentieth measure, that was its own affair. Thus the horse dealer demanded fifty gold pieces of the corn merchant." The Agellid asked: "What was your own opinion?" The boy said: "I thought that the owner of the horse had won the wager. For his horse had in fact taken the twentieth measure of corn. Thus the corn merchant must pay the fifty gold pieces to the horse dealer." The Agellid said: "I would have come to the same decision as you did. I can see that you have the same idea of justice and injustice as myself and that your judgment is clear. I am glad to find you are so wise, for now when I go away my mind will be at rest."

That night the two beautiful girls came into the boy's room and gave him their fifty gold pieces. They laughed softly and said softly: "We thank you. We care little for the loss of the fifty gold pieces in view of your own generosity. But as soon as our father goes away again we shall try another wager with you and this time we shall win."

A few days later the Agellid again went away. As soon as he had ridden out of the yard, his two beautiful daughters came to the boy and said: "Boy, you are so clever, handsome, and strong that we are again anxious to have dealings with you. Will you make another wager with us?" The boy said: "Yes, I am quite ready to do so. What is it you want?" The two beautiful girls laughed and said: "Both of us will take off all our clothes. Then, from evening until midnight, you will have to chase us, catch us, and throw us onto our bed. If you can disport yourself with us thus from evening until midnight without falling on us in order to swive us, we will pay you fifty gold pieces. But should you fall upon us and be unable to restrain yourself from swiving us, then it will be you who will owe us the fifty gold pieces." The boy said: "I accept your wager. But let me tell you in advance— you will lose your fifty gold pieces." The two girls laughed and said: "We do not care, so long as you will stay with us after midnight and sleep with us all night."

69

When evening came the two beautiful girls took off all their clothes. But the boy went into his room and, taking a piece of cloth, bandaged his penis to his leg. After a while the two naked girls came and gave the boy a pull. The boy jumped up, ran after them, caught them, and carried them to the bed, upon which he threw them down. After pressing them down on it, he stood up without doing anything else to them, nor did he try to prevent them jumping up again. The girls ran away, allowing themselves to be caught again, thrown onto the bed, and pressed down. Thus it went on for a long while without the girls being able to attain their ends. But not long before midnight the girls felt the boy and discovered that he had bound his penis to his leg. While he was rolling them on the bed they untied the cloth with which he was bandaged and, his penis thus set free, the boy could no longer hold back but fell upon the girls and began to swive them both, even though it was not yet midnight.

The girls laughed and said: "We are content. Go on with what you are doing. For now we are getting what we want and you will have to pay us the fifty gold pieces into the bargain." The boy said: "You can see how willing I am to comply with your wishes, both of you being beautiful girls. But it is you who will have to pay me the fifty gold pieces, for you untied my bandage and justice therefore is on my side. If you cannot agree with me and do not willingly hand over the gold pieces, I shall, like last time, ask the Agellid's opinion." The girls laughed and said: "No, we will not pay you the fifty gold pieces. We even demand the fifty gold pieces of you. If you bring up the subject as skillfully as before, we agree that you should obtain a decision from our father the Agellid and, like last time, we will abide by that decision. But for the time being stay with us."

The following morning the Agellid came back from his journey. The two girls hid in the stable and soon after the Agellid went into his room. The boy went to find the Agellid in his room and said: "While you were away the horse dealer and the corn merchant came to see me again, asking for a decision on a controversial matter. They had again made a wager with each other. This time the owner of the horse agreed to stand his animal at a given spot while the corn merchant was to place two buckets of corn, one to the right and the other to the left of the horse's head. The horse was to stand there from morning until midday and its owner undertook to pay the corn merchant fifty gold pieces if the horse, touched either of the buckets of corn before midday. The corn merchant undertook to pay the horse dealer fifty gold pieces if the horse, once in position, did not eat any of the corn before midday. Both agreed to the terms of the wager. The owner of the horse tethered his animal with a rope at the place they had agreed. The corn merchant put a bucket of corn on either side of the horse's head. For a long while the horse stood there without touching the corn. Shortly before midday, however, the corn merchant crept up and secretly severed the rope by which the horse was tethered. Being now able to move about freely, the horse at once made for one of the buckets and ate up the corn that was in it. Then it turned to the other bucket and by midday had just finished eating the corn. Now the corn merchant demanded the fifty gold pieces because the horse had not only touched the corn but had eaten it all up, and the horse dealer demanded the fifty gold pieces because the corn merchant had secretly severed the rope." The Agellid said: "Tell me how you, as my representative, decided the case." They boy said: "I decided that the corn merchant had no right to sever the rope just before midday when the horse had been standing there so long without touching the corn. For the owner of the horse had trained his animal to stand still in that way so long as its head was tethered. By severing the rope the corn merchant had deprived the horse dealer of all control over his horse and the horse of its understanding. Therefore the corn merchant must pay the owner of the horse the fifty gold pieces." The Agellid said: "Your decision was a very clever one. I could not have arrived at a better one myself. I am very glad that you were able to represent me so well while I was away.

At nightfall the Agellid's two beautiful daughters came to the boy's room, laughed softly, and said softly: "Here are the fifty gold pieces. We thank you. We would like to stay with you for a while."

In due course the Agellid's two beautiful daughters became pregnant. But this did not prevent them from continuing to visit the boy. One day the boy said to himself: "I have done this task for long enough. It is too much of a drain on my strength. Such fare may be all very well for a clever man but it is not honorable. This case has taught me that, though the best things are reserved for the clever, they are not wholesome unless, they lead to lawful enjoyment. I have no intention of remaining here to ruin my stomach."

One night, after the Agellid's two beautiful daughters had exceeded all bounds in the demands they made upon him, the boy packed his belongings and left the place without taking leave of anyone.

3. THE COFFEE-HOUSE OWNER'S WIFE   *Master*

The boy continued his wanderings and penetrated far into the country. Everywhere he went he asked what the people were like and what the women were like. Having arrived in a new district, he heard of an Agellid's daughter who was said to be exceptionally clever and beautiful. All those who spoke about her said that her father had built her a house of her own in which she lived. They related that the girl was exceptionally clever and had declared herself ready to test her wits against those of any man. This girl had also said that she would marry any man at all, though she would only keep for a husband one who was cleverer than she. What the people did not tell him, however, because they did not know, was that the girl had in the meantime taken a coffee-house owner for a husband. The girl had told the coffee-house owner that she was taking him only to see what kind of man he was. She told the coffee-house owner that she would deny him both house and marriage-bed should a man come along who could prove that he was braver and cleverer than he, or cleverer than herself. People did not tell the clever boy all of this because they did not know it. They only praised the beauty and cleverness of the Agellid's daughter. The boy said: "This Agellid's daughter would seem to be the wife that I am looking for." So the boy set out once more and went to the place where the Agellid's clever daughter was said to be living.

The boy arrived at the place. The boy settled with his belongings in a coffee-house. The boy did not know that the owner of the coffee-house was the man chosen by the Agellid's clever daughter to find out what sort of man he was. Now the boy lived in the coffee-house and did nothing at all. The boy said: "I will ask nothing and do nothing. What is going to happen will happen in any case. I shall wait until somebody shows me the way to my future wife."

For a month the boy stayed in the coffee-house, doing nothing and saying little. The coffee-house owner said to himself: "I must find out what this boy is doing here. I want to know because people keep asking me and I have no information to give to them." One day the coffee-house owner came up to the boy, greeted him, sat down beside him, and said: "You have been in my house for a month now." The boy said: "That is so. I have always paid for my board, lodging, and drink." The coffee-house owner said: "Certainly, you have always paid for everything. You must be wealthy to be able to go on paying for everything without having to earn your living. For it would seem that you do not work." The boy said: "No, I do not do any work. God has made me so clever, so handsome, and so strong that I never need anything." The coffee-house owner said: "Do you think that here, in this place, you will always get everything that you need?" The boy said: "Yes, if there are clever women in this place. But I do not believe that there are any clever women here." The coffee-house owner said: "You are quite wrong. There are some very clever women here. It is even said that the cleverest woman in the whole land lives in this place. In that house over there, for instance, there lives a young woman, our Agellid's daughter, who is cleverer than any other woman. Not long ago she took a husband who is busy all day. So as to make quite sure that no other man can intrude upon her while her husband is away, she has had her house fitted with seven doors to which there is only one key, and that key she gave to her husband, who always carries it with him. The clever woman has assured her husband that she will not allow into the house or receive any man not having the key to fit the seven locks.

She will not even receive her own relatives. This woman is very clever."

The boy said to himself: "The Agellid's girl has taken a husband. She has said that she will only receive the man who has the key to her house. I shall have such a key made. I shall go to her and see if she is really as clever as everyone says. If she proves to be really as clever, then I shall show her that I am cleverer than she or her husband, and after that I shall marry her. For after all, the coffee-house owner has already shown me where she lives." That evening the boy went to the house of the Agellid's daughter, taking with him a lump of wax. With part of the wax he took an imprint of the keyhole, then he pressed some more wax right into the lock. After that the boy went back to the coffee-house. Later that night the coffee-house owner went across to his wife's house. Putting the key into the keyhole, he opened the door. When he took the key out again he found the wards clogged with wax. The coffee-house owner said. "How can wax have got into my pocket and onto this key?" But he did not think about the matter for long. He removed the wax from the key and threw it onto the ground. Then he went into his wife's house through the six other doors, and left the house the following morning after having locked all the doors behind him.

During the night, however, the boy went out and looked for the wax which the coffee-house owner had thrown away. He picked it up and took it home with him. The next day he went to a smith and got him to make wards in accordance with the coffee-house owner's wax imprint. After that he went to one of the farms in the place and cut himself a good piece of wood which he carved to match the wax imprint that he himself had taken of the keyhole. Then he set the wards into the wood that he had carved. Towards evening he went to the house of the Agellid's clever daughter, tried his key in the lock and found that it fitted.

The boy opened the seven doors and locked them again. The boy walked into the room of the Agellid's daughter. The Agellid's daughter came towards him and asked: "How did you get in?" The boy said: Everyone has told me how clever you are. People have told me that you would only receive the man who had the key to your doors. Here is the key." The young woman examined the key and said: "It is not my husband's key." The boy said: "To take your husband's key would be an easy matter. One would simply have to kill him and take the key. People have told me that you would keep as your husband a man who was clever. Hence I had to produce a key of my own as the first proof of my cleverness." The Agellid's daughter returned the key to him, saying: "Sit down!" The boy sat down.

The boy examined the Agellid's daughter. She was strong and very beautiful. The Agellid's daughter examined the boy. He was strong and very handsome. The Agellid's daughter said: "What do you want of me?" The boy said: "First I want to sleep with you. Then I will see whether it would be a good thing for us to get married." The Agellid's daughter said: "But my husband will be arriving soon." The boy said: "We can make love until he comes. Then you can roll me up inside the mat and leave me lying in the corner. I shall sleep very well in the mat. Since he did not notice I had filled the keyhole with wax, then he will be too stupid to notice I am inside the mat." The Agellid's daughter laughed. The boy moved closer to her, saying: "You are beautiful." The Agellid's daughter said: "You are handsome and strong and clever." Then they lay down together. The Agellid's daughter said: "Now prove how clever you are. Oh, if only you were as clever as I would wish! If only you were the bravest and cleverest of men!" The boy laughed. The Agellid's daughter laughed.

They lay together until the husband of the Agellid's daughter began opening the doors. Then the boy got her to wind the mat around him and roll him in the corner, where he immediately fell asleep. The coffee-house owner came in and wanted to lie down beside his wife. The Agellid's daughter said: "You are not going to sleep with me tonight. In the next few days you will need to have all your wits about you, and so you must not weaken yourself. Do not forget the conditions under which I made you my husband." The coffee-house owner said: "I do not understand you." Then he went to his bed and lay down. In the morning he got up and went angrily out of the house. When he arrived back in his coffee-house he said crossly: "What is my wife up to? What can my wife mean? Why shall I need all of my wits about me?"

Not long after the coffee-house owner had left the house, the boy woke up, stuck his head a little way out of the mat, saw that the husband's bed was empty and that the Agellid's daughter was by herself, unrolled the mat, and stood up. The Agellid's daughter said: "Did you see my husband?" The boy said: "No, I did not have time. I was asleep." The Agellid's daughter said: "Come and talk to me." But she did not tell the boy who the husband was.

It was almost midday when the boy returned to the coffee-house. The coffee-house owner was used to the boy being there all the time. The coffee-house owner asked: "What were you doing last night? Your bed was not slept in last night, and it was nearly midday when you returned. You must have been with some pretty girl!" The boy said: "No, I was not with a pretty girl. I was with a beautiful woman. Did I not tell you that I always get what I need from clever women, and did you not tell me that the Agellid's daughter who lives in that house over there was clever? So I naturally decided to spend last night with the clever woman." The coffee-house owner asked: "So you slept over there, with the clever woman?" The boy said: "Of course." The boy said: "Did you not tell me that the clever woman would receive only the man who had the key? So I got a wax imprint made by the woman's husband by pressing wax into the keyhole. After the husband, who must be a real donkey, had pushed in his key, he pulled the wax off it, and left the imprint he had taken lying in the street. I made a key from the wax imprint. Then, yesterday evening, I went to the house, opened the seven doors, and afterwards lay with the woman. The woman is very clever and beautiful. When the husband came, I got the woman to wind me up in the floor-mat, which she then rolled into the corner. This morning, when the husband at last left his wife, I woke up, chatted to the wife for a while, and then came back here again. You were quite right. She is a very clever and beautiful woman. But as I said just now, her husband must in truth be a donkey." The coffee-house owner asked: "Then the clever woman did not tell you who her husband was?" The boy said: "No, she did not tell me

And why should she tell me?" The coffee-house owner
said: "Then you did not ask the clever woman who her
husband was?" The boy said: "No, why should I ask such
a thing? The clever woman does not want to talk about
her stupid husband, and he is no concern of mine." The
coffee-house owner said: "Why do you say that the husband of the woman you sleep with is no concern of
yours?" The boy said: "It is only the wife's business. The
husband will know about it soon enough when I marry
his wife." The coffee-house owner said: "What is that
you say? You want to marry this woman?" The boy said:
"I think that I will. But I have not yet made up my
mind." The coffee-house owner said: "Then tonight you
will go to the clever woman again and sleep with her?"
The boy said: "Of course I shall go." The coffee-house
owner said: "I do hope that you visit the Agellid's
daughter again tonight. It is rare to have an opportunity
to sleep with such a clever and beautiful woman." The
boy said: "That is very true. I should like to thank you
for drawing my attention to her." The coffee-house owner
went outside and began beating his head with his fists.
Then he went into his room and took out his sword to
sharpen it. As he sharpened his sword he kept repeating
over and over: "The man must in truth be a donkey!
The man must in truth be a donkey! The man must in
truth be a donkey! Just wait, my boy! Tonight I will get
you, and then the man who is in truth a donkey will teach
you to marry his wife!"

Towards evening, the boy went across to the house of
the Agellid's clever daughter. Again locking the seven
doors behind him, he went to find the clever wife. The
woman asked: "Did you tell anyone that you slept with
me last night?" The boy said: "Yes, I told a man who is
bound to pass it on to your husband more quickly than
anyone else, for I want to begin pitting my wits against
his as soon as possible." The woman said: "Whom did
you tell?" The boy said: "I told my friend, the foolish
coffee-house owner. Who else, seeing that he was so readily
available?" The clever woman laughed. She laughed and
laughed. The boy looked at her and said: "So it is the
coffee-house owner who is your husband? That is
regrettable." The woman laughed and then said: "Why
is it regrettable?" The boy said: 'Because I would

rather have tested myself against a cleverer man." The woman said: "Come and sit next to me." The boy stayed with the clever and beautiful woman until, in the street outside, they heard the coffee-house owner put the key into the keyhole of the outermost door. Hearing it, the boy said: "Roll up the mat, like yesterday. I will crawl into the wooden chest. It is long enough for me to be able to lie in it comfortably and sleep as I did last night."

The coffee-house owner came into his wife's room. He had brought his sword with him. After setting it aside, he tried to lie down on the bed beside his wife. His wife, the Agellid's clever daughter, said to him: "You will sleep with me neither tonight nor for several nights to come. For during this time you will need to have all of your wits about you and you must not weaken yourself. Let me remind you once again of the conditions under which I married you." Beside himself with rage, the coffee-house owner snatched up his sword and, wielding it with both hands, began to hack away with all his strength at the mat lying rolled up in the corner. And all the time he was hacking away at the mat, cutting it into little strips and pieces, he kept repeating over and over: "The man must in truth be a donkey! The man must in truth be a donkey! The man must in truth be a donkey! Just you wait! I've got you now, my boy. Now the man who is in truth a donkey is going to teach you to marry his wife!" When he had reduced the mat to shreds, and having blunted his sword as well, the coffee-house owner lay down and slept until the following morning. Then he returned to his coffee-house across the way.

Towards midday the boy walked into the coffee-house. The coffee-house owner looked at him in astonishment, saying: "Where have you sprung from, O boy?" The boy said: "I? Where have I sprung from? But you know that already. Did I not tell you yesterday that I intended to visit the clever and beautiful woman again?" The coffee-house owner said: "And did you go there again and sleep with her again?" The boy said: "Certainly, and I enjoyed myself very much. It was already late when the woman's husband came and wanted to lie down beside her on the bed. But his wife would not let him for, she said, in the next few days he would need all of his wits about him and must not weaken himself, and she reminded him of

78

the conditions under which she had married him. Then the husband, who must in truth be an exceptionally stupid donkey, flew into a terrible rage. He hacked at the mat which was still rolled up in the corner where it had been the night before. No doubt he thought that I would be spending the night in the same place and he hacked the mat into little pieces with his sword. And all the time he kept saying: 'The man must in truth be a donkey! The man must in truth be a donkey! The man must in truth be a donkey! Just you wait! I've got you now, my boy. Now the man who is in truth a donkey is going to teach you to marry his wife!" When the husband had ruined both the mat and his sword, he lay down. It was a good thing he lay down, for all the while I had been lying in the long chest next to the mat and I was finding it very difficult not to laugh. Trying not to laugh was such a strain that in the end it was nearly the cause of a shameful mishap, for I was on the point of wetting the chest. Now tell me, my friend the coffee-house owner, was that not a delightful adventure?" The coffee-house owner said: "Certainly, it was a delightful adventure! Most delightful! But tell me, my friend, will you again visit the clever and beautiful woman tonight in order to sleep with her?" The boy said: "Certainly, I shall. You yourself, a man of experience, told me how rare it was to have the opportunity of sleeping with such a clever and beautiful woman! Besides, I now want to marry the woman and I want to find out if we are suitable for each other, and if I am as clever as she is. For after all she wants to marry a clever man. It would seem that her present husband is far too stupid! The coffee-house owner asked: "Was that what the woman herself said?" The boy replied: "What can you be thinking of? I would not want to burden the woman by talking to her about the stupidity of the man to whom she is at present married!" The coffee-house owner said: "But tell me, what do you suppose is to become of the present husband of the Agellid's daughter? How do you propose to get rid of the man so that you can marry his wife?" The boy said: "Why should I have to get rid of the man? The man is so foolish he will undoubtedly be his own undoing." The coffee-house owner said nothing. He went running out. He slapped himself on the forehead and roared with rage. He picked up an axe and hacked away at a block of wood until he had reduced it to tiny splinters. Then, taking the axe, he set off for the blacksmith's, saying as he went: "Was that not a delightful adventure? Was that not a delightful adventure? And the man is so foolish that he will undoubtedly be his own undoing." Having come to the blacksmith he told him to temper and grind his axe until it was excedingly sharp. He remained squatting nearby to watch the work and all the time he kept saying to himself: "A most delightful adventure! A most delightful adventure! A most delightful adventure! Then he went home and carried on with his work in the coffee-house. But all the time he kept saying to himself: "A most delightful adventure! A most delightful adventure! A most delightful adventure!

That evening the boy again went across to the house of the Agellid's clever daughter, unlocked the seven doors, locked them behind him, and went to find the woman in her chamber. The woman asked: "How is my husband?" The boy said: "I told him about everything that happened here last night, but I did not say that I knew he was your husband. Things have gone so far that now only one more day is needed for him to bring matters to a close himself." The woman said: "How are you going to do that?" The boy said: "There is nothing for me to do. The man will do it on his own account. He is like a fly that will sting itself to death in its rage."

The woman said: "This time he will look through the whole house to find you. I know a good hiding-place. Later on, when he comes, get into the doves nesting-box. Once in there you must hold a dove by the legs in either hand. When he lifts the lid, let go of the doves. They will fly out and he is bound to say that if the nesting-box had been opened before, the doves would already all be flown. Then he will shut it again. But now come here to me again and we will get to know one another."

The boy and the young woman amused themselves until late into the night. At last they heard the coffee-house owner out in the street as he put the key into the keyhole of the outermost door. Then the young woman put the two doves into the boy's hands and told him to get into the nesting-box, and shut the lid after him. The young woman lay down on the bed. The coffee-house owner came in, carrying his axe. He immediately went across to the big chest which he split open in one blow. He smashed the big jars. He struck the wall. He struck the floor. He broke the axe. He went all about the place searching for the boy. And all of the time he kept saying out loud: "A most delightful experience! A most delightful experience! A most delightful experience!" He said: "Perhaps he is hiding in the nesting-box." He went across to it. He lifted the lid. The two doves came flying out into his face. He dropped the lid, saying: "If he had gone creeping in there, there would be no more doves left to fly out! A most delightful experience! A most delightful experience! A most delightful experience!" He searched all over the place but nowhere could he find the boy. Finally he threw himself down on his bed and went to sleep.

The next morning he got up and went across to his coffee-house. When it was nearly midday the boy arrived in his turn. The coffee-house owner greeted him and asked: "Did you pay yet another visit to the house of that clever and beautiful woman, the Agellid's daughter?" The boy said: "Certainly, I did. I have just come from there." The coffee-house owner asked: "And was the woman's husband there again?" The boy said: "Of course, he was there again. He was running around with an axe and began smashing the chest in which I had spent the previous night, going on to break up anything that came his way until he broke his axe on the floor. And all of the time he kept saying out loud: "A most delight-fu experience!" A most delightful experience! A most delightful experience!" The coffee-house owner asked: "And where were you hiding?" The boy said: "I was hiding in the doves nesting-box, holding a dove in either hand. When the man opened the lid I let go of the does so that they flew out into his face. Then he said: "If he had gone creeping in there, there would be no more doves left to fly out,' and then he dropped the lid. This man is stupid beyond belief!"

The coffee-house owner said to himself: "Just you wait, my boy! Your own gossiping will be your undoing, and the judge who will condemn you will be none other than your beloved's father himself. Just you wait!" To the boy, the coffee-house owner said: "Since we are now friends I will introduce you to my father-in-law's family. I have an invitation to eat there this evening. You will be able to make my wife's acquaintance as well. She is going along there in time for the midday meal because my father-in-law's youngest wife is indisposed, and my wife is going there to look after her small child. So come with me, my friend, and eat with me there." The boy said: "I shall be delighted to do so."

The coffee-house owner and the boy set off together to visit the former's father-in-law, the Ágellid. The coffee-house owner led the boy into the left-hand room of three that adjoined each other and were separated only by thin partitions. The Agellid's clever daughter was in the middle room where she was tending the child of her father's youngest wife. Having led the boy into the left-hand room, the coffee-houseowner went to find the Agellid in the right-hand room.

The coffee-house owner, after greeting the Agellid, said: "I have brought you a man who seduces young women throughout this district and who must therefore be put to death in accordance with our law." The Agellid said: "But our law declares that, if he is to be put to death, a husband must come to me and accuse him of adultery, and he must also provide absolute proof that adultery has been committed." The coffee-house owner said: "The boy himself will provide proof of adultery. For he relates everything in detail and boasts about his achievements." The Agellid said: "That is sufficient. Who will be responsible for the accusation?" The coffee-house owner said: "I will be responsible for the accusation." The Agellid said: "You would do better to leave the matter to others. For surely this case is not your own?" The coffee-house owner said: No, no, no, it is not my own case." The Agellid said: "Then leave it alone. For should you be unable to provide absolute proof I would have to accuse you of slander and to punish you in accordance with our country's laws. And, as you know, this as well as adultery is punishable by death." The coffee-house owner said: "No matter. I accuse the boy." The Agellid said: "Since you insist I will have to proceed. You will have to bear the consequences."

Leaving the right-hand room, the Agellid and the coffee-house owner went past the middle room and into the left-hand room. The Agellid's clever daughter remained in the middle room where she could hear all that was going on. The coffee-house owner accompanied the Agellid to the other room and said: "Here is the boy who can tell such pleasant stories. Tell us something, my friend." The boy said: "I cannot tell stories." "Well, then tell us what you have been telling me during the past few days about your adventures at nights." The boy said: "That can be of no interest to the Agellid." The Agellid said: "On the contrary, it does interest me. Now tell me!"

The boy said: "Recently a man told me that there was a very clever woman in this place. She was married to a man who always carried the only key to his wife's house on his own person so that no one else could get in to see her. Then I pushed wax into the keyhole with the result that the husband himself produced a model of the key. For having put his key into the keyhole, he then threw away the wax imprint. I went in, slept with his wife, and afterwards got her to wind me up in a mat and roll me across to the side of the room. In this way I spent the night in the room, remaining there even after the husband had come in. The following night the husband slashed the mat to pieces, but I was sleeping in the chest. On the third night, as the husband came in, I went and sat in the doves' nesting-box. He weilded his axe to such good effect that he smashed, not only the chest in which I had spent the previous night, but his axe as well. Then the husband opened the lid of the nesting-box where I was sitting. I let go of the doves and they flew out into his face, thereby causing the husband to let the lid fall to again just when he was on the point of discovering me."

When the boy had reached this point in his story, the Agellid's clever daughter in the middle room said loudly to the young wife's child: "Be quiet! That is enough! You will be getting yourself into trouble!" The boy heard what the young woman was saying. The boy understood her.

The boy said loudly: "When the husband let the lid fall, I woke up." The Agellid said: "What do you mean, you woke up?" The boy said: "Well, I woke from my dream!" The Agellid said: "So it was all just a dream?" The boy said: "Of course it was just a dream!" The Agellid said: "But you have been accused of having really done it." The boy said: "Who has accused me?" The

Agellid said: "This coffee-house owner here." The boy said: "What do you do about slander in this country?"

The Agellid said to the coffee-house owner: "Now speak. How was it? Where is your proof?" The coffee-house owner lost his head and said: "What shall I say? What shall I say? I cannot tell you it was your daughter with whom he committed adultery!" Angrily, the Agellid replied: "What presumption is this? Do you dare drag my daughter into this case? You are a slanderer, nothing but a stupid slanderer!"

The Agellid had the coffee-house owner executed. The boy married the Agellid's clever and beautiful daughter. On the day of his marriage he gave his wife the key to the house, saying: "keep the key to the house. For now I know what value I can set by it."

The boy and the Agellid's clever and beautiful daughter lived together in peace and happiness. When the boy, having forfeited some of his last years to Aini, came to the end of his allotted span and was nearing the point of death, the Agellid's clever daughter asked God if she might make over part of her own life to her husband. God granted her request.

Then the boy and the Agellid's clever daughter died on the same day. Thus it happened in the very way the boy had hoped it would some time happen with Aini, on that day so long ago when as yet he had known nothing of life.

MAMADI'S REVENGE   *Sahel*

The people of Wagadu said: "The first daughter to be born in Wagadu shall be given to Bida." The first girl was Sia Jatta Bari (Jatta Bari being her surname). Sia Jatta Bari was exceedingly beautiful. She was the most beautiful girl in the Soninké country. She was so beautiful that the Soninké and other peoples, when they want to describe a girl's beauty in the most flattering terms, would say: "She is as beautiful as Sia Jatta Bari." Sia Jatta Bari was intended for Bida.

But Sia already had a suitor, a boy named Mamadi Sefe Dekote. Everyone in Wagadu used to say: "How can we tell if we shall ever again have such a beautiful girl in Wagadu?" For this reason Mamadi Sefe Dekote was very proud of his beloved. One night, after the tam-tam, Sia Jatta Bari went to find her lover in order to spend the night with him (though not to make love). Sia Jatta Bari said: "In this world every friendship has to come to an end some time." Mamadi Sefe Dekote said: "Why do you say that?" Sia Jatta Bari said: "No friendship can last for ever and I am about to be handed over to Bida the snake." Mamadi Sefe Dekote said: "If that were to happen, Wagadu would be punished for it, for I will not tolerate it." Sia Jatta Bari said: "Do not make trouble, for thus it has been ordained and it is an ancient custom to which all must conform. I must become the wife of Sa (snake) Bida and nothing can be done to prevent it."

The following morning Mamadi Sefe Dekote sharpened his kitalalabong (sword) until its edge was as keen as he could make it. To find out if it was really sharp, he placed a grain of millet on the ground and with one stroke cut it in half. Then he put the sword back into its scabbard. On the wedding day the people dressed Sia Jatta Bari in all her finery, adorning her with jewelry and beautiful clothes, after which they formed themselves into a procession to accompany her to Bida the snake. Bida lived in a large, deep well outside the village. The festive procession made its way thither. Mamadi Sefe Dekote, having buckled on his sword and swung himself into the saddle of his beautiful horse, now joined the procession.

When Bida accepted a sacrifice, he would always raise his head three times out of the well before finally seizing hold of his victim. When the procession arrived at the place where the well was, Mamadi squatted down immediately beside it. Then Bida's head rose up out of the well for the first time. The people of Wagadu said to Sia and Mamadi: "The time has come for you to take leave of each other. Say goodbye." Bida reared his head up out of the well for the second time and the people of Wagadu called out: "Quick, say goodbye to each other, but do so quickly!" For the third time Bida reared his head out of the well. Then Mamadi Sefe Dekote drew his sword and at one blow severed the snake's head from its body. The head went flying high into the air. Before it fell to the ground again it said: "May Wagadu have no golden rain for the space of seven years, seven months and seven days." Then the head fell to the ground far away to the south and that is why gold is found there now.

The people of Wagadu heard the snake's curse. They yelled angrily at Mamadi. But with Sia on his horse's crupper, Mamadi galloped away in the direction of Sama-Markala, a town to the north of Segu on the Niger, where his mother lived. Mamadi Sefe Dekote had a good horse sired by Samba Ngarranja. There was only one horse in Wagadu capable of overtaking it and that was Samba Ngarranja itself. So the people of Wagadu asked Wagana Sako (who owned it) to ride after Mamadi Sefe Dekote and if possible to catch him and kill him. Jumping onto his horse, Wagan Sako went galloping after Mamadi, his uncle.

Wagana Sako soon caught up with his uncle, whose horse was having to carry two people. Seizing his spear, he rammed it hard into the ground. Then he said to Mamadi: "Flee as fast as you can, O Uncle, for if the people of Wagadu catch up with you they will surely kill you. I do not want to kill you because I am your nephew. Make haste and flee to Sama and your mother." With these words Wagana jumped out of the saddle and began pulling at his spear. After a little while the other people from Wagadu arrived. He said to them: "Help me to pull the spear out of the ground. I threw it after Mamadi Sefe Dekote but missed him and the spear has buried itself so deeply in the ground that I am having difficulty in pulling it out again. The people helped him to pull the spear out and then sent him off again in pursuit of Mamadi Sefe Dekote. Soon afterwards, having almost caught up with Mamadi, Wagana once more drove his spear into the ground, shouting as he did so: "Make haste and flee to your mother in Sama." For a second time he waited for the people of Wagadu so as to have their help in pulling his spear out of the ground. All of this happened yet a third time. By then Mamadi had gone to Sama.

Mamadi's mother came out of the town to meet the riders as they arrived at breakneck speed. She called out to Wagana Sako: "Turn back and let my son come to me in peace." Wagana said: "Ask your son. He will tell you how it was that I saved him and that if he is still in the land of the living, it is thanks to me." Mamadi Sefe Dekote said: "I killed Bida so as to save this girl whom I wish to marry. I cut the snake's head off. Before it fell to the ground Bida said: 'May Wagadu have no golden rain for the space of seven years, seven months and seven days.' This made the people of Wagadu very angry and they sent Wagana Sako on his horse Samba Ngarranja in pursuit of me, telling him to kill me. But he spared my life. Now I have arrived here with Sia."

Every morning in Wagadu, when Sia left Mamadi Sefe Dekote, he had used to give her gold to the value of mutukalle tamu (about a thousand francs). She had received this gift daily for the space of three months. Nevertheless she had not surrendered to Mamadi's embraces. Here in Sama, where there was no snake to enrich the lad with gold, these presents ceased. Sia tired of Mamadi. She wanted to be rid of him. So one morning she said: "I have a headache. Now there is only one remedy for headaches cut off a little toe from one of your feet so that I can moisten my forehead with the blood." Mamadi loved Sia beyond all measure. He cut off his little toe. After a while she said: "As yet it has done no good. My headache is as bad as ever. Now cut your little finger off. If I rub the blood on my forehead that should help." Mamadi was very much in love with Sia. He therefore did as she asked, but then Sia sent a message to her lover in which she said:

"I only like people with ten fingers and ten toes. I do not like people with nine fingers and nine toes." Mamadi received this message.

When Mamadi received this news he grew very angry. He grew ill with rage, so ill that he almost died. He sent for an old woman. The old woman came and asked him: "What ails you, O Sefe Mamadi Dekote?" Mamadi said: "I have grown ill with rage because Sia Jatta Bari has treated me so badly. It was for Sia that I killed Bida the snake. It was for Sia that I brought down a curse on Wagadu. It was for Sia that I fled from Wagadu. It was for Sia that I paid out so much gold every morning. It was for Sia that I cut off my toes. It was for Sia that I cut off my little finger. Now Sia has sent a note saying: 'I only like people with ten fingers and ten toes. I do not like people with nine fingers and nine toes.' That is what has made me ill with anger." The old woman said: "This is not difficult. Give me your snuff-box." Thinking that, like all old people, the old woman wanted to take a pinch of snuff, Mamadi handed her the box. She took it from him saying: "So that you can that it will not be difficult, look inside the box. Just now there was tobacco in it, and now, since I have been holding it in my hand, it contains gold. Your case is not half so difficult. It is easier to fill Sia with love than this box with gold. Tell me now, if I were to give you a karté cake (made of the butter from the butter tree), could you arrange for some of the butter to get onto Sia's head?" Mamadi said: "Yes, I could do that." Then the old woman prepared a karté cake with the help of borri (magic) and gave the magic stuff to Mamadi.

In Sama there was a woman who was especially skilled in dressing hair. This woman was called Kumbadamba. Mamadi sent for the woman and said to her: "I am prepared to give you gold to the value of mutukalla tamu if you will rub this butter into Sia's hair when you are dressing it. Are you prepared to do this?" Kumbadamba said: "That is not difficult. I am prepared to do it." Mamadi gave her the magic karté and left the rest to her.

One day Sia sent for Kumbadamba and said to her: "Dress my hair!" She said to her little slave: "Go indoors and get some karté!" (This vegetable butter is used in hairdressing). Kumbadamba said: "There is no need. I happen to have brought plenty of karté with me." Then she set to work. When she had finished dressing and arranging one side of Sia's head the girl sprang up saying: "Mamadi is calling me!" She hurried to him and said: "Did you call me, O big brother?"[1] Mamadi had not called her, the magic was already at work. Mamadi said: "No, I did not call you, for I have only nine fingers and nine toes, and I know that you like only people with ten fingers and ten toes." Then Sia went back to Kumba-damba so that she could finish dressing her hair. When the second side of her head had been dressed and the karté was being rubbed into it, Sia again jumped up hastily and said: "Let me go! Mamadi is calling me!"

---

[1] A term of extreme affection.

She hurried quickly away to Mamadi Sefe Dekote and said: "Were you calling me, O big brother?" Mamadi had not called and the magic was now at work on the second side of her head. Mamadi said: "No, I did not call you, for I have only nine fingers and nine toes, and I know that you like only people with ten fingers and ten toes." Then Sia went back to Kumbadamba to let her complete the work that she had begun. She smoothed the whole head, using large quantities of the magic karté, until Sia at last jumped up impatiently, crying: "That is enough! Mamadi is calling me!" In great haste she ran to Mamadi Sefe Dekote and asked: "Were you calling me, O big brother?" Mamadi said: "Yes, I was calling you, for I wanted to tell you to come to my house tonight." Sia said: "I will come and it will be our wedding night." Until now Mamadi Sefe Dekote had never succeeded in making Sia succumb to his embraces.

At his dwelling Mamadi saw to the preparation of house and bed. He had a young slave called Blali whom he could trust and who was responsible for the care of his fine horse. He called Blali and said: "Give me your old robe. I want to wear it. See that it is clean and washed. Then you are to wash yourself and tonight you will lie on my bed in my hut. At midnight a woman, Sia, will come to you. You are not to speak a word to her. Sia must think that it is I who am lying beside her, and she is used to my not saying anything. That is why I have been named Sefe Dekote. So do not speak to her, but make love with her. You must make love with her. If you have not done so by tomorrow morning I shall put you to death. Do you understand?" Blali said: "I will do it."

Sia came during the night. Mamadi had left his shoes beside the bed so that Sia should feel sure that he was there, for she would at once recognize them as his. She came, recognized the shoes, and lay down with the stableboy. She said: "Kassunka!" (Good evening!) So as not to betray himself, Blali merely made a clicking sound in reply. Sia said: "O big brother, I know that you never say very much. But speak to me tonight. I beg you to speak to me tonight!" Then Blali made love with Sia.

The following morning Mamadi Sefe Dekote, wearing Blali's clothes, went in through the door of the hut and

called: "Blali!" Blali answered: "Nam!" (master!)
Mamadi said: "Why have you not been tending my horse
this morning instead of sleeping here with this wench,
Sia?" Blali said: "If I have failed to do my work this
morning, O master, perhaps you will forgive me. For I
have made love with a woman of whom it is said throughout Wagadu that she is the most beautiful in the land. Is
that a good excuse?" Sia heard him and, as she lay there
on the bed, began to tremble in every limb. Trembling
she said: "O big brother, you settle your accounts well!"
All that day Sia did not dare leave the house for shame.
But in the night she crept back to her own house and
there she died of shame. Such was the justice meted out by
Mamadi Sefe Dekote to Sia Jatta Bari.

SIGA SANKE *Sahel*

Siga Sanke lived in the village of Söina in Kaarta. He
lived at the time of King Njagaleng Gara, a proud
Massassi who in those days ruled over Kaarta. At first Siga
Sanke was a close friend of the king. He would travel
around the country visiting individual dugutigis, and on
his return would usually tell the king: "Such and such
a one is not a loyal subject. Give me soldiers and I will
punish him in your name." At first the king did not sus-
pect that anything was wrong, and he was pleased at Siga
Sanke's loyal attitude. But when he discovered that Signa
Sanke was a wicked and dangerous sycophant, he at once
withdrew his favor from him.

Siga Sanke retreated in a great hurry to his village,
Söina, where he began to assume boastful and vain-glori-
ous airs. His town was very well fortified. Outside one of
its gates he set up a galla (platform) in the shade of four
trees and upon it twelve men would stand with their
drums in the evening to beat out the rhythm for the
people dancing below. Siga Sanke had become friendly
with a smith called Numuka Boji with whom he drank
honey beer while the drums kept up their rhythmic beating outside. In addition he had two women to sing to him.

One was Siga Sanke's wife, who sang: "Siga Sanke de firina mogo je (Siga Sanke fights with many)." To this the other woman made the rejoinder: "Siga Sanke mogo Bammana ndo nde (There is no Bammana like Siga Sanke)." They accompanied their singing on the guitar.

Siga Sanke drank a great deal. He took a gourd that had been newly filled. He put it to his lips and emptied it. He tilted his head back so far that his cap fell off. He said to Numuke Boji: "If you do nothing bad you will never make a name for yourself."

Thus he lived in a state of constant drunkenness. One day he heard that King Njagaleng Gara's son was travelling in that district. Thereupon he called his people and said to them: "Go to the place where the king's son is and kill him!" The people went and killed him.

Söina was a large village with seven gates. It was not at all an easy place to take. Siga Sanke very rarely left it, except twice a year: once when the fields were being newly sown at the beginning of the rainy season, so as to inspect the sowing; and once when the harvest was ripe, so as to inspect the fruit. Now one day, after he had had the king's son assassinated, he sent for twelve dialli whom he ordered to help out the drummers on the galla. Then, one day after the king's son had been murdered, when the twelve dialli were playing alongside the drummers, he put four large tobacco tins filled with gold on the ground in the middle of the square.

Siga Sanke drank.

He turned round and said: "Who is there?" A slave answered: "I am here!" The slave stepped forward. Siga Sanke, taking one of the tobacco tins full of gold, said: "Take this gold and carry it to the king of Segu and tell King Daga that in a month's time I am going to be attacked by King Njagaleng Gara of Kaarta who is already preparing for war. Tell him that if he is here in a month's time and helps me in the war, I will pay him tribute thereafter." The messenger left with the gold.

Siga Sanke drank. He turned around and said: "Who is here?" The slave said: "I am here." Siga Sanke said: "Come here!" Siga Sanke picked up a tobacco tin filled with gold, gave it to the messenger, and said: "Take this and carry it to King Njagakeng Gara. Tell him that I admit having done him a cruel wrong but that I am sorry

91

for it. I would beg him forgiveness. Tell him further that in a month's time the King of Segu is going to sally forth against my town in order to subdue me. But since I once was friends with the king of Kaarta it would only be right for him to receive my tribute. He should therefore send a force strong enough to rout Segu's army. The messenger took the tobacco tin full of gold and went.

Siga Sanke drank. He turned around. He said: "Who is here?" The slave said: "I am there." Siga Sanke said: "Come here!" The slave stepped forward. Taking the fourth tobacco tin full of gold, Siga Sanke handed it to him saying: "Take this. Carry it to the King of Sharo. Tell King Bina Salogo Traore that the King of Massina is preparing a big force with which to attack and conquer my town. Tell him to arm a strong army so that next month he can send it to my aid. For I would rather pay tribute to King Bina Salogo Traore of Sharo than become the king of Massina's vassal." The messenger took the tobacco tin full of gold and went on his way.

When the next month had come Siga Sanke, the twelve dialli, and the two women went up one evening onto the roof of a house and began a merry drinking-bout. He ordered the seven gates of the town to be locked and himself took possession of the keys. The diallis played. The women sang. Siga Sanke drank.

That night Segu's ton-jong (auxilliary forces) arrived, shouting their war-cry: "Daga! Daga!" Then the armies arrived from Kaarta, shouting their war-cry: "Dese! Laba! Dunkoro! Mussira!" (the names of former chiefs of Kaarta). They fell upon each other, and that night the forces from Segu and those from Kaarta were joined in bloody battle.

In the course of the same night the king of Massina's troops arrived outside the gates of the town of Söina. But at the same time fighting men arrived from Sharo, sent by King Bina Salogo Traore, and, on hearing the warriors from Massina shouting "Amadu-Amadu!" they set upon them so that here, too, under cover of night, a battle was waged in which no life was spared.

And when dawn approached and the sun began to rise, all the bravest on both sides had fallen in battle and all around the town lay the corpses of horses and warriors. When the sun rose, Siga Sanke said to the drummers:

"Now stop!" He said to the dialli: "Now stop!" Siga Sanke went up onto the roof of the tallest building, looked out across the sea of corpses, and shouted: "You four bands of warriers! I sent for all four of you and all four of you come. You have fought valiantly throughout the night. You have lost the flower of your armies. Do you know why I did this? I did it to fertilize my fields. And now my fields have been fertilized with the good blood of the corpses of the brave. My harvest will be a good one." Then he called Boji the smith and said: "Strike the walls so that we can tell from the sound whether they are good or bad." Boji the smith smote the walls and said: "They are good!" Siga Sanke called out to the warriors: "You have heard the sound. The walls are good. And why are they good? Because my men who built them wore old trousers, my women who built them wore old clothes. They did not work in new garments but in old ones, and that meant that they worked with a will. As for me, I only go out of the town twice every year, and so excellent is the work on the walls, that it is you who'll have to pay the piper!"

Then they all departed. Sira Bo, the king of Kaarta's brother and commander of the army sent by King Njaga-leng Gara, was the only man left outside the gates of Söina. Siga Sanke shouted to his people: "Mock him!" Then all Siga Sanke's people yelled: "Ho, Sira Bo! Ho, Sira Bo! Ho, Sira Bo!" They yelled it three times. Sira Bo shouted "You may jeer at me today, Siga Sanke, but one of these days I shall see you spitting your teeth out!" Then Sira Bo sent a message to Siga Sanke which said: "Go to another country and leave Söina! Once my mother had her garden there. This country belongs to the Massassi!" Then he too went his way.

When the next rainy season set in, Siga Sanke decided to have a new field made between Söina and King Njaga-leng Gara's town. He ordered the scrub and trees to be cleared from the place and decided to ride out himself to inspect the work and the land, for it was in any case his custom to go outside the gates of Söina twice a year. But Sira Bo had sent out two knights, having told them: 'Go to Söina and mark well when Siga Sanke leaves the town. As soon as you hear of it, come back at once and tell me." Now when the two watchers heard that Siga

Sanke intended to inspect the field between Söina and the king's town, they returned hotfoot to Sira Bo and said: "Tomorrow Siga Sanke will be inspecting his field. Siga Sanke has called this field Kulanieni or Bolanieni (he looks for Bo)." Sira Bo set off at once with his men and formed a wide circle round the place.

The next morning Siga Sanke mounted his horse and rode with a few of his people to the field called Bolanieni. There he dismounted and began walking about. No sooner did Sira Bo perceive this from his hidingplace than he called out to his men: "Close in on him, but do not harm Siga Sanke. I shall drive him in front of me." Siga Sanke heard him. He saw the danger. He made a dash for his horse, meaning to leap into the saddle and escape. But his horse had taken fright and broken free and now it was running away. Siga Sanke just managed to get hold of one of the horse's legs, but the animal kicked out and its hoof struck him in the mouth, knocking out four of his teeth, two from the upper and two from the lower jaw. Spitting them out, he again made after his horse. He caught up with it and attempted to leap into the saddle as it galloped but he fell off on the far side. As he fell, his head struck against a heap of stones and once again he had to spit out four of his teeth, two from the lower and two from the upper jaw. Then Sira Bo shouted: "Did I not tell you that one day I should see you spitting your teeth out?"

Finally, however, Siga Sanke did succeed in leaping into the saddle and he rode away as fast as his horse could carry him. He even succeeded in breaking out of the circle, but Sira Bo was hot on his heels and now struck him in the ribs with the butt of his gun. Siga Sanka cried out: "Hëig!" and wept. He yelled: "Don't kill me." Three times he yelled it before he reached the gates of Söina.

Sira Bo shouted: So you are weeping? that shows that you are a njamogode (commoner), but I am a njerre ulu (pure-blooded one). I am a Massassi. You were weeping!" Then Sira Bo went home. Siga Sanke was saved. On arriving back in the town he asked his people: "Where is the drum?" His people answered: "You left it outside on the field called Bolanieni."

By now Siga Sanke had picked quarrels with all of his

94

neighbours. One day the king of the Surakka also said: "Let us attack Siga Sanke." Taking all of his people with him he arrived outside Söina. His people surrounded Söina.

Although Siga Sanke had managed to close the gates before they arrived, he feared that this time things might take a bad turn.

Calling for his son and his brother he said: "Go to King Njagaleng Gara of Kaarta and say that I have wronged and injured him. But I would beg his forgiveness. In the future I will be his vassal. But now I would ask his aid against the Surakka." The two men set out and arrived at the court of the king of Kaarta. When they had delivered their message King Njagaleng Gara and his people shouted: "Now we have two of the brood. Kill them!" At that time, however, the judge was a Numu. He said: "No, do not kill these men. The king should set out with his army." Then the king and the people gave up the idea of killing the two emissaries, who were sent back with the message: "My men will be coming in three days' time."

When King Njagaleng Gara was already on his way with his warriors, the king of the Surakka sent him a message, saying: "Leave Siga Sanke to me. I will have him beheaded and will send you the weight of his head in gold." The king of Kaarta agreed. He now considered how Siga Sanke could be lured into a trap, for it was impossible to destroy the walls of Söina. Siga Sanke came out to negotiate with King Njagaleng Gara's emissary. But, having guessed their intentions, he abandoned his horses and escaped into the town.

It is said, however, that in the end Njagaleng Gara succeeded after all in killing Siga Sanke.

SIDI BABA   *Sahel*

Sidi's father was called Baba and Baba's village was called Tonna. Baba had married a wife whose name was Shokolo. He cared nothing for his wife's family. When Baba and Shokolo had been married three years she said: "You have never visited my father and mother." Baba said: "If that is what you wish, it can be done at once. I shall leave without delay." He armed his band of warriors and set off.

When Baba came to the village where his wife's parents lived, he speedily prepared an attack. He made the attack. He burnt the village down. He took his wife's mother and father prisoner. He killed them, cut off their heads, put the heads into a sack, and took the sack with him. When he got home again, Baba said: "I went, as you asked, to the village where your father and mother lived. I embraced them both very affectionately and they gave me some pretty trinkets for you. Here is a sack. Look inside it." The wife opened the sack. She took out a head. Baba asked: "What is that?" His wife said: "That is my father's head." She pulled out another head: Baba asked: "What is that?" Shokolo said: "That is my mother's head." Baba said: "Take both the heads and use them to stand on under your cooking-pots. Then cook my food over them."

The woman, Shokolo, did not say a word. She took the heads and laid the fire around them. She set her cooking-pots on top of them. She prepared the food for her husband on them, but she did not say a word. The two heads were blackened and burnt, but the wife did not say a word.

When time enough had gone by for Baba to forget all this and when he really had forgotten it, his wife Shokolo went to a smith, from whom she obtained a very sharp knife. Armed with this knife she went very early one morning to the house in which her mother-in-law, the mother of Baba, her husband lived. She did not say good-morning to the woman but cut her throat. Then she went on to slit open the woman's belly, removing from it all that there was of usable fat. Leaving the corpse where it was, she went home, taking the fat with her. With the fat she prepared a dish. The food she made was incomparably delicious.

Meanwhile the day had begun and everybody of note had assembled in the square where they sat talking to each other. Baba's wife took the dish that she had prepared and carried it out into the square. She knelt down in front of her husband (as ancient custom prescribed) and handed him the platter. The men began to eat. One of them said: "Ah, this is excellent." Another said: "Ah, this has been exceptionally well prepared." Baba himself said: "Yes, it is the tastiest meal that I have ever had in my life."

It was Baba's custom to send a messenger every morning to his mother to enquire after her health. On this particular day he called a house slave as usual and said to him: "Go to my mother and ask her how she is." The house slave went. He arrived at the house. He saw the body lying in a pool of its own blood and with its belly slit open. He went back to Baba. Baba asked: "How is my mother?" The house slave said: "I cannot tell you." Baba said: "Tell me at once or I will kill you."

The house slave said: "Kill me, but I cannot possibly tell you what I have seen." Thereupon Baba had the slave put to death.

Baba said to another house slave: "Go and ask my mother how she is." The house slave went. He saw the bloody corpse, came back, and said: "I cannot possibly tell you what I have seen." Baba had this slave put to death also. He called a third house slave and said to him: "Go and ask my mother how she is." The house slave went. He saw the bloody corpse, came back, and said: "I cannot possibly tell you what I have seen." Baba had him put to death also.

Then a musician said: "Baba, you should not have your men slaughtered like oxen or sheep." Baba said: "Very well. If you do not like it, why not go yourself to my mother's house to ask her how she is?" The musician went. He saw the bloody corpse, came back, and said: "Baba, what your salves have said is true. This thing cannot possibly be told." King Baba said: "Tell me at once, or I will have you put to death as well."

The musician said: "Baba, your mother is dead. As for the rest, you must go and see for yourself." Baba went. He saw the bloody corpse with its belly slit open. The king was exceedingly angry. He sent a message throughout the region which said: "All heads of families must at once make inquiries to find out who killed my mother. If this has not been found out by this evening, I shall have a thousand people put to death." Thereupon everyone began to hunt around, searching for tracks, but nobody succeeded in finding a single one. It was not discovered who had killed Baba's mother.

Now after everyone had been searching in vain, and when King Baba was sitting in the square conferring with the elders and musicians, Baba's wife appeared. She knelt down in front of Baba (as ancient custom prescribed) and asked: "Did I not prepare a dish for you this morning and bring it to you out here in the square?" Baba said: "That is so. We enjoyed it very much and I myself told you I had never had a tastier meal in all my life." Shokolo said: "In preparing this food I used the fat from your mother's belly. It was I who killed your mother. Now do with me what you will."

One of the men sitting in the square said: "This woman should be put to death." Another said: "She should be shot." A third said: "She too, should have her belly slit open." A fourth said: "She should be burnt alive." But amongst them there was an old man who was greatly respected in the council. He said: "I think she should be allowed to live. Nothing should be done. We must wait. A bad father and a bad mother produce bad children." He stood up and went. Nothing was done.

Two years later the woman gave birth to a son who was called Sidi Baba because his father's name was Baba. The child flourished. When he was ten years old his favorite occupation was setting snares for pigeons. One day a squirrel got caught in one of his snares. When Sidi Baba approached it the creature was so frightened that it eventually succeeded in breaking free from the cord. Then it escaped into its hole.

Sidi at once began to search the ground so as to dig out the squirrel. He dug and dug. Sidi Baba dug for a whole day and a whole night with no thought for anything else. When a night had gone by and the boy had not returned, Baba sent out emissaries to look for his son. One of them found Baba. He said to Sidi Baba: "Your father has sent out emissaries to search for you." Sidi said: 'Tell my father that there was a squirrel caught in my snare, but that it escaped at the last moment and slipped into its hole. I am now digging out its burrow." The messenger went back to inform Baba.

Sidi went on digging and at long last discovered the squirrel and killed it. Then he set off for home.

But before he got home again his father died and his kingdom was made over to Baba's brother. A great feast had been prepared at which a great deal of besu was drunk and the new king lavishly inaugurated. When Sidi arrived they told him: "Your father is dead. Your uncle has been made king." Sidi Baba at once said: "Show me where my father is buried." They showed Sidi the place. Sidi said: "Open up the grave." They did so. Standing nearby was the slave whose function had always been to give floggings. Sidi Baba said: "Give Baba here fifty blows with the knotted stick for having died behind my back. For this is going to stir up strife."

Then Sidi Baba sent his uncle a message with the question: "Who inherits this kingdom at my father's death?" On hearing this his uncle grew afraid and said: "I am in no way king. All I do is drink a little and enjoy being alive." Sidi Baba said: "You can take all of my father's women, and my mother as well. But you will get nothing else." Then Sidi Baba became king.

When Sidi Baba had thus made himself king, having ousted his uncle, he said: "O elders! I know what you are like! You want to be rid of me!" Sidi Baba had five great halls. He sent a proclamation throughout the land, saying: "There is to be an assembly of all the elders knights, farmers, musicians, and smiths. All are to assemble at Sidi Baba's farmstead." They came in from all directions, forming a great crowd in the courtyard, and many believed that they were to be honored. But when all were assembled Sidi Baba proclaimed throughout the land: "Today every elder is to make way for his son. Age desires that youth should come into its own. None of the elders wishes to die behind the back of his heir and thus make difficulties for him over his rightful inheritance. Therefore Sidi Baba informed you that from today the old are making way for you."

Sidi Baba had all of the elders killed. Then he summoned the musicians and said: "Now take the bari (gourd piano) and sing to it. The elders no longer have any use for the bari." The elders fields he gave to the young farmers. He gave the young knights their father's overlordship. The elders' workshops he gave to the young smiths.

In that region there was a country called Garrio, not

far distant from the land of Fara Maka. In the place called Garrio there was dancing and playing every day. This annoyed King Sidi Baba. Every day the noise of it came across to him and annoyed him so much that one day he said: "The king of Garrio is too much addicted to merriment. I shall make him a little less noisy." Between his village, Tonna, and Garrio there was a wilderness called Nampala. The Nampala Wilderness is known throughout the world. To cross this territory of desert and scrub requires two or three days journey. There is no water to be found. Sidi Baba set out with his warriors to march to Garrio. When, on the first evening, he camped in the Nampala wilderness he said to his men: "There is no water here. On awakening tomorrow morning I want to see water. Dig a well. If you have not completed the well by tomorrow morning I shall have you all beheaded." Then Sidi Baba lay down to sleep. His warriors worked the whole night through and the following morning, when Sidi Baba awoke, the well was finished. The well was at least seventy fathoms deep. It can still be seen today. The well lasted for many, many years but in the course of time it has become silted up.

Having arrived at Garrio, Sidi Baba captured it.

When he had left Tonna, Sidi Baba had taken with him ten thousand long, stout pieces of rope. These he now caused to be joined together, beginning by having a prisoner bound with the first piece, another then being tied behind him, and so on. Nose to tail, they resembled a file of sheep. He overthrew a hundred villages, each time adding the conquered to the train with what remained of the ten thousand pieces of rope. His men said to him: "Lord, you have already done so much. Now return home." Looking along the train of bound captives he asked: "Is there still any unused rope?" His men said: "Yes, there is still some unused rope." Sidi Baba said: "Then we have not finished yet, nor can we yet return home."

He subdued the country as far as Barbé and Fantala in the Kumari district. By then almost the whole of the rope was used up. But on returning to the Namapala wilderness he found that there were still two hundred pieces of rope trailing behind and not yet in use. Then he said:

"We have exactly two hundred djongwaldes.[1] We have exactly two hundred pieces of rope left. We shall use these two hundred pieces to tie the two hundred djongwaldes' hands behind their backs. Then I shall sell the two hundred djongwaldes. But if their wives and children raise an outcry, I shall not hesitate to have all two hundred djongwaldes killed." Thus the two hundred overseers were sold, and Sidi Baba bought drink with the proceeds.

Sidi Baba died after a reign of thirty years. During his lifetime he captured six hundred and twenty villages. Sidi Baba belonged to the Kulloballi tribe. Today his successors still live between Gumbu and Sokolo. They are Bammanas.

A SIMPLETON'S LUCK   *Kabyle*

A boy had a mother, but his father was no longer alive. The boy was an orphan. His mother prayed often and never missed the hour of prayer. But the boy was a foolish chatterer. When at four in the morning the muezzin called the faithful to prayer from the mosque, his mother would rise and begin praying out loud. And when he called the faithful to prayer at night she would again rise and pray out loud.

But the boy liked to sleep late in the morning and his mother's praying disturbed him. One morning when the muezzin had woken her as always at four o'clock, thereby disturbing the simpleton's sleep, the latter took up his cudgel, went out and clubbed him so hard on the nape of the neck that he fell down dead. Then he picked up the muezzin's corpse and carried it to the well. He was pleased about what he had done.

In joyful mood he went home and said to his mother: "The muezzin will never disturb my morning sleep again. I have killed him and thrown him into the well." The widow took fright. She said to herself: "My son will tell everybody about this!" The widow went to the sheep-pen, pulled out a sheep, killed it, carried it across to the well, and threw it in.

---

[1] Slave overseers; perhaps at an earlier period district or military leaders.

The simpleton ran to the men's assembly place, and went gleefully about the people, crying: "No, the muezzin will never disturb my morning sleep again. I have killed him and thrown him into the well!" The men said: "That is terrible!" Taking ropes and hooks they ran to the well and tried to fish up what lay at the bottom. Finally their hooks caught in the wether which the widow had thrown in shortly before. They pulled it up and laughed. They said to one another: "Not a bad joke for a simpleton, calling the muezzin a wether!".

One day his mother gave the simpleton a carpet to take to the market and sell. Taking the carpet the boy went to market, offered it for sale, waited, bargained, but all in vain, for no one that day wanted to buy his carpet. In the evening he set out for home with it. On the way from the market to the village where his mother lived there was a river past which the simpleton had to go. As the simpleton walked beside it the river was murmuring. The boy asked: "What are you saying? Are your feet cold? Do you need a carpet? Will you pay for my carpet next market day? You will? Then I will lay the carpet over your feet." The simpleton flung out the carpet, spreading it out over the river. The river carried the carpet away. The boy called after it: "Do not forget to pay me next market day!"

The boy returned home. Gleefully he said to his mother: "I have sold the carpet." His mother said: "Where is the money?" The boy said: "I shall get the money next market day. The river bought the carpet." His mother asked: 'Who bought the carpet?" The boy said: "The river bought it. The river had cold feet. It is going to pay me next market day." His mother said: "Do not forget to take the shovel with you. You will have to shovel out all the money that the river will bring for you in its bag."

When market day came the boy set out with his shovel over his shoulder in the direction of the market. As he walked along the river bank he said: "Now show me what you have in your money bag." It was daylight and the river was whispering as always, but the sound meant nothing to the boy. The boy said: "You are taking your time about answering today. I shall have to look for your money bag myself." The simpleton began digging holes in the bank and the river bed. The mud formed dams in the river. Soon the river was diverted from its course. It returned to the old one which farmers had already laboriously deflected it from in order to irrigate their fields. The farmers at work in the fields became aware of the danger threatening their crops. All of the farmers set off together to walk upstream. They came upon the simpleton.

The farmers asked: "What are you doing there, boy?" The boy said: "I have dealings with the river which concern only myself. It is a business matter." The boy continued his work. The farmers asked: "What kind of business is it?" The simpleton said: "As I was passing this way a short time ago, bringing back a carpet from the market, the river complained of having cold feet and asked me to sell it the carpet. It was going to pay me for it today. Now I am trying to find its money bag. Now I want to work. Do not disturb me with stupid questions, or I will never be finished."

Going a little way apart, the farmers said to one another: "If the boy goes on working up here much longer he will ruin our fields down below. Would it not be better for us to club together and pay for the carpet?" The farmers all agreed. Returning to the boy, they said: "This river has sent you this money from downstream." The boy took the money, counted it, and said: "That is the right amount." Then he picked up his shovel, ran home, and gave his mother the money, saying: "This is what I have been paid." The boy then went to the place of assembly and sat down with the men, saying: "It is bad business to have dealings with people. I have dealings with the river. It pays more money."

On the next market day the simpleton's mother gave him a burnous and told him: "Take this burnous to market and sell it." The boy took it and went to market. He showed the burnous to many different men. No one wanted to buy the burnous, for the boy was asking far too much money. The boy became bored. He went out to the place beyond the meat market where the vultures were. He asked them: "Would you like to buy the burnous? Here! You can look at it!" The boy threw the burnous to the vultures. The vultures picked it up and flew off with it. The simpleton called out after the vultures: "Hooo! Do not forget! I will be back here next market day! Then you must pay me for my mother's burnous." The simpleton went home and told his mother: "I sold the burnous well. A whole family bought it." His mother asked: "Have you brought the money?" The boy said: "No, I have no money. I sold the burnous to the vultures. They are going to pay me next market day." His mother said: "Then you will probably have to visit their home to get the money." The boy said: "I have plenty of time. I do not mind how far I have to go."

The following market day the boy put his shovel on his shoulder, went to market, and looked about for the vultures. Having found the vultures in the meat market he said: "Have you brought me my money?" The boy waved his shovel at them. The vultures screeched and flew away. The simpleton said: "My mother is a clever woman. She told me that I would have to climb up to the vultures' home to get my money. And now they are calling me!" He shouted after the vultures: "Do not fly so fast. I have to follow you."

The simpleton climbed up the mountainside after the vultures. He saw their nest. He went towards the nest. Screeching, the vultures flew off. The boy said: "All right. Go if you want. I will be able to find the money for myself." Taking hold of his shovel, he began to loosen the ground. Buried in it he found two jars filled with gold and silver coins. The vultures had collected the gold and silver. The boy looked at the gold and silver, saying: "Is all of this for me? I can't even carry it all!" The boy ran off.

The boy ran home and said to his mother: "Mother, you spoke the truth. The vultures will only pay you at their home. They had two big jars full of gold and silver coins for me to take away. Now bring two baskets so that I can carry the money home." His mother picked up two baskets. She said to herself: "If what the simpleton has said is true, I am going to be pestered by other people's greed, for the boy will spread the news everywhere. I shall have to spice this matter with pepper." The woman filled one of the baskets with eggs and the other with cakes. She said: "I am ready. I will go ahead." As his mother walked in front she let fall a cake, now an egg. The simpleton picked up the cake. He picked up the egg. He ate every cake and egg dropped by his mother as she went on her

way. As they walked his mother said: "It is raining today." But it was not raining. The sun was shining The
son said: "Is it raining today?" Dropping another cake
and another egg the mother said: "Yes, it is raining today." The boy ate the cake and the egg and said: "Yes, it
is raining today."

The mother and her son arrived at the vultures' nest.
The woman saw the gold and silver in the nests. After
packing the coins into the two baskets she set off for home,
where they arrived in the evening. The following day the
boy went to the square where all the men were gathered,
and said: "My mother and I are rich now. We found jars
of gold and silver." The boy said: "It was on the day
when it rained cakes and eggs." The people laughed. The
people said to each other: "Truly, the boy is a simple-
minded chatterer."

One day the simpleton was walking along the road. He
was chattering away out loud to himself, saying: "If God
lets me find a hundred gold pieces in the road, I shall
pick them up and take them away with me. If God leaves
only ninety-nine pieces of gold, I shall let them lie." Walking just behind the boy, though he did not know it, was
a cunning merchant. The cunning merchant said to himself: "If the simpleton should do what he says and were
to be brought before a judge, it could cost him a pretty
penny, which would be profitable to the man who had
put down the ninety-nine gold pieces." The cunning
merchant hurried ahead of the boy and laid down ninety-
nine gold pieces on the road. The simpleton, coming to
the spot and finding the gold pieces, picked them up and
counted them, saying: 'Ho! I would not have expected
that of God. Now God still owes me one gold piece. Listen
to me, God! Make sure that you pay me that last gold
piece very soon." The simpleton went on his way.

The cunning merchant came out of his hiding place
and said: "You have taken away my ninety-nine gold
pieces." The boy asked: "Do you mean that you left
ninety-nine gold pieces lying in the road, or did God cause
you to lose them?" The merchant said to himself: "I cannot declare before the judge that I put the ninety-nine
gold pieces there." The cunning merchant said: "No, I
did not leave them lying in the road. God caused me to
lose them. Come with me to the judge." The simpleton

said: "I have no good clothes and so cannot come with you to the judge!" The cunning merchant gave the boy some new clothes. The boy said: "I cannot go on foot." The merchant gave him a mule. In his new clothes and riding the mule the simpleton accompanied the cunning merchant to the judge. The merchant said: "This boy has robbed me of ninety-nine gold pieces!" The boy said: "Ho! And now you will say that you gave me the clothes that I am wearing on my back and the mule that I am riding?"

The cunning merchant said: "Certainly, I gave them to you." The judge said to the merchant: "You are notorious for your cunning. What you have just admitted is so foolish that I do not believe a word of anything you have said." The simpleton said: "O judge, ask him whether it was not through him that God gave me ninety-nine gold pieces." The judge asked: "Is that so?" The cunning merchant said: "That is what I have said: God caused me to lose them." The simpleton said: "And God caused me to find them, and he still owes me one gold piece. I ask you, O judge, to make the cunning merchant pay me God's gold piece." The judge laughed and said: "Listen, O cunning one! If God caused you to lose the money, and if you had not laid it down on the road merely for the purpose of blackmail, then in God's name pay the boy the hundredth gold piece. Otherwise I shall be compelled to view the matter in quite a different light."

The cunning merchant handed over the hundredth gold piece and went. Pocketing the gold piece, the simpleton said to the judge: "God has put me to more trouble over this hundredth gold piece than over all the other ninety-nine together."

SAMBA KULLUNG THE FOOL   *Sahel*

The name Samba Kullung means Samba do-nothing or Samba the coward. When Samba was a child a hand suddenly raised would cause him to start with fear. A shriek would send him scuttling away as fast as his legs could carry him. Thus he was as a child and thus grew into a man. His father gave him a horse, a dialli musician, and a groom named Munjo Kadi. The dialli's name was Sirima. Kullung was now grown up.

Nevertheless, Samba was still Samba Kullung, Samba the coward. He was tall and strong and very handsome but because of his cowardice he was a general laughing-stock. Samba's mother said to Sirima the dialli. "Everyone speaks badly of my son. Cannot something be done about it?" Sirima the dialli said: "Nothing can be done, nothing at all. Every day I try to rouse him. I tell him all kinds of things trying to stir up his enthusiasm for adventure but it does not work. His nature was thus in his childhood, and will remain so as a man." The mother said. "Oh, what a disgrace for my family. I shall never live it down! Oh, what a disgrace! But listen, Sirima the dialli, would it not be possible to find a sweetheart for him? Every girl taunts a man and makes him desire war-like adventure. Would it not be possible to find him a sweetheart?" Sirima the dialli replied: "Nothing could be simpler, for Samba Kullung is the handsomest man in Kala."

The next day Sirima the dialli brought Samba Kullung a pretty girl called Kumba. Samba Kullung was sitting on the end of his bed. The dialli and the pretty girl also sat down on the bed. Kumba sat in the middle. After a while Sirima the dialli stood up and went out, leaving the pair alone together. For the whole of that day until the following morning, Samba Kullung remained alone with the pretty girl. Then he came out. Sirima the dialli asked: "Well, what happened?" Samba Kullung said: "What do you suppose happened? We sat side by side on the bed. She said nothing and I said nothing either. She did not move and I therefore did not move either." Sirima the dialli said: "That is no way to act. A man sitting next to a pretty girl should take her by the arm. Try doing that."

Sirima the dialli went into the house with Samba Kullung. He sat down on the bed alongside Kumba and Samba Kullung. Then he went out. Then Samba Kullung took Kumba gently by the arm. But Kumba, as women always do, pushed him away. Samba Kullung got up and left her. Outside he met Sirima the dialli. "Well?" asked Sirima. Samba Kullung replied: "When I took hold of Kumba she pushed me away. So I went away." Sirima the dialli said: "I see that you are still very ignorant about women and their ways! They always act that way. Try once more, and if she pushes you away again, give her a gentle spanking. That is the way women like it, no more, or less."

Samba Kullung at once went back into the house. This time he did not immediately come out again. They remained in there a whole day. When the next day Sirima the dialli asked him what had happened, Samba Kullung replied: "Listen, O Sirima the dialli, it was very wrong of you to keep from me for so long the best this world has to offer. When she pushed me away again, I gave her a spanking and found it so pleasurable that I began to wonder what else might be done, and then I lay with Kumba. Oh Sirima the dialli, why did you not tell me before that there was such a thing in the world as this!"

The next day the boy's mother came to Sirima the dialli and asked: "Well, did it do any good?"

Sirima the dialli said: "It was a good suggestion. He already shows signs of improvement."

A few days later the tabele[1] was sounded because a battle had begun nearby. Sirima the dialli went to Samba Kullung, sat down beside him, and said: "The tabele is being sounded!" Samba Kullung did not reply. After a while Sirima the dialli said: "The tabele is being sounded. Should we not go out to fight?" Samba Kullung replied: "You surely do not suppose that because you brought me Kumba I too should go out to fight? That idea is far from my mind. I will stay at home." Samba Kullung's father said to Samba Kullung: "My son, you have not gone out with the others to fight?" The youth replied: "No, I do not want to go out to fight. I want to stay at home." The father said: "I am ashamed of you! Get out of my sight. Away with you!" Samba Kullung's mother said to her son: "When I look at you I can only feel shame. Get out of my sight." Samba Kullung went.

Samba Kullung called Munjo Kadi his sufa, and said: 'My parents have disowned me because I do not want to go into battle. Therefore saddle my horse. I shall ride away to some far off place where there is neither war nor strife." Munjo Kadi saddled the horse. Sirima the dialli

[1] War drum.

108

came to him and said: "I will stay with you. I will go with you to another country." The three set forth, rode out of the town and into the wilderness. For a month and a half they wandered in the wilderness. Then they arrived at the edge of a big village.

The village was ruled by a powerful chief who had a very beautiful, unmarried daughter. One day this girl's slave had gone to the edge of the bush to gather wood. She had put the bundle on her head and was about to return home when she saw the three travellers. When, her gaze fell on Samba Kullung she was so overcome by the young man's beauty that she threw down her bundle and ran home as fast as she could. When she got there she said to her mistress: 'A very handsome horseman is on his way here with his dialli and his sufa. Tell your father to give him a worthy welcome and offer him a good farm." The chief's daughter went to her father and told him what she had heard.

Samba Kullung, his dialli, and his sufa arrived in the big village. He was given a friendly welcome by the Dugutigi, who led him into a fine large farm and killed a sheep in his honor. Everyone was saying: "How Handsome this young man is!" Samba Kullung settled down comfortably there for a period of two days. For two nights he lay with the Dugutigi's daughter.

On the third day the tabele was sounded. Samba Kullung sat in his house. He paid no attention to the summons. But the chief's daughter came to the door, fell on her knees as a sign of respect, and said: "Listen, Samba, the tabele! Samba, are you not going into battle?" Samba jumped and said: "Do you suppose that because your father killed a sheep for me I should now go into battle? No, I will not do so! I do not like fighting. I am Samba Kullung. My father and mother drove me out of their house because I am Samba Kullung and did not want to go into battle. Do you suppose that I shall now go into battle because of your father's sheep?" The girl jumped up and said: "So that is what you are like! You are Samba Kullung? Well, I do not want to have anything more to do with you. Be off with you! You are no concern of mine now."

Samba Kullung called his sufa. He said to him: "Munjo Kadi, saddle my horse. We are going away from this place." Munjo Kadi replied: "Very well!" He did as he was told. Samba Kullung mounted his horse. But Sirima the dialli said: "I shall go home and not stay with you any longer. For you will not change and all I can expect from you is disgrace and dishonor." Sirima the dialli went home. But Samba Kullung and his sufa rode on together.

Now there was a large town governed by a great king. He was rich, having much land and many followers as well as a very clever and beautiful daughter who, as yet, had followed no man into wedlock. One of this princess's slave-girls was washing her mistress's clothes in a pond outside the city gates. She looked up from her work and her gaze fell on Samba Kullung who was riding towards her with his groom, Munjo Kadi. Immediately the girl, so struck by the rider's handsome appearance, abandoned her washing and hurried back to her mistress in the town. The girl came to her mistress and said: "Fatoumata, I have just seen a rider, a very handsome man, coming towards our town. You should at once ask your father, the king, to welcome the stranger as he deserves, for never have my eyes beheld so handsome a man as this rider." Fatoumata went to her father and said: "Father, I have heard that a very fine and handsome rider is coming to our town. I hope that you will welcome him as he deserves and extend the hand of friendship to him." Then Fama, the king, had a big farmstead prepared for Samba's reception, and on the latter's arrival he ordered an ox to be slaughtered. Fatoumata said to her slave: "You were right. He is the handsomest man that I have ever seen." And Fatoumata gave her slave a pretty loin-cloth.

Samba Kullung felt very much at ease in his fine dwelling and everything seemed to him exceptionally agreeable. For five days he lived in great comfort. Every day several excellent meals were served up to him and every night was spent with the beautiful Fatoumata. The king also showed him great honor. But on the sixth day towards evening the tabele was sounded and everywhere people were saying: "The enemy is upon us! The enemy is upon us! We must go out to meet them." Samba Kullung, however, pretended to notice nothing.

For a while Fatoumata watched from her house to see what Samba would do. When she saw that nothing was happening on his farmstead she went across and threw

110

herself down on her knees before him. She said: "Samba, the tabele has sounded. Have your horse harnessed and ride out with the other warriors against the enemy." Samba said: "I will not go! Because I despise fighting my father and mother drove me away from home. Because I cannot stand fighting they called me Samba Kullung. Because I am Samba Kullung another beautiful girl has rejected me. And even though your father may kill oxen for me, I will not start fighting now. If you do not like me as I am then I will leave."

Now Fatoumata was beautiful and proud and very clever. In recent days she had spent a great deal of time talking to Samba. She had recognized his nature and because Samba was extremely handsome, she had grown very fond of him. She said to Samba: "Even though you are Samba Kullung I will not give you up. But I will put on your clothes and mount your horse and ride out against the enemy with the others. It is so dark that nobody will see my face, but they will recognize the clothes." There were one or two slaves present who had heard and seen all that had happened. Having put on Samba Kullung's trousers and coat, Fatoumata said to the slaves: "If any of you, either today or later, tells what he has seen here, I will have him put to death." Fatoumata mounted Samba Kullung's horse and rode out into the night. Samba Kullung watched her go and stood long gazing after her.

The tablele had been sounded for nothing. It was a false alarm. The information had been wrong and no enemy had arrived. All of the warriors returned that same night and Fatoumata changed back into her own clothes. Samba's eyes remained fixed upon his robe which Fatoumata had been wearing. The following day Samba was crossing the main square of the town. A dialli was sitting there. He was singing: "Last night I saw a splendid horseman who, though he was not one of our townsmen, went out to ride against the enemy. If there had been a fight, he would have shot many of the alien marauders. His achievements would have been very great." Samba Kullung stood at the corner for a long time listening to the dialli. Then he went home.

It greatly distressed Fatoumata that so handsome a man as Samba should not be inclined to fight. After thinking for a long time and considering Samba Kullung's character, she decided that he was very young.

One day Fatoumata's father said to his daughter: "There is going to be a fight between ourselves and our neighbours this evening. You may tell Samba, but take care that no one else in the town hears of it too soon." Fatoumata pondered the matter. She said nothing to Samba Kullung or to anyone else but instead went to the market where she bought a big gourd of honey beer. When evening fell she went across to Samba's house, taking the honey beer with her. Samba Kullung asked: "What is that?" Samba Kullung was still so inexperienced that he did not know what an intoxicating drink was. Fatoumata said: "Oh, this is nothing more than a good drink for the stomach. You may have some" Samba Kullung drank.

Samba Kullung drank. He said: "Why has no one ever told me before that such wonderful things exist?" Samba Kullung drank and became intoxicated. He took Fatoumata onto his knee. Fatoumata said: "Everyone in the town is saying that if you wanted to you could vanquish a whole horde of robbers single-handed." Samba Kullung laughed. Samba Kullung drank.

Samba Kullung drank. Outside in the big square the tabele was sounded. Fatoumata heard it. Fatoumata stood up. Samba Kullung heard it. He said to Fatoumata: "I suppose you think that you can go to war for me every time? No, Fatoumata. You are going to hear the diallis sing about me. Tomorrow they will be singing the Pui[1]. Today the tabele has sounded for me alone, for is not everyone in the town saying: 'If Samba Kullung really wanted to, he could vanquish a whole horde of robbers single-handed?' Do you hear how they are sounding the tabele for me?" Samba Kulling called for Munjo Kadi. He said to his sufa: "Harness my horse. I want to ride out to battle."

Munjo Kadi saddled the horse. Samba Kullung rode out. He rode with the others. He killed an enemy. He came back to Fatoumata and said: "Today I had no luck, for I have only killed one enemy." Then he went to sleep.

Not far from the town in which Fatoumata's father was

[1] Epic Saga

king there lived a hunter whose name was Gomblé. He was a very wealthy man and by nature violent and hot-tempered. He owned a large estate and numerous slaves who tended his fields. One thing he did not like was for a horse to set foot in his fields. Many had ridden across his fields unknowingly and had been attacked by him. Since he was very strong, they had all been killed. Having killed a victim, he would at once cut off its head and hang it up in one of the trees that grew around his fields. Everyone went in such fear of Gomblé that no one would have dared to mention his name when going out to fight. Nor did anyone dare to venture in the direction of his farm.

When Fatoumata saw what effect the beer had had on her Samba Kullung, and when she heard the diallis singing about his good looks and his courage, she bought a large quantity of durra[1] and with her hands brewed some excellent home-made dolo. One morning she placed the dolo in front of Samba Kullung and he began to drink. He took Fatoumata onto his lap. When Samba Kullung had drunk enough, Fatoumata said: "Everyone is singing your praises because you are so brave." Samba Kullung said: "Oh, I have not done anything yet. But I have heard of a hunter called Gomblé." Fatoumata said: "Ah, do not speak of him! No one dare pronounce his name. Still less would anyone dare attack him.'

Samba Kullung seized hold of the pot of dolo. He drank. He set Fatoumata down on the ground and said: "Go to your father and tell him to have the tabele sounded for me, and then to let me have some men who will show me the way to Gomblé's estate." Fatoumata immediately went to her father and said: "Have the tabele sounded for Samba. He wishes to go and fight Gombolé and ask you to let him have some men who can show him the way there." Fama said: "That is good news." He ordered the tabele to be sounded.

Samba Kullung mounted his horse and took his musket. He was followed by a hundred freemen, a hundred diallis, a hundred noumous[2] and a hundred slaves, all on horse-back. When they had ridden some distance they came to a parting of the ways. To the right there was a wide, much

[1] Maize.
[2] Blacksmiths.

113

frequented road. To the left there was a narrow path which led to Gomblé's estate. The men said: "We must turn left. That is the way to Gomblé's." On hearing this all the many gapers who had accompanied them out of the town remained rooted to the spot and gazed after Samba Kullung as he took the left-hand fork. After a while the hundred slaves said: "We do not like the look of this business. We would rather have no more to do with it." And the hundred slaves would go no further. After a while the diallis and noumous said: "We have followed so far, and beyond that hill are the first of Gomblé's fields. The noumous and diallis remained where they were. But the hundred freemen dismounted and accompanied Samba Kullung a little way further on foot. Then they too remained by the wayside.

Now Samba Kullung rode on by himself and soon found himself at the edge of Gomblé's fields. Seven hundred slaves and sons were tilling Gomblé's fields. Gomblé himself, however, was sitting at the field's edge under a butter tree, drinking his beer out of a gourd. Pretending he had not seen Gomblé, Samba Kullung rode onto the hunter's field and advanced a little way towards him. For a while Gomblé watched this boldness in astonishment. Then he called out: "Hey there, my fine fellow, are you a stranger or a man of this country?" Samba Kullung replied: "I am a stranger in the land."

Gomblé said: "What? Was there no elder, no friendly counsellor in the district from which you have come or in the town you must have ridden through, to tell you the circumstances concerning me and my fields? I am Gomblé, a hunter and a man of evil disposition. All those whose horses' hooves have trodden the soil of my fields have up till now suffered a miserable fate. I have caught and killed them, and hung their heads on the trees. Now you know where you are!" Samba Kullung said: "Then I must be knocking at the very gates I was seeking. For it was Gomblé with whom I wished to speak."

Gomblé said: "Very well. I will talk with you, for you are a handsome young man and I should be glad to strike up an acquaintance with you. But you must dismount at once and lead your horse to the field boundary. Then take off your cap and use it to carry the soil trodden by your horse's hooves, and set it on one side. This I insist

114

upon. After that we can be good friends." Samba Kullung said: "You have misunderstood me! That is not my intention. I am going to lay hold of you." Gomblé said: "Do not make tricks! If you were not a handsome youth I would have hanged you a long time ago. But I will make you an offer. Perhaps you are a starveling who is willing to stake his happiness against his keep. If you are in need, then take two of these slaves over there. I will give them to you for your handsome looks!"

Samba Kullung said: "You misunderstand me. It is you I want to lay hands on and no one else!" Gomblé said: "Do not provoke me too far, for I have already been more patient with you than with anyone else. Take those slaves over there if you want and then be off!"

Samba Kullung said: "You still do not understand me. It is you and you alone I am going to get my hands on. Stand up!" Gomblé said: "As you will!" With his gun held high, its butt to the fore, Gomblé rushed towards Samba Kullung. Then he turned the gun about in order to shoot. Gomblé pulled the trigger but the gun misfired. Then Samba seized him by the chest and swung him high into the air. But Gomblé called out to his sons and laborers, saying: 'Do not let this little misadventure to disturb you at your work!"

Then Gomblé said to Samba: "Samba, you took unfair advantage[1] of the fact that my gun misfired!" Samba Kullung said: "No one shall accuse me of taking unfair advantage! Feed these two cola nuts to your bashis and see if it makes them protect you better." He then let Gomblé slide to the ground and threw him two cola nuts. Gomblé went to one side.

After a time Samba Kullung said: "Are you ready, O Gomblé?" Gomblé said: "I am ready. Come!" Gomblé picked up his musket and fired. Samba Kullung ducked down and the bullet struck his cap. The bullet removed his cap without so much as grazing his head. Samba Kullung galloped towards Gomblé, caught hold of him for the second time, and swung him high in the air. Samba Kullung said: "Now, Gomblé, if I can catch you and swing you in to the air three times, will you become my bondsman and sufa? Will you then be my slave?" Gomblé

---

[1] Literally: "you robbed".

said: "It cannot happen three times!" Samba said: "Let us see!" Samba let Gomblé slide to the ground. But Gomblé called out to his sons and bondsmen: "Nothing that happens here must be allowed to disturb you at your work."

Gomblé went to one side. Samba Kullung asked Gomblé: "Are you ready?" Gomblé replied: "Yes, come!" But as Gomblé was about to pull the trigger, Samba Kullung bore down on him so tempestuously that he was able to knock the gun to one side before he had had a chance to fire it. Then he seized hold of Gomblé for the third time and swung him high into the air. At the same time he said: "Now, Gomblé, was not that three times in all?" Gomblé's seven hundred sons and laborers were about to assail the handsome youth, but Gomblé called out: "What concern is this of yours? Return to your work!" The seven hundred sons and laborers went away again, but to Samba Kullung Gomblé said: "Samba, you have vanquished me thrice. I will follow you as your bondsman wherever you lead me."

Then Samba Kullung set off for home. Gomblé followed behind him. They encountered the hundred freemen, the hundred noumous, the hundred diallis, the hundred slaves. All the people exulted, crying: "Samba has vanquished Gomblé. Gomblé is alone and is now Samba's bondsman. Look, there he is behind Samba! Samba is braver than he! Look at Samba! But Gomblé addressed the people, saying: "I would advise you not to jeer at me, for it might be the worse for you! I am Samba's bonds- man, but I am not yours. It was not you who vanquished me." Samba said: "Gomblé is right. You must not jeer at him." Gomblé said: "But you should sing my master's praises, for Samba is strong and handsome and brave!" Then the people began to shout: "Samba is the bravest of all men!"

In this way they arrived before Fatoumata's dwelling, with Gomblé following behind Samba Kullung as his slave. Thereupon Samba Kullung was appointed Kelletigi and as such the townsmen's leader in all their future wars and fueds. Indeed, this town had never known a warrior as powerful and magnificent as Samba Kullung.

One day Fatoumata had brewed some dolo of unusual excellence. Thereupon Samba Kullung arose and sallied forth against the enemy. Single-handed, he captured all their oxen and cows, a considerable herd, and brought them home. On another occasion when Fatoumata had made an exceptional brew of dolo, Samba Kullung again sallied forth, returning with a herd of cows and oxen even bigger than the first one. Fatoumata prepared yet another brew of excellent dolo. For the third time Samba Kullung sallied forth against the enemy, seizing an exceptionally fine herd so that he became the richest man in that town and indeed throughout the whole land.

Everyone declared that for strength and heroism the country had never seen his like before.

Samba Kullung herded all of his cattle together and entrusted them to Fatoumata. He said to Fatoumata: "Take all that I have acquired. I myself am going to Kalla to visit my parents. They drove me from home because I would never fight. Now I will show them what I am really like. I shall come back. Farewell, and take care of all I have won for you."

Then Samba Kallung set off for Kala. He arrived home. He found his parents again and stayed with them for a little while.

When Samba Kullung had ridden away there was a general uprising of all those that the Kelle-tigi had subdued, and the man at their head was Gomblé. Gomblé said: "The town has lost its strongest defense. Now we shall attack it." All of the town's enemies gathered together to attack the town. The town was surrounded by enemies. The danger was very great.

While he was on his way back, Samba Kullung encountered a marabout. He was not, however, an honest man but had been hired by Gomblé and his men. The marabout said to Samba Kullung: "The town of Fatoumata and her father is being attacked and Gomblé is in command of the enemy. If you return there now and if you succeed in capturing seven of the assailants, the town will be free." But there was no truth in what he said, for his was a false prophecy and was intended to lure Samba Kullung into a trap.

Samba Kullung arrived outside the town. He flung himself upon two of the assailants and took them prisoner. He flung himself upon two more of the assailants and took them prisoner. He flung himself upon three more of the assailants and took them prisoner. But then Gomblé's men came on the scene and Samba Kullung was himself taken prisoner.

Two of Gomblé's men led Samba Kullung to their master, who was on his estate. On the way there Samba Kullung said to one of them: "Give me some water. I am thirsty." The man said: "Why should I? Last year you killed my father. I will not." Turning to the other man, Samba Kullung said: "Give me some water. I am thirsty." The man said: "Why should I? Last year you killed my father. You will get nothing from me!" Then the two slaves perceived that Samba Kullung who had journeyed far and fought arduously, was growing faint and they killed him.

The two men came to Gomblé and said: "Your enemy, Samba Kullung, is dead." Then Gomblé grieved and said: "How did he lose his life?" The two men said: "Samba Kullung was thirsty. We gave him nothing to drink, for he had killed our fathers. When he grew faint we put him to death." Then Gomblé grieved and said: "It was an evil thing to do, for a man so brave as he and capable of such great things should be courted for his friendship. As for you, you are nothing but a pair of miserable robbers."

BUGE KORROBA

Sahel

Bugé Korroba had four wives. Among them was one called Njelle who was his favorite wife. Because of this woman, Njelle, he would never listen to the tabele or war drum, he never left this wife, for he loved her very much. Also he had everything he wanted in the way of slaves, horses and cattle. The other three wives were jealous and told the women in the town: "Because of this woman, Njelle, Bugé Korroba will never go out to fight. It is a calamity for this place." The women of the town said: "One of these days when Njelle comes to the well, we will give her a good beating so that she sends her husband out to fight."

The women of the town lay in wait for Njelle, and one

day Njelle came to the well. Some of the women said to her: "Beware!" Njelle said: "Why are you angry? I have done nothing to harm you." The women said: "Because of you, Bugé Korroba always stays at home and never goes out to war, and that is bad for this place." They beat Njelle. Taking off their bracelets, they rained blows on Njelle. On her forehead Njelle had three wounds in a row. The women said: "Now do you know, Njelle, why we have been hitting you?" Njelle said: "You did right to hit me."

Bugé Korroba had two diallis. Every day they had to play the guitar to him. They had to sing the Pui. When they began it, he flicked their guitars with his fingers. The diallis asked: "Why did you do that?" Bugé Korroba said: "I want you also to sing about me." The diallis said: "But you never go to war!" Bugé Korroba said: "I love a beautiful woman and the backs of horses."

Bloodstained and dirty, Njelle came home. Bugé Korroba said: "What has happened to you?" Njelle said: "The women of Kalla have beaten me because you love me too much to leave me, and staying at home instead of riding out to war." Bugé Korroba said: "One of these days the people of Kalla are going to get a surprise! It is not because I am afraid that I do not ride out to war. Because of this affair the surprise I shall give the people of Kalla will not be a pleasant one."

Three days later robbers from Massina came and took away all the cows and bullocks belonging to the people of Kalla. Only Bugé Korroba's cattle was left untouched. His herd was kept on an island. On hearing what had happened, Bugé Korroba mounted his horse. He took with him two kossongallas,[1] his own and Njelle's. He rode out of the village. When the people of Kalla saw him riding away they jeered at him, saying: "What? Are you riding out to war? Your fighting won't be up to much!" Bugé Korroba said: "I am not riding to war but only going to look at my herds on the island. For it was your herds the robbers took. They left mine alone."

Bugé Korroba rode away. First he went to look at his herds, then he rode after the robbers but, instead of following the same winding track, he took a short cut and to

[1] Blankets from Segu.

such good effect that when he rejoined the path he was far ahead of them. There he dismounted. Laying one of the kossongallas on the ground, he sat down on it, then wound the horse's bridle round his feet. After that he covered himself with the other kossongalla in such a way that his face could not be seen. In this guise, he sat and waited. After a time one of the robber band's diallis arrived. Seeing the man on the track, he turned back and told the robber chieftain: "One of your men is sitting on the track waiting for you." The robber chieftain's men deliberated, asking: "Who can it be?" Some suggested this man, others suggested that. No one thought that it might be a man from Kalla.

The men of the robber band proceeded on their way, driving the herds before them. It was not long before they came upon the man swaddled in his blanket and apparently asleep. They stood around him in a circle, considering who this man might be. After a time, however, Bugé Korroba spoke. He said: "Who is your chieftain?" One of the robbers said: "Are you dreaming or babbling nonsense? Do you not know your own chief?" But the man sitting on the ground replied: "I know very well what I am saying. It is you who are confused. I am not seeking war or strife, nor have I come to pick a quarrel with you, for you took nothing away from me, Bugé Korroba. But I would like to take back to the people of Kalla their cattle. My people are not used to drinking the sap of the baobab tree instead of milk. Therefore, refrain from strife and give me back the cows that belong to the people of Kalla." The robbers said: "No!" Bugé Korroba said: "See that you act justly."

Among the robbers was a man called Samba. He was known to all as one who never lied and whose judgement was respected by king and slave alike. The robber chieftain said to Samba: "Now, Samba, tell us if there is any justice in this man's plea."

On hearing this, Bugé Korroba took up his blankets, stood up, folded the blankets, and after placing them across the horse's cruppee, swung himself into the saddle. Samba said: "The judgment in this case is easy to make but very difficult to accept." Seeing which way the wind was blowing, the robber chieftain said: "Yes". One of the robbers shouted: "I think we ought to kill Bugé Korroba and not indulge in all this talk about justice."

The Suboli[1] realizing what Samba's judgment was going to be, tried to forestall it by saying to Bugé Korroba: "Listen, Bugé Korroba, we will give you half. Take them back with you to Kalla and I will take the other half with me to Massina." Bugé Korroba said: "I do not want half. Either you send me back to Kalla with all the cows so that my people can have their milk tomorrow morning, or else, besides taking the cows I will take your horses too." Angrily the robber chieftain exclaimed: "Bugé Korroba, I have already offered you half, but now you will get nothing."

Burgé Korroba took his gun and shot the Suboli dead. Once more he took his gun and shot the Kuntigi[2] dead. He shot them. The robbers saw it. Overcome with fear and horror, they made off as fast as they could. Bugé Korroba, however, took all of the cattle and the four horses and herded them all onto his island. Then he galloped back to Kalla.

Outside his farmstead he pulled in his horse with a sudden jerk and shouted: "Njelle!" Njelle came out. Bugé Korroba asked Njelle: "Why did the other women beat you?" Njelle said: "The women of Kalla beat me because you love me too much to leave me, staying at home with me instead of riding out to war." Bugé Korroba said: "This evening all of the men and women whose cattle was stolen and all of those who beat you must come here. I have brought all the cows back. If the people of Kalla want to have their milk tomorrow morning, then they must come to me this evening to discuss all of these matters."

In the evening all of the men and women foregathered. They all said: "Bugé Korroba is the bravest of all, for he has brought back all our cows, and the robbers' horses besides. He did this alone." The diallis came and said: "Bugé Korroba is now in the Pui." Bugé Korroba came with Njelle. In front of the people he asked his wife: "Njelle, why did the women of Kalla beat you?" Njelle said: "The women of Kalla beat me because you love me

[1] Robber Chieftain.
[2] Leader of the band.

121

too much to leave me, staying at home with me instead of riding out to war." Bugé Korroba said: "You have heard what happened. I have your cows. If you want to get your cows back and to drink milk tomorrow, then you must make your wives dance the slave dance[1] here."

The men said: "Your complaint is a just one. Our wives treated your wife very badly. Your wife was beaten by our wives. We, too, will beat our wives." Bugé Korroba said: "Do what you want." Then every man in Kalla gave his wife fifty strokes with a rope, after which they said to Bugé Korroba: "Now justice has been done. Give us the cows." Bugé Korroba asked his wife: "Njelle, why did the women of Kalla beat you till you bled, and leave you with three scars on your forehead?" Njelle said: "The women of Kalla injured me because you love me too much to leave me, staying at home with me instead of riding out to war." Bugé Korroba said: "You have heard what happened. I have got your cows. If you want to get your cows back and to drink milk tomorrow, then you must make your wives dance the slave dance here."

The men said: "It is too much to ask. Our wives beat your wife. They have been beaten in return. Your wife received three scars from our wives. We shall give our wives three as well." Bugé Korroba said: "Do what you want!" Then the men made their wives cut three horizontal scars into the center of their foreheads in the same position as Njelle's scars. Then they said to Bugé Korroba: "Now justice has been done. Give us back our cows." Bugé Korroba said to his wife: "Why did the women of Kalla humiliate you?" Njelle said: "The women of Kalla humiliated me because you love me too much to leave me, staying at home with me instead of riding out to war." Bugé Korroba said: "You have heard what happened. I have got your cows. If you want to get your cows back and to drink milk tomorrow, you must make your wives dance the slave dance."

The wives were sitting on their stools. When they again heard this they stretched out their right hands in a gesture of horrified protest and pressed their left hands to their sides, crying: "Never!" But this position, left hand to the side and right raised in protest, is the first position

[1] A sexual dance.

of the sexual dance. Bugé Korroba laughed and exclaimed: "You say Never! but you have already taken up the first position!" Then everyone burst out laughing.

GOSSI THE HERO   *Sahel*

Gossi was renowned as the bravest Fulbe ever to have lived. He was immune to pain. If he trod on a thorn and it penetrated his foot, he did not feel it. When addressed, he never took any notice until his name had been repeated, for to turn around immediately would betray alarm. He would not notice anything that went on behind him. In order to attract his attention it was necessary to catch up to and address him from the front.

There had been only three times since he had grown up when Gossi had been afraid. But nobody except God and himself knew that he had been afraid.

One evening at six o'clock when it was already dark, the people were drawing water from the well outside the town. Suddenly the rope to which the gourd was attached broke in two. Then nobody could think of how to draw up the water needed that night. In the darkness no one dared to climb down into the well, for the whole world knew that in its depths there lived a dangerous snake, a korongo. All the people were standing around the well and none of them knew what ought to be done.

Gossi happened to come that way. He said: "What is wrong?" The people said: "We have no water in our village, the rope has broken, and the gourd has fallen to the bottom. We shall have to wait till morning when it is light, for now it is black night. Also the korongo is down there." Gossi said: "What does that matter. Tie this rope around my body and lower me down. I will get the gourd." Some of the people said: "But now it is darkest night!" Others said: "The korongo is down there!" Gossi said: "What does that matter. Now lower me down." So they lowered Gossi into the deep shaft of the well.

Down below the korongo had meanwhile settled down snugly into the gourd. Gossi, seizing hold of the broken end of rope, tried to tip out the snake. But he could not. Three times Gossi tried without success. But in the meantime the thirsty cattle had shouldered their way through to the well where they were waiting to be watered. A playful bull tried to mount a cow. But in the darkness neither animal saw the shaft of the well and both of them fell into it. And there they stuck not very far from the top, entirely blocking the shaft. Now Gossi was trapped. The rope was jammed fast. Above him were the cow and the bull, below him the water and the snake, and all around was total darkness. The people cried out in horror.

The people said: "We must dig a hole at an angle so that Gossi can get out." When he heard them, Gossi shouted: "Do not go to such unnecessary trouble, for I would not come out. Leave me here till tomorrow morning. When daylight comes you will be able to pull out the cow and bull and that will be the moment for me. But now I will not come out." The people said: "If that is how Gossi wishes it, we cannot do anything."

The next morning they returned and began by pulling out the cow and the ox. Then they called out: "Gossi!" But Gossi would never answer the first time he was called. Again they shouted: "Gossi! Are you still alive?" Gossi shouted back: "Yes, I am still alive. During the night the rope broke again and I fell into the water." The people added a strong piece to the rope and let it down, calling: "Loop the rope around your body and let us pull you up." Gossi answered: "No, I will not let you pull me up. I am going to stay down here and die. For I have fallen into the water and thus made it unclean for the Fulbe. I have become the laughing-stock of the Fulbe women."

Then all of the women gathered round the well and said to Gossi: "Come up, Gossi, come up. Remember that the village has only one well. If you die down there, we will not be able to draw up any more water. Then all of the people and all the cattle will die of thirst. But you are the bravest of men. For you were the only one who dared climb down into the well and you stayed there all night with the terrible snake." Then Gossi allowed himself to be pulled up, saying: "The Fulbe shall not die of thirst because of me." When he arrived at the top he threw the corpse of the snake, which he had crushed to death in his bare hands, onto the ground beside the well.

When the cow and bull had fallen in, Gossi had been frightened for the first time. But except for himself and Allah, no one else had been aware of it.

In that region there was another man called Gossi, a relation of Gossi the great here. This other Gossi was excessively jealous of his wife and had therefore built a house for himself and his wife outside the gates of the town. For if a fly had so much as settled on another man's skin he did not like it to touch his wife's hands afterwards. This Gossi was a keen hunter and he liked to hunt at night. He had slung a bell about his horse's neck and thus could always be heard when he was approaching or riding away.

People would joke with Gossi the hero, saying: "You are a great hero, but you would not dare go into your jealous cousin's compound and visit his wife during her husband's absence!" And Gossi would say: "Aha, so you think so." One day he took his double barreled gun, mounted his horse, and rode to his jealous cousin's compound. The man was not at home. Gossi, after tethering his horse outside, took off all of his clothes and hung them all around where anyone could see them. Then he went in to the wife.

He remained with the woman. Laying his head in her lap he went to sleep. After some time the woman heard the bell her husband's horse wore hanging from its neck.

The woman nudged Gossi, saying: "Do you not hear?" Gossi woke up and asked: "What is it?" She said: "Listen, that is the bell worn by my husband's horse. He is coming. If he finds you here he will kill you!" Gossi said: "What? You wake me up for such a trifle?" Then he turned over and went to sleep again.

Meanwhile the other Gossi had ridden into the yard. He tethered his horse. He noticed that there was another horse there. He walked towards his wife's house. There he saw all of his cousin's clothes hanging up outside. Thereupon he flew into a terrible rage and loaded his double-barreled gun. He went into the house. He took aim and fired at Gossi. But in his fury he had used too much priming, so that when he fired the first barrel exploded. Again he aimed the gun and fired. But as he did so the second barrel also exploded, for in his fury he had again rammed in too much powder. Gossi the hero said: "Like all hunter's guns, yours is in poor condition, for hunters allow water and rain to wet their guns too often. Take my gun. It is in good condition and properly loaded besides. It is standing behind the plank bed."

The other Gossi snatched up the gun but he was trembling so much with rage and excitement that he was unable to pull the trigger. After a second or two Gossi the hero said: "If you are not going to fire, then I will not remain here." Taking leave of the other Gossi's wife, he went out, put on his clothes, and rode away. The other Gossi said: "You were saved by God and your total lack of fear. It is true that you are never afraid."

When the hero got home, he realized that he had left a cord with a string amulet hanging up outside the other Gossi's entrance door. He said: "If I send someone else to get it, people will say that I am afraid. If I ride past quickly and snatch it as I ride, people will say that I am afraid." He saddled his horse, rode back slowly, dismounted outside the other Gossi's house, conversed with him for a while, and then said: "I forgot something here this morning." He went over to the entrance door, took down the trinket, hung it around his neck, made sure it was hanging properly, took leave of his cousin, and rode slowly home.

That was the second occasion on which Gossi was afraid. But except for himself and Allah, no one was aware of it.

Bakari, a Fulbe, had heard of Gossi's heroic deeds. He came from a great distance and said to Gossi: "I have heard that you are a hero of exceptional courage and that you are quite fearless. Would you consent to take me with you the next time that you go out? For I wish to experience something out of the ordinary in your company and have the chance of witnessing your deeds with my own eyes." Gossi replied: "Follow me. We can set off at once, in any direction you choose."

After a while they came to a part of the bush through which seven hunters were making their way. Bakari said: "Should we not attack them?" Gossi said: "These people are too dangerous. I am afraid of such people." After a while they came upon some laborers working in a field. Bakari said: "Are we not going to attack them?" Gossi said: "I am afraid. These are very dangerous people. Also, if we start a fight here, we shall have the laborers in front of us and the hunters in our rear." Then Bakari said: "I can see that you are not really a valiant hero after all, since you seem to be afraid of everything. Perhaps it is your generosity towards the musicians that influences them so much in your favor and leads them to sing your praises as they do?" Gossi said: "No doubt that is exactly how it is!" After a while they came to a town. Outside the gates were a number of people who were going into the bush to relieve themselves. Sarcastically, Bakari asked: "How about them? Shouldn't we attack them?"

Then Gossi flared up and said to Bakari: "You are such a coward I feel ashamed to have ridden with you. Are you completely without shame? Are you not afraid that by attacking harmless hunters and laborers you will become the laughing-stock of the Fulbe women? I blush for you!" Bakari said: "What are you really thinking of doing?"

Gossi said: "Ahead of us lies a royal city. Inside it the king keeps two valuable horses. You can take one of them and I will take the other. Then we will ride home with them. That would be worthwhile, for each of the two horses is guarded by twelve well-armed sufas." Bakari said: "Are you going to do this in the daylight? If so I will not go with you!" Gossi said: "Then do not come at all. I will ride in by myself and fetch out the horses." Bakari said: "No. Wait until nightfall and then we will do it together." Gossi said: "Very well, since you refuse to do it any other way."

When evening came, they rode into the town. They passed the sufas unmolested, for the sufas took them to be innocent travellers. They came to the place where the two horses were tethered. The moon was out. By the light of the moon they went to the place and untied the horses. Hearing the sound of horses' hooves, the sufas shouted: "The horses have broken loose!" Others called out: "Stop the horses! Catch the horses!" Gossi shouted: "There is no need for you to worry about the horses. They are not alone. I am with them, I am the man who let them loose." When the sufas heard that, they made all speed to shut the gates. Then having captured Gossi and Bakari, they handed them over to the head jailer. The men said: "Early tomorrow we can put these two men to death above the royal sanctuary." Gossi and Bakari were put in irons. Gossi said to the men: "Go to the king and tell him that I am accustomed to have a drink of milk every evening." The men replied: Horse-thieves do not get milk!" Nevertheless they told the king. The king said: "He is a Fulbe. Give him milk." They brought milk to Gossi. He drank half of it and handed the rest to Bakari. Bakari said: "I do not want any." Then the salves' overseer took charge of them both. The two men were chained together.

In the middle of the night Bakari called out: "Gossi!" But Gossi never answered the first time he was called. Bakari again called out: "Gossi!" Gossi said: "Why are you disturbing my sleep?" Bakari said: 'What? Are you able to sleep on the night before your execution?" Gossi replied: "How could I show any endurance tomorrow if I did not sleep now?" Bakari said: "If it pleases you, we will escape now. For I know that you will only do things your own way." Gossi said: "Do not annoy me! How could we get away, chained together as we are? If you persist in such foolishness I shall call the head jailer." Bakari said: "Do not get angry." Gossi began to call out, but Bakari put his hand over his mouth.

Then a tremendous storm blew up. The town was veiled in clouds of dust. After a while Bakari said to Gossi: "Gossi, we would easily get away. We may be chained together, but we could walk if we place our feet carefully. We can climb out of here, then over the wall." Gossi said: "Very well. Let us go." The two men set out for the wall. It was completely dark, but since the storm was a thunder-storm there were frequent flashes of lightening that lit them on their way. Step by step, Gossi and Bakari slowly made their way to the wall.

When they had reached the wall Bakari said: "We only have to jump down and we will be outside." Gossi said: "No, I will not do that. We can not break the iron. But if we jump down we shall break our ankles and the scar made on my foot by the iron will always remain for everyone to see. Then we shall be the laughing-stock of the Fulbe women. No, I will not do that. I would rather die tomorrow above the royal sanctuary." The storm roared over their heads. The thunder rolled. The rain pelted down onto the ground. Lightening flashed from the sky.

Then Bakari gave Gossi a push. Both men fell from the wall.

Below there was a lioness who had had nothing to eat for a long time, so that her cubs were empty. She was standing below with her cubs. When Bakari and Gossi crashed down from the wall, they fell on the cubs. The iron fetter struck the cubs and killed them. But the lioness flung herself on Bakari and tore open his throat.

The lightening flickered across the sky. The lioness had flung herself on Bakari and begun to eat him. Whenever the lightening flashed the lioness, her bared fangs dripping with blood, would turn on Gossi, still fettered as he was to Bakari. Each time Gossi would strike her in the face and each time she would turn back to Bakari, burying her fangs in his body and crunching his flesh. The lightening flashed. Gossi struck the lioness. The lioness devoured Bakari. Gossi lay alongside. At long last the lioness bit off Bakari's feet. Gossi, with the fetter still on his leg, could get up and go. Stopping only to give the lioness a parting blow, he made for home. Though he could not walk very fast, he managed to make some progress. In this way Gossi got home. That was the third time that Gossi was afraid. But except for Allah, the lioness and himself, no one was aware of it. After that, Gossi was never afraid again.

Gossi lived in the land of Bakunu. In Gossi's day, Hamadi was king of the Bakunu Fulbe. Now Hamadi insisted upon a strict observance of the country's ancient customs in two respects. His first concern was for the sacred bull. No one might strike or jostle the bull, and any failure to observe this rule was at once punished by death. Secondly, the king insisted upon unfailing respect being shown towards the women of his court and household. No fewer than seven hundred soldiers were constantly on guard at the gates leading to his living quarters.

Twice a week, on Mondays and Fridays, the women were accompanied down to the river by the body of soldiers. Anyone who found himself in the path of the procession was to hide and anyone who, in defiance of this rule, dared to look at the women or to remain where he was, would be put to death. Also, anyone wither at the royal court or anywhere else who happened to see a woman of the king's household was supposed to turn away and cover his face with his hands or his cloak. Among these women there was one whom the ruler loved above all the rest. Her name was Njelle. He could never refuse her anything that she asked for, and it was to her that he entrusted the care of all his treasure.

Now there was a Fulbe by the name of Bulloballi. Having heard of Gossi's deeds, he set out to find the hero, for he wanted to see him in person. He travelled a long way, found Gossi, and said: "I want to see something terrible and outrageous." Gossi said: "That is easy. Wait a few days and I will show you so much outrageousness that your curiosity will quickly be satiated." Bulloballi said: "I will wait."

One Monday everyone was gathered together in the market place. The diallis were playing the guitar and singing the Bowdi.[1] . . . Flicking their guitars, Gossi said: "Come, Bulloballi, today we will play paddi[2] . . . on the south bank of the river." Gossi and Bulloballi went down to the river and began to play. After a while Gossi saw that the train of royal women, led and protected by the seven hundred soldiers, was advancing towards them. He did not move. Bulloballi turned around. He too saw the train of women. Overcome by fear he at once sought the shelter of a hole in the river bank.

Gossi stood up. He saluted the royal women by falling on to his knees and touching the ground with his forehead. As the procession passed beside him, however, he stood up, looked at the train of women, and called out: "Njelle!" Njelle answered at once: "I am here!" Gossi said: "Njelle, I am thirsty. Please bring me a small bowl of water." Njelle went down to the river, she went into the water up to her knees, and filled the bowl for Gossi. She returned with the bowl. She knelt down in front of Gossi and handed the hero the water. Gossi drank.

Blankets had already been spread out on the ground for the women. With the flat of his hand Gossi now brushed away the sand that had settled on one of the blankets and said: "Sit down next to me, Njelle!" The seven hundred soldiers and guards, and the women of the

[1] Epic.
[2] A game of dice.

130

royal household, all watched this outrage. No one dared move or say a word. Njelle, however, sat down next to Gossi. They talked for a while. Then Njelle said to Gossi: "There are no real men left among the Fulbe of Bakanu!" Gossi said: "Yes, there are some real men in Bakunu. Only you do not know them. If you want to get to know a true Fulbe hero, wait for me tonight in your house. For despite the seven hundred guards and the sacred bull I will spend the night with you." Njelle said: "Ah, I can hardly wait for the evening! I wish it were tonight already!"

Then Njelle and Gossi parted and the women and their guards went back to the town and the king's compound. Bulloballi now emerged from his hiding place. He said: "Quick, come home! I have had my fill of outrage!" Gossi said: "No, we cannot go. Let us play a little longer." Bulloballi said: "Let us go!" Gossi said: "Then go by yourself." Bulloballi remained. They played paddi. When his turn came to play, Gossi remarked: "A woman has said that there are no real men left among the Fulbe of Bakunu. This gives us an opportunity. We have to prove that there are." Just then a lioness appeared out of the bush. But Gossi never looked behind him. He could hear the animal padding over the ground and he could hear it snarling, but since it was coming up behind him he paid no attention to it. Bulloballi said in alarm: "A lioness!" Gossi said: "It is your turn to play." Bulloballi leapt up and again took refuge in his hole. Gossi neither moved nor stirred.

Then two hunters came that way, thereby scaring the lioness who sprang quickly back into the bush. Bulloballi said: "I am going home." He came creeping out of the hole and, as he passed Gossi, he said: "I have had too much outrage today!" He hurried away.

When evening came, Gossi took two spears and went with them to the king's quarters. Ngare togo sholi, the sacred bull, was tethered outside one of the gates. No one might strike or jostle him under pain of death. Taking one of his spears, Gossi plunged it into the bull's flank. Then he took the second spear and plunged that into the bull's flank. The sacred bull dropped down dead. Then Gossi walked through the gatehouse and into the king's quarters. He asked a woman where he could find Njelle's house. The woman pointed in a certain direction. He asked another woman the way to Njelle's house. She showed Gossi Njelle's house. Gossi went inside and slept with Njelle.

Gossi spent three days in Njelle's house and slept with her. All of the men and women knew about it. But no one dared carry the news to the king, for they were all afraid of his anger. On the third day Hamadi's first wife went to the king and said: "Gossi the hero has spent three days in the royal quarters, in your wife Njelle's house, where he has been sleeping with her." When the king heard this, he summoned all of his notables and wise men to council in the great courtyard.

The king said: "I once gave a law that anyone who struck or jostled Ngare togo sholi should be put to death. I gave a law that anyone who saw my women and failed to turn away on their approach should be put to death. But now Gossi has come and, not content with striking Ngare togo sholi, has killed it! He has not only looked at my women, but has slept with my favorite wife! He has been with Njelle for three days and does not fear my anger. If blows and looks are enough to have a man executed, what is to be done in the case of killing and lovemaking? What advice have you to give?"

Some said: "He can only be put to death." Others said: "He can be boiled in a big cauldron." Much else of the same kind was deliberated. Among the company however, there was a brother of Gossi, one who was older than Gossi. He said: "Do not kill Gossi, but banish him from the land." In Njelle's house Gossi could hear everything that was going on in the square outside.

When Gossi's elder brother had said: "Do not kill Gossi but banish him from the land." Gossi said to Njelle: "I am too hot in here. I will go and walk around the big courtyard for a while." Njelle said to him: "I will come with you." Then Gossi and Njelle walked hand in hand out of the house and into the big courtyard where the council was being held. Gossi said to Njelle: "Now go back." Njelle said: "no, I will stay with you, for you are a real man and the bravest of all the Fulbe!" Hand in hand they went on walking towards the council and the king until Gossi said: "Farewell, Njelle!" Njelle said: "Farewell, Gossi!" Njelle went back into her house.

When the assembled men saw Gossi and Njelle hand in hand coming out of the house and walking across the courtyard, some turned their heads away, others covered their eyes with their hands, and yet others veiled their faces, in obedience to the king's order that all should look elsewhere upon the appearance of a royal woman. Thus it was that Gossi was able to walk across the courtyard and sit down next to the king. Overwhelmed with terror at the sight of such fearlessness, the king, timidly moved apart.

Gossi sat down beside the king and said: "Just now my elder brother said: 'Do not kill Gossi but banish him from the land.' If it were not my brother who had uttered these scandalous words, my brother born of the same father and mother as myself, I should kill him right now. Punish me as you think fit. You can put me to death. But never shall I be banished from the Fulbe community!" When he had spoken Gossi stood up and went back to Njelle's house. All the while that Gossi had been sitting beside him the king had been filled with fear. Now that Gossi was gone he felt a sense of relief.

After Gossi had left the courtyard and gone back into Njelle's house, a breathless messenger arrived before the council. He had come hotfoot to announce that a strong band of warriors had made its appearance outside the capital, where it was causing trouble. Then King Hamadi said: "For now we shall have to leave the case against Gossi and go out to meet the enemy." A man from outlying parts said: "If we go away from here, Gossi will flee at once and escape his punishment." But one who belonged to the town said: "It is easy to see that you do not belong here for otherwise you would know that this man is a hero and would never flee." After this the army under King Hamadi's leadership went forth against the foe.

Now Gossi had been listening to all this. When the others had gone he said to Njelle: "O Njelle, I hear that there is fighting, and here I am, sitting idly with a woman! Njelle, if only I had a horse!" Njelle said: "Here at the royal court there are two fine horses. One of them cost seven slaves and the other ten. Go and choose one for yourself." Gossi went and chose a horse. He came back and said: "Njelle! If only I had a good gun!"

Njelle had all the keys to all the store-houses. She showed him where to find the gun store. He went there and from a pile of fifty he took a double-barreled gun. Njelle showed him where the powder and ammunition were stored. She said to Gossi: "Take plenty of powders and bullets." Gossi said: "I shall need only enough to fire two times." He loaded the gun and said: "Farewell, Njelle!" Njelle said: "Farewell, Gossi!"

The fighting was going very badly for King Hamadi's army. The enemy force was very strong and had almost succeeded in pushing back the Fulbe. There were two valiant heroes among the enemy who wished to kill King Hamadi or take him prisoner. One had just levelled his musket to fire point-blank at King Hamadi. The other had already stretched out a hand to seize hold of the king. At this moment Gossi galloped forth. First he shot the man who was levelling his gun at King Hamadi, then he shot the one who was reaching out to seize hold of the king. Both men fell dying to the ground. Seizing the bridles of their two horses, Gossi handed them to the king and said: "Take good care of these two horses." The king tied the horses' reins together and held them, and thus it was that King Hamadi became the sufa of Gossi the hero.

But Gossi flung himself into the fighting, riding here and there wherever the enemy was strongest, and soon King Hamadi's army turned back the invader.

While Hamadi's army was reassembling, Gossi galloped back to the town as fast as he could. He tethered the horse outside Njelle's house and then went in. Gossi said: "Now Njelle, bring me hot water so that I can bathe, for the work that I have done was very tiring." Then Njelle laughed for joy and got everything ready. The hero washed himself.

Hamadi's army reassembled on the battlefield and returned to the town. Once more the council gathered in the big courtyard. When everyone was present the king said: "We must now complete the case of Gossi the hero, for we left it unsettled. Gossi killed Ngare togo sholi and went into the house of my favorite wife to sleep with her for three days. We were unable to think of any penalty severe enough to make up for these crimes. Meanwhile, however, things have greatly changed. Gossi has saved

my life on the battlefield. It is because of him that the
enemy did not conquer us. Therefore, instead of punish-
ing Gossi the hero, I shall give him my wife Njelle."
Gossi's elder brother went to call the hero and to tell
him what the king had decided.

Gossi came out. He went into the council. Boldly and
without hesitation he sat down beside the king. He said:
"King Hamadi and all the rest of you! You think that I
have done what I did for the sake of the woman Njelle. I
would not do such a thing, for Njelle is the king's wife.
But a Fulbe woman had said to me that there were no real
men left among the Fulbe. It is a disgrace when Fulbe
women can say such a thing. What I have done I did to
show that there still are real men left among the Fulbe.
I will not take your wife away from you. Keep her, King
Hamadi."

Then Gossi the hero rose and left the royal quarters.

Later Gossi the hero said: "I am the bravest of all the
Fulbe. Only three men could show more courage. The
first is the man who washes himself in warm water, and
then does not scratch himself. The second is the man who
has a hangnail and can peel it off along his finger towards
the back of his hand instead of removing it by biting or
cutting it. The third is the man who draws a drink of
water at night and drinks it without looking first to see
what he is swallowing."

SIRA MAGA NJORO   *Sahel*

Sira Maga Njoro became one of Massina's great heroes.
His birthplace was the village of Keke and he was the
son of the king of Massina. His father was called Ardo,
and at that time Massina was tributary to King Daga's
kingdom of Segu.

On the day Sira Maga Njoro was born, King Ardo made
inquiries throughout the country to find out where other
boys had been born on the same day. The inquiries re-

vealed that a hundred boys had been born. Then Ardo sent one batang[1] as a gift to each of the mothers of the hundred boys, and a message saying: "As soon as your son has been weaned from his mother's breast, send him to my home. I wish to bring up, along with my own son all the hundred boys born on the same day as Sira Maga Njoro. I will see that they never want for anything. The hundred young people are to live together for as long as their lord, Sira Maga Njoro, remains alive."

King Ardo then built a large and splendid manor containing ten beautiful buildings. Each of these ten houses was to serve as a dwelling for ten of the hundred boys. One after another, the hundred boys were brought to the manor by their mothers and there they lived. From then on they all led the same life there as Sira Mago Njoro. They all ate the same food. They all wore the same clothes. When they had grown big enough, they were all circumcised together. Then, all at the same time, they were given horses to ride and weapons to hunt and fight with, and experienced men were chosen to teach them various skills, and musicians to sing to them about the valiant deeds of the past. They all rose at the same time every morning, spent the day doing the same things, and went to bed at the same time. And so it continued until the boys were grown-up.

At the time when the boys were still quite young, Massina was not independent but King Ardo paid a yearly ussuru[2] to the ruler of Segu. Every year that country would send out a message through all the land and would have sheep brought in which the emissaries from Segu would take back with them. When the hundred boys were still no more than half-grown youths an emissary arrived one day from Segu. He was seated in the king's great hall. Next to the king a robust youth was sitting. The emissary from Segu could not take his eyes off him, for a large fly had settled on the boy's forehead and was sucking his blood. The fly's body swelled as it continued to suck. But the boy took no notice of it. At last, gorged with blood, the fly fell dead onto the youth's knee. His eye happening to light on it, he flicked it with his finger so that it

[1] 10,000 cowrie shells.
[2] Tribute.

136

quashed against the wall. The wall was stained with blood.

Out of the corner of his eye the emissary watched this small incident with interest. Then he left. Outside he asked a man: "Who was the lad sitting next to King Ardo?" The man said: "That was King Ardo's eldest son. His name is Sira Mago Njoro." The emissary returned to Segu and, having delivered the sheep, said: "King Ardo of Massina has a son called Sira Maga Njoro. When he is fully grown it will not be so easy to collect ussuru from Massina. The boy had a blood-sucking fly on his forehead which drank its fill before it fell off. He did not even notice it and did not once put his hand to his forehead."

The following year the emissaries again arrived from Segu to collect ussuru. They saluted Ardo. One of them happened to drive some of the animals past the meadow where Sira Maga Njoro and his companions were playing. Catching sight of the man driving the sheep, the king's son called out: "Hullo there boy! Where are you taking those sheep? Whose sheep are they?" The man from Segu said: "These are some of the sheep that the king of Massina is sending to the king of Segu as ussuru." Then Sira Maga Njoro cried: "What does ussuru mean?" The emissary said: "It means that Massina is weaker than Segu, so that your father has to pay tribute to the king of Segu in order to remain on friendly terms with him." Sira Mga Njoro said: "What? Is not Sira Maga Njoro now a grown man in Massina? No, we will not pay ussuru so long as I am alive! Are there any more sheep-drovers of this kind?" The people said: "There are seven men engaged in driving the ussuru to Segu." Sira Maga Njoro said: "Well, drive these seven brave men along in this way!" All seven men from Segu were brought as he had asked. When he saw them all in front of him, Sira Maga Njoro ordered their heads to be cut off. This was done. Sira Maga Njoro was still not fully grown at that time, but such was his influence that his orders were obeyed.

When King Ardo heard what had happened he at once sent Sira Maga Njoro a messenger with instructions to warn him that this was not to happen again. It was an old dialli that Ardo sent. The old dialli came to Sira Maga Njoro and said to him: "Your father has sent me to explain the circumstances to you and to point out how foolishly you have acted. Today Segu is powerful, very powerful, but Massina is weak, very weak. Segu, if it is so wished, could take everything away from us. We could not defend ourselves." Sira Maga Njoro was carrying three throwing spears. He took one of them and hurled it in a great arc so that it flew right into the river. He took the second spear and hurled it in a great arc so that it flew right into the river. He took the third spear and hurled it in a great arc so that it flew right into the river. Then he said: "Tell my father that if Segu tries floating up that way, it will tangle itself in my harpoons. And that will be so as long as I am alive." The dialli went and told King Ardo what he had heard. King Ardo said: "It is well. We shall see what happens."

One day Sira Maga Njoro's people told him: "Your father's brother is going to be married." Sira Maga Njoro said to his men: "Find out whether the girl is young or old. My father's brother is old. A young girl is not suited to him. If she is young I will take her away from him." His people went to see the girl. Then they came back and said: "The girl your uncle wants to marry is young." Sira Maga Njoro said: "Then come with me." He set off with his horsemen and rode to the village where the girl was living. He took her away from the village and married her himself.

When King Ardo's brother heard what kind of trick Sira Maga Njoro had played on him, he at once set forth. He was exceedingly angry and decided to use all the forces he could muster against Sira Maga Njoro. He journeyed to Segu, to the overlord of Massina, and said to King Daga: "My bother's son, Sira Maga Njoro, has done me a grave injury and has taken the girl that I intended to marry. Now lend me your warriors so that I can march against him with your men and mine and put him to death." King Daga of Segu said: "You have good reason for complaint. But I myself have fared even worse. For what did this boy, Sira Mago Njoro, do but go and kill seven men I had sent to Massina to collect the tribute. Nor would he allow any tribute to be sent to me from Massina. Now let us wait, you and I, until next year and then we will both go to war against Massina and Sira Maga Njoro."

One day Sira Maja Njoro was in a house together with his dialli and his hundred heroes. Sira Maga Njoro said: "I excel all other men in three things. First, I am the handsomest man in Massina. Second, I am the most generous in distributing money to the people. Third, I am the most fearless of all."

King Ardo's brother was passing outside. Hearing the opening words of the discourse he said to his companions: "Stop for a moment. My brother's son in there is making great claims. Let us wait and listen." They all stopped. Sira Maga Njoro said: "First, I am the handsomest man in Massina." The eavesdropping uncle nodded and said: "That is true." Sira Maga Njoro said: "Second, I am the most generous in distributing my money to the people." The eavesdropping uncle nodded and said: "That is also true." Sira Maga Njoro said: "Third, I am the most fearless of all." At this his uncle shook his head, saying: "No, that is not true. He is exaggerating. I, for example, have more courage than this inexperienced boy. Now come!" He rode away. Now Njidi, an old bondsman of Sira Maga Njoro's, had been standing not far off listening unseen to the remarks the uncle had made. In accordance with his usual habit, however, he did not say a word.

The following day the slaves, with Njidi at their head, went into the bush to cut wood. Njidi took them so far that they no longer knew their way. Njidi said: "Wait here in the forest and I will find the way back." The slaves remained where they were. Njidi went out of the bush in the direction of Keke. It was already dark and there was no moon. Then it began to rain. When he had come close to the village Njidi climbed a tall tree and let out a screech.

The people in the village were startled and asked: "Who was screeching?" Others said: "Where did that come from?" Others said: "It must be a band of warriors coming to attack the town." Others said: "And the slaves are not back yet." Others said: "That will be the army from Segu, coming to surprise us. They will have come upon our slaves on the way here and taken them prisoner." All of the men fetched their horses and weapons and rode out of the city gates behind Sira Maga Njoro and King Ardo's brother.

The heroes rode in the direction of the screech until they arrived under the big tree in which Njidi was sitting, Sira Maga Njoro stopped on one side and King Ardo's brother on the other. Above their heads Njidi gave another screech. This filled Sira Maga Njoro's uncle with such terror that he went galloping back to Keke at break-neck speed. His men followed in his wake. Meanwhile Sira Maga Njoro remained quietly standing where he was. He called up into the tree: "Who is it up there?" Njidi, however, gave another screech. Again Sira Maga Njoro asked: "Who is it up there?" Then Njidi answered: "It is I, Sira Maga Njoro's slave. The other slaves and I have lost our way." Sira Maga Njoro said: "Very well. Come down and climb up behind me. We will ride home."

When the uncle at last reined in his horse outside the gates of Keke, he asked: "Where is Sira Maga Njoro?" His men said: "Sira Maga Njoro stayed under the tree. He never moved from the spot." Then the uncle was ashamed and rode back again. When he met the young hero he said: "My horse bolted. I lost all control over the animal and it went galloping back with me to Keke. Not until then did I regain control over it." Nobody said anything in reply but all turned back across the dark plain.

As they rode back across the plain some animal close by gave a roar. This frightened Sira Maga Njoro's horse so that it reared. But Sira Maga Njoro's strong hand on the reins forced the animal down again. A little while later two lions roared somewhere very close by. Sira Maga Njoro's horse again reared up and then made several bounds forward. But it was forcibly restrained by the young hero. On seeing the horse trying to bolt, the uncle said: "You see! That is just the way my horse behaved!" Sira Maga Njoro said: "But mine did not get as far as the walls of Keke."

Now contrary to his usual habit the old slave Njidi for once opened his lips and said: "Yesterday evening when I was in the place where I prepare my master's food, I heard my master Sira Maga Njoro say three things and I heard another who was passing by say three things. What the other said was wild and uncontrolled, like the bolting horse of King Ardo's brother. What my master said was

proud and strong like the hand that curbed Sira Maga
Njoro's horse."

Then Sira Maga Njoro's uncle was ashamed.

Sira Maga Njoro said: "Who knows whether I still
have more than a year to live. For I have already done two
things for which restitution will be demanded of me. I
have had the ruler of Segu's emissaries killed and I have
taken a woman away from my uncle. Let us enjoy ourselves therefore. Let us play paddi." Sira Maga Njoro did
not, as others do, play paddi with pebbles or pieces of
wood, but with dice of gold and silver. They began to
play. He picked up the silver dice. The others said:
"Why, since you are the king's son, do you not take the
better ones, the golden dice?" Sira Maga Njoro said:
"White is clean, yellow is dirty. I only want what is pure.
You have what is dirty if you prefer it."

They began the game. Sira Maga Njoro, whose turn it
was, said: "I begin. Everything I order to be prepared
for you, you can eat without detecting anything bad or
disgusting." Polor, an older and much esteemed house
slave, was also playing. He was regarded as a truly exceptional man and hero, and legend said that whenever in
battle Sira Mago Njoro killed a man on one side, Polor
would fell an enemy on the other. It was Polor's turn to
play after Sira Maga Njoro. He said: "I think we can
eat everything that the king's son puts before us, except
cow-dung. We should be able to detect that."

The following morning Sira Maga Njoro called for his
cook Njidi and said: "Take a dish of rice, a dish of cow-
dung, and a sheep and make them into a succulent meal
for my heroes." Njidi did as he was ordered. He prepared
an aromatic dish. When the others gathered for their
meal, Sira Maga Njoro said: "You will have to eat without me for I am not feeling well today. I have a stomach
ache." Then the others ate the dish prepared for them by
Njidi and found it delicious. They ate the gourds clean.

Afterwards they began to play paddi again. This time
too, Sira Maga Njoro opened the game saying: "I begin.
Everything I order to be prepared for you, you can eat
without detecting anything bad or disgusting." Polor
said: "I think we can eat everything that the king's son
puts before us except for cow-dung. We should be able to
detect that." Sira Maga Njoro said: "You have just eaten

cow-dung without noticing it. The saying is therefore of no avail." The others laughed and said: "You got the better of us! In play too, you are king!" Sira Maga Njoro said: "But now can see that I was right to choose the silver dice which are always pure, and to leave you the gold ones."

One day Sira Maga Njoro said to his comrade for he was always on such friendly terms with his slave that he called him thus: "O Polor, harness my horse, Sopre Kange!" Polor asked: "Where do you intend to go?" Sira Maga Njoro said: "Who can tell whether I still have more than another year to live? So I should at least get married. I am going to the Konare country where I shall bring back the daughter of its ruler, Galadio, to be my bride." Now Galadio lived in the village of Gundaka. Around Gundaka there grew a thick belt of scrub consisting in stiff, thorny tomonong bushes. A single path led through this secure barrier to the village of Gundaka.

Sira Maga Njoro, and the hundred heroes set out together and rode to the Konare country. They camped for the night on the ground outside the barrier of tomonong bushes. Sira Maga Njore laid twelve light throwing spears on the ground, covering them with a blanket. This served him for a bed. At the head of the bed he set up a heavy spear. Two diallis squatted down beside him and played the Baudi. Flicking the guitars with his fingers he said: "Go at once into the town to Galadio. All you need say is: 'Sira Maga Njoro has come. He wants to marry your daughter and take her back with him to Keke.' In addition you can tell Galadio: 'Your daughter Fatoumata is the first girl in Massina. Sira Maga Njoro is the first boy in Massina. Hence they belong together and their union will make Massina strong.' To this Sira Maga Njoro's companions replied: "Do not send such a message, for it is contrary to all custom. The ruler of Konare will be affronted and will send out his twelve kambodjes[1] against you." Sira Maga Njoro said: "What is to be will be. I want you to deliver my message in this form."

The two diallis set off. They rode along the path between the thorn trees until they reached the market place. There they saw Galadio seated among his men, all

[1] Knights who have proved themselves in single combat.

of them swathed in beautiful white robes, while twelve diallis were playing the Baudi. It was a noble gathering. Having made their salutation, the two musicians from Keke said: "We have come to you with important tidings." The king said: "If what you have to say is good, I shall be glad and will show my gladness to you. But if the news you bring is bad I shall see to it that you lose half your clothes on the tomonong bushes out there." This frightened the diallis. They said: "Then we will go away again, even though our master is a brave man." Galadio said: "Do as you think fit." Then the two diallis returned.

The two diallis came back to Sira Maga Njoro. When they appeared in the distance one of the prince's companions said: "Look, there come your two diallis again." Sira Maga Njoro said: "Why have you come without Fatoumata?" The diallis said: "If a little of your beard is inherited from both father and mother, then you will have a goodly beard. Galadio spoke to us so uncivilly that we left without delay."

Sira Maga Njoro laughed and said: "Polor, harness my horse, Sopre Kange. Today I will take all Konare's cattle and tomorrow Fattoumata will be given to me for a bride. If I do not succeed in doing this, then, whenever you see me, you can heap insults on me and call out: 'There is the dog! He is running away!'" Then he and his horsemen went out and rounded up all of the cattle of Konare.

When Galadio heard of this he caused the tabele to be sounded. Sira Maga Njoko heard it and he said to Polor: "Drive the cattle home at your leisure. The hundred heroes will help you. I will wait here, for I have heard the tabele sounding. There is no need for any hurry, and if the cattle want to graze a little on the way, let them do so. I will see to it that, while I am alive, no horseman will come past me through these tomonong bushes to attack you. Proceed, therefore, at an easy pace." Polor and the hundred heroes then drove the cattle away.

Sira Maga Njoro sat down on the ground between the thorn bushes, tied his horse's bridle to his foot, swathed his blankets around him and waited with his thirteen spears ready to hand to see what would happen next.

When the tabele had been sounded, the twelve Kambodjes came to King Galadio and asked: "What is happening? Why have you had the tabele sounded?" Galadio said: "Sira Maga Njoro has come into our country and stolen all of our cattle. He is driving them away." The Kambodjes said: "But surely it was not worth having the tabele sounded and mustering every one of us just because there is a cattle-thief out there in the bush?" Galadio said: "You are wrong if you believe that Sira Maga Njoro is just an ordinary cattle-thief. He has his hundred heroes with him." The Kambodjes said: "But knowing us as you do, you must be aware that just one of us is able to take on a hundred men? Choose, then, one of us twelve and send him out in pursuit of this Sira Maga Njoro." Galadio said: "You would seem to know nothing at all about this Sira Maga Njoro. He is the bravest and most fearless hero in Massina." The Kambodjes said: "Very well, if that is what you wish, all twelve of us will go out against him." Galadio said: "Even that is not enough for my liking. I and my other horsemen will also accompany you." Then the whole band rode off and soon arrived at the town gates.

Seated beside the town gates was an old dialli. As Galadio rode past him he called out: "Galadio! Galadio! Galadio!" He had to call out three times before the king heard him. Galadio said: "What is it?" The old man said: "What I have to say to you may make you angry. But it is good that you should hear it. Yet in your anger you might kill me." Galadio said: "I will not kill you." The old man said: "How can I be sure?" Galadio said: "I will not kill you." The old man said: "All the same, you might grow angry afterwards. Therefore you must swear!" Galadio said: "I swear by my name that I will not injure you."

Then the old dialli said: "If someone like this Sira Maga Njoro rides out against your three hundred and thirty villages with his hundred horsemen, he is a brave man, a hero! And Sira Maga Njoro *is* a hero! So do not fight him, for if you were to kill this one man it would cost you too many brave warriors. Therefore I advise you to ride out and meet him, and discuss this matter with him in peace. Salute him in the name of your common ancestry. Shout Diko[1] when you see him." As Galadio rode on, he turned the matter over in his mind.

Sira Maga Njoro was sitting on the ground in the same position as before. He was singing the Baudi to himself, accompanying his song on a guitar left behind by one of his diallis. Upon the king's arrival, Sira Maga Njoro jumped up. This startled Galadio. He remembered what the old dialli had said and called out: "Diko!" Sira Maga Njoro had not been expecting this. He had been looking forward to a fight. When the king saluted him thus, he gnawed his lips so fiercely that the blood spurted out of them. Only then was he able to reply. Thereupon Galadio said: "Listen, O Sira Maga Njoro, we belong to the same family and are both of royal descent. Why should we weaken each other by fighting? It would be better to seek to strengthen the Fulbe families than to murder each other and decimate our people. It would be better to share between us what there is of good or ill in our families. If you had a daughter I would ask for her hand in marriage. If you want to marry my Fatoumata, I will gladly give her to you, for you are a member of my family and a hero. This is how we should act. We should not fight each other and steal from one another." Sira Maga Njoro said: "You are right. We will not continue as we have begun. I will give you your cattle back and take your daughter for my wife. That was my intention. You will keep your word as I am used to do."

The king said: "I will send someone to fetch back the cattle. You can stay here." Sira Maga Njoro said: "It would be better if I were to call back my people myself." King Galadio said: "That is your affair. I am content that it should be so." King Galadio sent out the twelve kambodjes and three hundred warriors to tell Polor to send back the cattle. Galadio took the kambodjes on one side and said: "Should Polor refuse, you must kill him and the other hundred men. At all costs you must bring back the cattle." Those who stayed behind sat down beside Sira Maga Njoro. The diallis played the Baudi.

Meanwhile Polor was saying: "O hundred heroes, go on driving the cattle forward at an easy pace. I will cover your rear and see that none of Galadio's horsemen gets

---

[1] Name of the noble family to which they both belonged.

past me." Soon after leaving their king, the kambodjes galloped ahead, while the three hundred horsemen remained far behind them. When Polor turned around, he saw the twelve strange horsemen on the horizon. He at once galloped back to the hundred heroes and said: "Our hero Sira Maga Njoro must have been killed, for I have seen that we are being followed by hostile warriors. You can go on slowly, driving the cattle. I will not let anyone past me." Once more he remained behind the rest. And now, in the distance beyond the twelve kambodjes, he saw the three hundred horsemen advancing. Once again he rode back as fast as his horse could carry him and said to the hundred heroes: "You can go on slowly driving the cattle, for I shall have plenty of work to do. A number of horsemen are coming. Wait for me by the water over there and let the cattle graze. I will come back as soon as I have settled this matter."

As Polor went galloping back he said to himself: "Sira Maga Njoro has never yet told a lie. Today he said: 'While I am alive no horseman will get past me.' Therefore he must be dead. I shall make these people pay for that." Polor rode on at full gallop. He saw one of the twelve horsemen raise his hand. But he himself was yelling so stridently that he failed to hear the other shout: "Stop, Polor! A message!" Taking aim, he shot the other man, the leading kambodj, so that he fell from his mount. Again he raised the gun and shot the second kambodj. Thereupon the other ten kambodjes turned and fled.

As soon as the three hundred horsemen saw this, they did not wait, but turned their horses around and galloped for home. They galloped ahead, behind them the ten kambodjes with Polor hard on their heels. Again he fired. Again a kambodj fell from his mount. Only nine remained. From time to time he fired on the kambodjes. He never missed. Eleven kambodjes were killed in all. But by then they had reached the spot where Sira Maga Njoro had remained with Galadio.

Sira Maga Njoro called out: "Stop, Polor!" At that Polor lowered his gun and Sira Maga Njoro's cry saved the life of the last kambodj. Polor exclaimed: "O Sira Maga Njoro, you have never told a lie before. But today you have told an untruth. For not long since you said to me: 'I will see to it that, while I am alive, no horseman will come past me through these tomonong bushes.' And yet I see that you are alive." Sira Maga Njoro said: "You forgot that I added: 'To attack you.' But these people did not come out to attack you. They came bearing a message." Galadio said: "Now eleven of my kambodjes have been killed and only one is left alive!" Sira Maga Njoro said: "Did I not tell you that it would be better if I called my people back myself?"

Afterwards, Sira Maga Njoro sent the cattle from Konare back to Galadio and a little later Sira Maga Njoro married Fatoumata, the daughter of King Galadio of Konare.

Meanwhile King Ardo's brother, who had been robbed of a woman by Sira Maga Njoro, was pressing King Daga of Segu to go to war against Massina. King Daga said to him: "I will give you ten bands of warriors. You can lead them with your own men against Sira Maga Njoro." Ardo's brother said: "That is not sufficient. You do not know this Sira Maga Njoro. No hero like him has ever before been born of a Fulbe woman." King Daga said: "Then take my whole army and lead it against Massina and Sira Maga Njoro." Ardo's brother said: "Thas is not sufficient. Unless you accompany your army, good luck and strength will not be ours in this campaign." At long last Daga agreed to everything that Ardo's brother asked for. He said: "Very well, I will ride out with you and I and my army will accompany your men. If we are not then victorious, it will mean that our cause has not found favor in the eyes of God." They armed themselves and set forth.

A rumour eventually reached Keke that a powerful army was on its way and that King Daga himself was leading his forces. Sira Maga Njoro called for his younger brother, Mussa Ardo, and said: "Listen O brother, something serious is afoot. Ride out and see whether there is any truth in the rumor that King Daga himself is marching against me at the head of his whole army. Make sure the information you obtain is correct and complete." Taking a sufa with him for groom, Mussa Ardo rode towards Daga's army as fast as his horse could carry him.

When they had journeyed for six days they came to a part of the bush in which men of the hostile army were cutting wood to build a camp. At the edge of the bush they were cutting grass to provide fodder for their horses. Hardly had Mussa Ardo's sufa heard the sound of wood-cutting than he said to his master: "Let us turn around quickly, for we have reached the camp. We can say that we have been in the enemy's encampment." Mussa Ardo said: "I promised to bring my brother a report that was correct and complete, and I can only turn back when I have seen the warrior bands with my own eyes." They rode on. They came to the enemy's encampment. The sufa said: "Well, now we have seen the enemy troops. That is enough. Quick, let us return! For what good would it be to your brother if we were killed? Then he would be left without any news at all!" Mussa Ardo said: "I promised my brother to learn whether Daga himself was leading the Segu army. Therefore follow me!"

Mussa Ardo rode into the very middle of the enemy camp, as far as the spot where a hut had been built for the king. Daga himself was standing there. Mussa Ardo dismounted, went towards the king, and saluted him. The king replied: "Hail, O traveller. I am King Daga of Segu, and I am on my way with my army to carry war into Massina, the land of Sira Maga Njoro, the hero. Who are you?" The other answered: "I am Mussa Ardo, brother to Sira Maga Njoro, the hero. I have been sent out by my elder brother to find out for certain whether the army of Segu is on its way to Massina and whether King Daga himself is at its head." Daga said: "Then you can inform your brother that I am on my way and that he should prepare himself for war." Mussa Ardo said: "That I will do." King Daga said: "You must be tired, for you have come a long way." Mussa Ardo said: "Truly, I am tired!" King Daga said: "Spend the night here in my camp to recover. I will have a good sleeping place set up for you." Mussa Ardo said: "I accept your offer." Soon afterwards King Daga sent the hero a hundred red cola nuts for his refreshment. But the hero's sufa said: "Do not eat them. They are most certainly poisoned though you will not be able to taste it." Shrugging his shoulders, Mussa Ardo unhesitatingly placed several nuts in his mouth. After a while King Daga sent food and a black ox as provision for his journey. Mussa Ardo accepted it with thanks. The sufa said: "In Allah's name do not eat any of this meat. The ox is black and that is proof enough!"

Mussa Ardo slit the bull's throat, had an ample meal prepared, lay down to rest on the couch that had been got ready for him, and slept soundly until the following morning.

The next morning King Daga called for Mussa Ardo the hero and said to him: "Mussa Ardo, tell your brother that I am glad you came. I had intended to leave today and go to Keke as quickly as possible. Now that I have seen you here I will put off my march for eight days. And tell Sira Maga Njoro on my behalf that if his spears are not in good condition, he should have them mended and sharpened. If any of his guns are broken, he should have them repaired. If there are breaches in the town walls, he should have them filled in." Mussa Ardo said: "I will tell my brother what you say."

As the hero turned his horse and was about to ride away, his eye fell on Kaba Mbadji. He was a chief from the Segu district and a captain in the king's army. He was a very handsome and powerful man. Mussa Ardo said: "Who is that? A freeman or a bondsman?" Daga said: "He is a freeman and a hero." Mussa Ardo said: "Good. Kaba Mbadji, we shall meet again outside Keke. We two will do battle together and you will be the first man to fall by my hand in this war."

Then Mussa Ardo rode home, sought out his brother, Sira Maga Njoro, and said: "The entire royal army of Segu, with Daga at its head, is on its way here. I rode into the camp and talked to the king. He gave me a place to stay during the night, offered me food and presents, and sent word to you that he would remain where he was for eight days, thus giving you time to prepare yourself for war."

Daga's army rode across the land. So numerous were the bands of warriors that they stirred up the dust like a whirlwind and drove it before them, and even the antelopes sought refuge in the town of Keke. The Segu army moved forward to camp close beneath the walls of Keke. The king, together with King Ardo's brother, camped beside a tommi[1] tree which stood on a hill offering a view of the entire army. They camped there although Ardo's brother had warned King Daga, saying: "So exposed a

[1] Tamarind.

149

place is not good for you and me, for if Sira Maga Njoro takes up arms he will fight his way through all the warrior bands down there until he reaches this point which can be seen from afar."

For some days there was nothing but skirmishing. Every now and again the men of Keke would make a sortie against the forces of Segu. Many valorous deeds were to be seen, for every man in Keke regarded himself as a hero in the service of the bravest man in the country. Whenever a very bold spirit issued from the gates of Keke and laid about him amongst Daga's people, the king invariably asked: "Can that be Sira Maga Njoro?" But each time King Ardo's brother laughed and said: "When my brother's son takes up arms, you will know him. When that happens you will not even ask, but you will say at once: 'That is Sira Maga Njoro!'" So it went on for two days.

On the third day Sira Maga Njoro said: "Today I will ride out against the enemy." He clothed himself in scarlet trousers, a scarlet cloak and a scarlet cap. He mounted his horse, Sopre Kange. He went galloping to the gates. He galloped out of the town. Everyone shouted: "That is Sira Maga Njoro! That is Sira Maga Njoro!" The hero hurled back the enemy to the right and to the left. He went galloping into the thickest of the fray and wherever he appeared men fled before him, crying "That is Sira Maga Njoro! That is Sira Maga Njoro!"

King Daga saw it from his position under the tommi tree. King Daga said: "Yes, that is Sira Maga Njoro." The hero was fighting his way ever closer, until he reached the tamarind tree. King Daga and King Ardo's brother fled in terror. Sira Maga Njoro, however, rode up until he was beneath the tree. Plucking a branch from it, he went galloping back into the town of Keke.

The following day he again put on his scarlet clothes and rode out of the city gates. Again he smote those to the right of him and those to the left of him and went galloping into the thickest of the fighting. Everywhere his coming brought panic and terror, and when he reached the tamarind tree, King Daga and King Ardo's brother fled in flight. But Sira Maga Njoro plucked a branch from the tamarind tree and carried it back to the town.

King Daga became thoughtful. He said to his men: "In

this way we are suffering a loss of power, respect and renown. What can we do against so strong a hero?" The people said: "Let us consult a wise marabout." Summoning a wise marabout, they asked him: "Can you tell us how King Daga can subdue this hero?" The marabout reflected for a long time.

After some while the old marabout said: "Tomorrow Sira Maga Njoro the hero will again ride out of the gates of the town of Keke and do battle with the king's warriors. During the night you must have a copper arrow made. Then you must give a bow and the copper arrow to a jepege[1] and hide him while it is dark in the tommi tree. Tomorrow when Sira Maga Njoro comes out to ride against the king, the jepege must shoot the arrow at him from above. If the arrow finds its mark, Sira Maga Njoro will die. If it fails to find its mark, Sira Maga Njoro cannot be killed by this means, and any attempt will be made in vain." Daga said: "It will be done."

They at once set about forging the copper arrow. They gave a jepege a bow and the copper arrow and during the night they sent him up into the tamarind tree.

The following day Sira Maga Njoro once again clothed himself in scarlet. Leaving the gates open, he rode out against the enemy. Now to the right and now to the left he wounded and killed the enemy. Under the fury of his onslaught, the boldest military leaders went down, the most stalwart bands were scattered. He rode up to the tamarind tree. King Daga and King Ardo's brother had fled. Sira Maga Njoro reached out for a branch of the tamarind tree. The jepege drew his bow. The arrow found its mark. The hero, feeling death upon him, tore off the branch and galloped back to Keke. The gates closed behind him. Then he sank to the ground.

Sira Maga Njoro was dead. His people tore up the earth all over the town to form mounds that looked like fresh graves. But Sira Maga Njoro they buried in a hidden place and they did it most secretly so that no one should know where, how, or whether Sira Maga Njoro had died. For they knew that King Daga would have the graves opened in order to find Sira Maga Njoro. For three days the people never stirred out of Keke. Then Mussa Ardo

[1] Albino.

151

said: "I will ride out instead of my brother. Give me his scarlet clothes."

When Sira Maga Njoro had galloped back into the town of Keke everyone kept asking the jepege: "Did your arrow find its mark or did it not?" The jepege answered: "It did find its mark!" Shaking his head, King Daga said: "Sira Maga Njoro broke the branch off the tamarind tree and rode back into the town." But the jepege said: "We shall see whether or not the hero comes out of the town." When on the next day he failed to appear on the battle ground the people said: "Then he must be dead!" When on the second day he failed to appear on the battle ground, everyone said: "Then he is most certainly dead." When on the third day he failed to appear, they all began to shout: "Sira Maga Njoro is dead! " Sira Maga Njoro is dead! "

On the fourth day the gates of the town flew open. Out of them there rode a horseman in a scarlet robe who galloped up to a band of warriors, killed men to the right and to the left, unhorsed brave heroes, went galloping up to the tamarind tree, putting King Daga and King Ardo's brother to flight, and broke a branch from the tommi tree. Then all the enemy bands began to shout: "Sira Maga Njoro is not dead! Sira Maga Njoro is still alive! Sira Maga Njoro is not dead!" The hero clad in scarlet rode back into the town. Not a man among the enemy knew that it had not been Sira Maga Njoro but his brother Mussa Ardo.

The following day and the day after that Mussa Ardo performed the same feat. By then the forces of Segu were overwhelmed by fear. But during the night Mussa Ardo mustered all of his troops and led them out of Keke. He crossed the river and rode away.

When King Daga and King Ardo's brother realized that the town had been abandoned, they broke down the gates and went inside. There they found many new burial mounds. They opened them to see if Sira Maga Njoro was buried there or not. But they did not find Sira Maga Njoro's body, for it had been far too well hidden. Thus the king never knew whether or not the hero was dead.

During the war against King Daga of Segu and King Ardo's brother, Polor had not been in Keke but had ridden with thirty-five horsemen to another land. On his return to Keke he was told of all that had happened, including Sira Njoro's death. Then he covered his face with his hands and wept. He went on weeping thus for a whole day until he fell asleep in the same position. When he woke he mounted his horse and rode away with his thirty-five heroes. No one ever knew where they went. But whenever it thunders people say: "That is Polor making war out in the bush."

GOROBA-DIKE   *Sahel*

One of the descendants of the royal Ardo family, which ruled over Massina for five hundred years, was Goroba-Dike. But, being a younger brother, he was not heir to any kingdom and he spent his time wandering about in the Bammana country. Discontented and irritable, he would vent his bitterness arising from his own ill-fortune upon the wretched inhabitants. Thus Goroba-Dike grew to be a brutal, cruel and violent man. When he dismounted in the evening in a Bammana village, he would have a small child killed and pounded in a mortar, its remains being then mixed with water and given to his horse to eat. Arriving at a smithy, he would order the smith to temper his knife and spears without using either fire of bellows. Or upon encountering a leather worker, he would demand that he cobble a hippopotamus' skull with leather. He did so many things of this sort that the Bammana tribes went in terror of his savagery.

In their distress the Bammanas turned to Alal the Mabo,[1] Goroba-Dike's clever musician. They brought him a big chest full of gold and presents, saying: "You are the only man who has any influence on what Goroba-Dike chooses to do. We are bringing you these gifts in order that you should tell him that his actions are only bringing destruction to this land without any benefit either to us or to himself. Could you not try to change his attitude?" Alal the Mabo said: "Very well. I will see what I can do about it." He accepted the chest of gold. It was indeed

[1] Fulbe caste of singers and weavers.

153

true that he was the only man to whom Goroba-Dike would listen. A few days later he said to Goroba-Dike: "Listen, these Bammana have never done you any harm. If I were in your place, I would do something against my own countrymen, the Pulos. For do they not owe you a kingdom?"

Goroba-Dike said: "You are right. Which town should I visit first?" Alal the Mabo said: "How would it be if you were to journey to Sariam, a place where Hamadi Ardo is king?" Goroba-Dike said: "Very well. We could do that. Let us ride there."

The two men arrived in the neighbourhood of Sariam. They halted at a farm in that district. The farm belonged to a Dimadio,[1] and there they dismounted. Goroba-Dike said to his Mabo: "For the time being you must stay here. I will go and have a look at the town on my own." He then took off his good clothes, asked the Dimadio to give him one of his labourers' oldest and most tattered garments, and in this ragged disguise set off on foot for the town. The first man he addressed was a smith to whom he said: "I am a Pulo who has fallen upon evil days. In return for a little food I am prepared to work diligently for you." The smith said: "There is nothing that I can use you for except to work the bellows." Goroba-Dike said: "That I will gladly do." He began to work at once. He worked well.

As they worked he asked the smith: "Tell me, who owns this town?" The smith said: "The town belongs to Hamadi, a member of the Ardo family." Goroba-Dike said: "So it belongs to Hamadi Ardo? Does he have any horses?" The smith said: Oh, he has horses beyond number! He is rich in every way. Both he and the town are rich, very rich. He has everything he needs. He also has three daughters, and two of those daughters are married to brave Fulbe men." Goroba-Dike said: "Is the third daughter still only a child?" The smith said: "No. Far from being a child, she could already herself have had several children. But Kode Ardo is the proudest Fulbe girl in Massina. She wears a silver ring on her little finger and will only marry a man who can fit that ring onto his own little finger. For she says that a true

[1] Fulbe caste of serfs.

154

Fulbe must have very fine limbs and delicate fingers. Otherwise he cannot be a true Fulbe."

As on every other day, all the most noble young men among the Fulbe gathered next morning in front of Hamadi Ardo's house where they stood about talking to each other. Then Kode Ardo, the king's small proud daughter, came out of her house, pulled the silver ring off her finger, and began to search among those present for a man upon whose finger it would fit also. One who tried it could not even get it over his finger-ip. Another succeded with difficulty in getting it as far as the first joint. A few were able to push it down as far as the second joint, but no one could get it any further, no matter how much they tried. For everyone there would have been overjoyed to have Kode Ardo for his wife. To possess her would have been a proof of pure breeding. And as the King's daughter she would bring her husband a fine estate.

The following morning exactly the same thing happened. Once again, among all the Fulbe who had come in from far and near, there was not one who was able to put on the ring. But by now Hamadi Ardo's patience was completely exhausted. He said to his daughter: "Now you will have to marry the first man who comes along." Among those who heard this remark was the smith for whom Goroba-Dike was working. He said: "Oh, I have a man working in my house. He is not well dressed. He is a countryman. He says that he is a Pulo, but it is clear from his appearance that he is a Fulbe." Hamadi Ardo said: "Go and fetch the man. He, too, shall try on my daughter's ring to see if its fits." The smith and several others went to Goroba-Dike and said to him: "Come at once. The king wishes to speak to you!" Goroba-Dike said: "What? The king wishes to speak to me? But I cannot go like this, in these ragged clothes!" The smith said: "Do not worry. That is how the king wants it."

Goraba-Dike went with the smith to the big marketplace where King Hamadi was standing with Kode Ardo and the rest of the distinguished company. He went in his rags and tatters. The smith said: "Here he is." Hamadi Ardo asked him: "You are a Fulbe?" Goroba-Dike said: "Yes, I am a pure Fulbe." Hamadi Ardo said: "What is your name?" Goroba-Dike said: "That I cannot tell you."

155

Hamadi Ardo took his daughter's ring and said: "Try to push this ring onto your little finger." Goroba-Dike took the ring and pushed it onto his finger. The ring fitted. King Hamadi Ardo said: "You will marry my daughter."

The Kode Ardo began to cry, saying: "No, I will not marry this country fool, this ugly, dirty creature!" But the king said: "It was by your own choice. Now you shall marry the man." Kode Ardo went on crying the whole of that day, but she was forced to marry dirty Goroba-Dike. The marriage was celebrated on the very same day. That night Goroba-Dike slept with his wife. The next morning Kode Ardo wept. She went on weeping the whole day through and said: "Oh, what a dirty creature my father has married me to!"

One morning the Burdama raided the district and stole all of the cattle belonging to King Hamadi Ardo and to the town of Sariam. The shepherds came hurrying in and cried: "The Burdama have stolen all of our cattle. You must go after them at once." Everyone in the town armed himself. But Goroba-Dike continued to lie idly in a corner. King Hamadi Ardo went over to him and asked: "Are you not going to mount a horse and ride to war with the others?" Goroba-Dike said: "Mount a horse? I have never ridden a horse in my life! I was born of poor people. Give me a donkey. I will not fall off a donkey!" Kode Ardo wept. Goroba-Dike mounted his donkey and, having beaten it, rode off in the direction opposite to that taken by the rest of the warriors. Kode Ardo wept and wept. She said: "Father, father, what a misfortune you have brought down on my head!"

Goroba-Dike rode to the Dimadio's hamlet where he had left his horse, his weapons and his Mabo. Jumping off the donkey's back he said: "Alal, I have got married!" The Mabo said: "What? You are married? And whom have you married?" Goroba-Dike said: "I have married the proudest girl in the town, Kode Ardo, daughter to King Hamadi Ardo." The Mabo said: "What? Can you really have been so fortunate?" Goroba-Dike said: "Yes. But today there is something more important. The Burdama have stolen my father-in-law's cattle. Now hurry get me my clothes and weapons and harness my horse. I want to catch up with the others." The Mabo got everything ready, handed him what he wanted, and asked: "Can I go with you?" Goroba-Dike said: "No, not this time." Then he rode off as fast as his horse could carry him.

He soon caught up with the others and now he rode level with them but always keeping a short distance away. King Hamadi's two sons-in-law and the other Fulbe men saw him approaching on their flank and said to one another: "That must be Djinar.[1] We must see if we can get him on our side. Then we should be sure of victory and of getting back our cattle." One of them said: "We ought to speak to him." Some of them rode across to Goroba-Dike and asked him: "Where are you going? What are you doing?" Goroba-Dike said: "I ride out wherever there is fighting and lend my aid to whomsoever I choose." The men said: "Then you must be Djinar." Goroba-Dike said: "Of course I am Djinar." The men asked: "Will you help us?" Goroba-Dike answered: "Why should I not help you?" How many of King Hamadi Ardo's sons-in-law are there with you?" The men said: "There are two of them with us." Goroba-Dike said: "If each of them agrees to reward me with one of his ears I will help you." The men said: "That is impossible. What would people in the town say?" Goroba-Dike said: "It is simple enough. The two sons-in-law can say: I was holding my head thusand the blade glanced off it. And what is more, this will be to their honour." The men rode back and told the king's two sons-in-law. At first they refused to agree, but finally each of them allowed one of his ears to be cut off and sent it across to Goroba-Dike. He put the ears in his pocket. Then Goroba-Dike went to the head of the column. He said to the Fulbe men: "You are not to tell anyone that Djinar has helped you." The Fulbe men said: "No, no. We will not tell anyone."

They came upon the Burdama. They fought with the Burdama. Goroba-Dike killed several of them and captured their horses. He gave them to the sons-in-law. The Fulbe won the battle. Then the Fulbe drove their cattle home. But Goroba-Dike went off in another direction and rode to the Dimadio's farm where his Mabo was waiting for him. Having dismounted, he laid aside his clothes and

[1] The devil.

his weapons, put on his rags and swung himself onto the donkey's back. Then he rode back into the town. As he rode through Sariam he was seen by the smith with whom he had lived when he was first in the town. The smith shouted: "Keep away from my threshold. You are no Fulbe, you are either an infamous bastard or a slave, but one thing is certain, you are neither a warrior nor a Fulbe!" On hearing this, the smith's wife said to her husband: 'Enough of such talk! A Fulbe is a Fulbe, and you yourself have not wits enough to know what might be happening behind all of this!'"

Meanwhile the victorious Fulbe had returned with the herds which they had so happily recovered. They were joyfully acclaimed by all. King Hamadi Ardo himself came out to meet them and said: "You have shown yourselves true warriors. You are real Fulbe after all. Some of you must be wounded, too!" One of the sons-in-law said: "When I was making a flank attack thus, a tall Burdama aimed a blow at my head with his sword thus. I inclined my head and the sword sliced off my ear but I myself was saved." The other son-in-law said: "When I was attacking on the other flank, a small Burdama aimed an upward blow at my throat with his long sword. It might have cost me my head had I not turned away thus, thereby losing my ear. But my head was saved." King Hamadi Ardo said: "Such tales gladden the heart. You are heroes. But tell me, did no one see my other son-in-law?" Then they all laughed and said: "Oh, *him*! He rode away in the wrong direction at the very beginning. No, we did not see him."

Goroba-Dike came into the town from the other side. As he drew closer he began beating the donkey so that it bounded forward at the gallop. When Kode Ardo saw him approaching thus, she began to weep bitterly and said: "Father, Father, what misfortune you have brought down on my head!" That evening the Fulbe nobles lay around in a circle re-telling the deeds they had done. Goroba-Dike, clad in his rags, lay in a corner listening to all that was going on. One man said: "When I galloped ahead of everyone else into the midst of the enemy . . ." Another said: "When I captured their horses . . ." A third man said: "Aye, you are not like Kode Ardo's husband. You are real heroes!" The two other sons-in-law had to tell once again the story of how they had lost their ears in the heat of the battle. Goroba-Dike, however, sat on one side, his hand in his pocket, his fingers toying with the two severed ears. When it was night he went to his house. Kode Ardo said to him: "You cannot sleep next to me. You must go and sleep over there!"

The following day the Burdama fell upon the town in large numbers. When they first appeared on the horizon, all of the able-bodied men foregathered. But Goroba-Dike swang himself onto his donkey's back and galloped off. Everyone yelled: "Goroba-Dike is running away! Goroba-Dike is running away!" Kode Ardo burst into tears. She wept and said: "Father, Father, what a misfortune you have brought down on my head!" Goroba-Dike rode to the Damadio farmstead where he had left his clothes, his weapons, his horse and his Mabo. As soon as he got to the village he jumped off the donkey's back saying to his Mabo: "Hurry! hurry! Harness my horse, give me my weapons. For to-day something very important is going to happen. Powerful bands of Burdama are attacking the town and no one is there to defend it." Alal the Mabo asked: "Can I ride out with you?" Goroba-Dike said: "Not this time." He put on his other clothes, snatched up his weapons, sprang into the saddle and galloped away like the wind.

Meanwhile the Burdama had attacked and surrounded Sariam. Moreover, some of them had already entered the town and were advancing towards the royal compound. Goroba-Dike, approaching from the rear, broke through their ranks. Unhorsing Burdama warriors to the right and to the left, he arrived at his father-in-law's compound at a critical moment. For just then the Burdama were about to seize hold of Kode Ardo with the intention of carrying her off. When Kode Ardo saw the brave Fulbe coming towards her she called out: "O big brother, come and help me, for the Burdama want to drag me away and my husband has fled like a coward." Goroba-Dike thrust aside an enemy with his spear. But one of the man's companion's dealt Goroba-Dike a blow that left a gaping wound, only to be felled himself by the hero. The remaining Burdama fled. Seeing that Goroba-Dike had been badly wounded, Kode Ardo called out: "Oh, big brother, you have saved me! But you yourself are wounded." She at once tore off half her dress and used it to bandage Goroba-Dike's bleeding leg. Then Goroba-Dike galloped off, pressing forward into the midst of the enemy and scattering them on every side. Spearing one man here, striking down another there, he spread terror among the Burdama. They jostled each other in their haste to get out of the town and went galloping away in headlong flight, with the Fulbe hot on their heels.

But Goroba-Dike rode away in the direction of the Dimadio's farm, where Alal, his Mabo, was waiting. There he dismounted, discarded his clothes and weapons, covered himself with his rags, and returned to the town mounted on his donkey. When he was riding past the smith which had been his first lodging, the smith shouted: "Just look at him, the miserable bastard, the stray dog, the coward! Now be off with you! I do not want you dawdling outside this house!" The smith's wife said: "That is enough of such talk, for this man is a Fulbe and no one should ever insult a Fulbe!" But the smith shouted: "Hold your tongue, woman! Let me speak, woman! How can I do anything but curse this wretch who ran away just when there was dire need for all the men we could muster!" Goroba-Dike said: "What did you expect? Ever since I have been here I have done nothing but say that I was born of poor parents."

Then he beat his donkey so that the animal went bucking into the market place. There was a large crowd of Fulbes around King Hamadi Ardo and they were discussing what had happened that day. Kode Ardo was also there. When Goroba-Dike arrived in this fashion she began to weep, saying: "O Father, why did you inflict such a miserable fate upon me when there are so many Fulbes who are brave and daring men?" Goroba-Dike said: "The very first day, when we were married, I told you that I was born of poor parents. And did I not tell your father that I know nohing of horses or the practice of war?" But Kode Ardo wept and said: "You coward! You miserable coward! Never again shall you share my bed!" Quite unconcerned, Goroba-Dike lay down in a corner.

The Fulbes continued to sit together until evening, talking about the events of the day. One said: "When I repulsed that pary of Burdama . . ." Another said: "When

I scattered the Burdama in such and such a place . . ." A third said: "When I put the main body of the Burdama to flight . . ." But many of them mocked Kode Ardo, asking her: "Where was your husband?" Kode Ardo said: "Leave me alone. It would have been better if my father had married me to a monkey than to this coward! O, how ashamed I am!"

Then night fell. The Fulbe went back to their houses. Kode Ardo could not sleep. She was thinking about her cowardly husband and the brave stranger who had come to save her. At midnight she looked across to the bed on the other side of the room where her husband lay sleeping. She saw that his clothes had slipped to one side, she saw that the rags had fallen off, she saw blood. She raised herself and stared across. The blood was dripping from a bandage round his thigh, and that bandage was part of her dress. It was the part of her dress which she herself had torn off that very day in order to bandage the brave Fulbe. The bandage was round the thigh of her husband, he who had come home riding on a donkey. Kode Ardo got up, went across to her husband, bent over him and said: "Goroba-Dike, where did you get that wound?" Goroba-Dike said: "Try to remember!" Kode Ardo asked: "Who was it that tore her dress and used it to bandage you with?" Goroba-Dike said: "Try to remember!" Kode Ardo asked: "Who are you?" Goroba-Dike said: "A king's son." Kode Ardo said: "I thank you!" Goroba-Dike said: "Say no more for now, but go and warm up some carite[1] and put it on my wound." Kode Ardo fetched some tree-butter. She warmed it up. She dribbled it onto the wound. She bandaged the wound. Then she crept out. She went to her mother, sat down beside her, wept, and said: "My husband is not a coward. He did not flee. He is the man who today saved our town from the Burdama. But do not tell anyone else." Then she crept back.

The following day Goroba-Dike again mounted his donkey and rode to the Dimadio's farm where he had left his Mabo, his clothes, his weapons and his horse. He said to his Mabo: "Alal, the day has now come when we can present ourselves properly and as we really are before the

---

[1] Tree-butter.

proud Hamadi Ardo and the town of Sariam. Therefore harness my horse and harness your own as well." Goroba-Dike put on his clothes and took up his weapons. He rode into Sariam. His Mabo rode behind him. He dismounted in the big market place where a great many Fulbe were assembled. Then the Mabo knocked the horse-pickets into the ground. They were made of silver.

Goroba-Dike called his wife to him. She greeted him and laughed. Then he turned to the Fulbe and said: "I am Goroba-Dike and this is my wife, Kode Ardo. I am a king's son and it was I who, yesterday and the day before yesterday, vanquished the Burdama." King Hamadi Ardo said: "I do not believe it. We have never seen you ride anything but a donkey." Goroba-Dike said: "Then ask those who fought in the battle." The others said: "It is true." Only the king's first two sons-in-law said: "We cannot be sure.' 'Then Goroba-Dike brought out the two ears and asked: "Do you not recognize these ears?" At that the two men fell silent and went to one side.

King Hamadi Ardo, however, went up to Goroba-Dike. He knelt down in front of him saying: "Forgive me. But receive my kingdom at my hands." Goroba-Dike said: "King Hamadi Ardo, I am no less a man than you. If I am now king, my first order concerns the smith who has reviled me on several occasions, though he is a smith and nothing more. I order that he be given fifty smacks on the buttocks with the knotted stick." And so it was done.

THE MONKEY GIRL   *Kordofan*

An emir had three sons who slowly grew up to be tall young men. One day their father said to them: "Take your spears and ride with me out of the village." The sons went and fetched their weapons, mounted their horses, and rode out with their father onto the plain. The father said: "Now, my sons, I would like to see if you can handle your weapons skillfully enough to be able to defend a wife with them. Do you see those gazelles over there? Go and hunt them with your spears so that I can watch how you go about it."

Then the three sons rode off as fast as their horses could carry them while their father followed them more slowly some little way behind.

From a distance the father observed the skill with which they used their spears in pursuit of the animals. When they returned a few hours later, each of them had succeeded in killing three antelopes. The father said: "Now come back with me to our village. Let us return home. As we ride through the village each of you may plunge his spear into the ground before the house of the girl whom he wishes to marry. I myself will then later approach the girl's parents and settle the matter with them."

The father rode through the village with his sons. When they came to the house of a highly respected man with a beautiful daughter much coveted by all the young men of the village, the eldest son drove his spear into the ground. The emir said: "Very well. I will arrange things for you in due course." When they came to the farm of another respected man who likewise possessed a much coveted daughter, the second son drove his spear into the ground and once again the emir nodded, saying: "I am satisfied, and this matter too, shall be settled."

Then they rode on until they had gone through the whole length of the village. The youngest son cantered his horse playfully, twirling his spear between his fingers. But he showed no signs of thrusting it into the ground in front of any of the dwellings. When they reached the far end of the village, the father said: "What is you intention now, my son? Have you no desire to get married?" The youngest son laughed and said: "Of course I want to marry. But none of the girls in this village are pretty enough. The desert must provide a beautiful girl for me." The young man laughed and dug his spurs into his horse's flanks and it reared up on its hind legs. He threw his spear in such a way that it was borne far out into the desert by the wind.

Then the emir shook his head, saying: "You are young, my son, otherwise you would not play about like this, either with your weapon or with us. How could I ride out there to settle matters with a woman whose name and family I do not know? You yourself, my son, will have to ride out in search of your spear and you yourself will have to settle the business of your wife. There is nothing more that I can do about it." Turning his horse, the emir rode back through the village to his seriba, accompanied by his two elder sons.

The youngest son remained where he was, looking out over the desert. He was very much ashamed of himself, for he could see that his father was offended and that he had been the cause of his taking offence. The young man was exceedingly handsome and the women and girls all loved him very much. But he himself had never felt any particular inclination towards them and this was why he had been unable to think of anything better to do with his spear than hurl it out into the desert.

The youngest son rode out into the desert, keeping his eyes open as he went in the hope of finding his spear. He rode for the space of an hour and did not find his spear. The youngest son said: "My spear has been my best friend ever since I was a child. It cannot have run away from me like a rebellious slave!" The youngest son rode further and further, always in the direction in which he had thrown the spear. He kept going in the same direction and searched diligently, now to his right and now to his left, but nowhere could he see what he was looking for. The youngest son said: "My father was right. It was a thoughtless game I played. Now I realize that my spear cannot possibly have covered such a distance all by itself. There is more to this than meets the eye and I shall doubtless have something to contend with. But now that I am on my way, I will not seek to avoid whatever it is that lies in wait for me."

When the youngest son had ridden on a little further, he saw, rising out of the desert, a solitary tree with his spear firmly embedded in its trunk. Having arrived beneath the tree the youngest son looked up into its branches. Sitting crouched in their midst was a young female girda.[1] The youngest son looked at the female girda. The youngest son said: "So you are the bride that I have chosen for myself?" The female girda said: "That is so." The youngest son said: "Well, at least you can talk. Even if you cannot provide valuable carpets and a

[1] Species of monkey.

soft angareb, or oil and delicious food for my household, you can at least talk."

The female monkey said: "Yes, I can do that. But do not forget that by throwing your spear you yourself chose me for your bride." The youngest son said: "No. I will not forget it. But my father will not want to come out to settle the matter with your parents. Therefore you must come with me on my horse so that I can take you home."

The youngest son wrenched his spear out of the tree trunk. He held out his arm to the monkey. Taking hold of it, the female girda lowered herself onto the horse's back. Then the youngest son rode home with the female girda.

In the house he showed the monkey the angareb. The female girda lay down on it and went to sleep. The youngest son went to his father and said: "You were right, O father. I threw my spear into the desert and when I rode after it I found it stuck in the sand outside the house of a female girda." His father asked: "What did you do?" His youngest son said: "I have brought the female girda back with me." The emir said: "You must settle the matter yourself." The youngest son said: "Now I shall have to make the best of what my wife does for me in the house. I have given the female girda an angareb. She will be given her food and her drink. There is nothing else I can do."

The emir's two elder sons got married. Their wives furnished their houses. They provided carpets and cushions and all manner of other things. One day the emir said to his eldest son: "My son, tomorrow I shall pay you a visit and will eat with you. For I would like to see how you are living now that you are married." The eldest son hurried back to his wife and said: "Tomorrow my father is coming to eat with us. You must see to it that he is pleased."

The next day the father arrived and was welcomed by his son. The son led his father into the house and invited him to take his place on the cushions and carpets. Finely dressed slaves arrived bearing aromatic sherbet, after which they came in carrying a beautiful sinia on which there were many different kinds of food. The father observed everything and it was late when he finally rose to go. He said to his son: "I can see, O eldest son, that you have married well and that your wife looks after you and your household most excellently."

The following day, the father visited his second son in the same way, having warned him beforehand that he was coming. Here, too, the emir found rich furnishings and good, well-organized hospitality. He also wished his second son all happiness in his domestic life.

The emir's youngest son had ridden away from his house during the afternoon and went wandering around the countryside, for since the monkey had been living in his house, he no longer felt at ease within its mud walls. And whereas before he had never found his dwelling ugly, now that it was shared with the female girda, and by comparison with the fine homes of his happily married brothers, it seemed to him unendurable. The youngest son turned to go home and on his way back met his father who had just been entertained by his second son. The youngest son greeted the emir. The emir said: "How are things with you, my youngest son? Yesterday I dined with my eldest and today with my second eldest son, and the food in each case was excellent. Both of them have been living very happily since they got married." The youngest son said to his father: "Father, I cannot invite you to dine with me tomorrow."

The youngest son arrived home late at night. He sat down on his angareb and sighed. He sighed and was disconsolate. In the room next door the female girda was stretched out on her angareb. The female girda heard her husband's sighs and groans and came in to him. The female girda sat down on the angareb beside the young man and said: "Tell me what is troubling you. Perhaps it is something that can be smoothed out." The youngest son said: "You are a kind monkey since you are concerned about my sorrow. But nothing can be done about it, for just as you, a girda girl would be better off with a male girda than with a man, even though he were the son of an emir, so my household would be better provided for by any girl or woman, even though she might be less warm-hearted than you are." The female girda said: "Listen, you are an emir's son, but you are just a man and as such cannot know what a girda girl is like, how she feels, and what she can do. So tell me what is troubling you." The youngest son said: "Kind girda girl, you became my bride on the same day that my elder brothers chose their wives. Now their wives have furnished their houses and made them comfortable. The day before yesterday my father dined with my eldest and today with my second eldest brother, and he found everything very luxurious and comfortable, their wives having provided them with fine, rich furnishings. Tomorrow I myself ought to entertain my father. But how could I serve him with food between these bare mud walls and on this floor of beaten earth?" The female girda said: "Is that all?" The youngest son said: "It is enough to make me sad."

The young girda said: "Nothing could be simpler! Quick now! Saddle your horse and take me back into the desert this very night. Then you will not be troubled any more by your ugly little girda. Now, out in the desert there is a town in which there are rich and beautiful women. I will show you the way. You can win the hand of a beautiful woman. She will come with all her possessions and by tomorrow evening she will be able to furnish your home for you. Believe me, there is no difficulty about this matter." The youngest son said: "You are a kind little monkey. But tell me, what would then become of you?" The female girda said: "I would die." The young man said: "You are a kind little girda and you shall not die. I won you for my wife by throwing my spear and I will not be the cause of your death. Go back to your angareb and sleep. I can go on living like this, and there is no need at all for my father to visit me. But thank you for coming to me and asking me the cause of my sorrow. That sorrow has gone away."

The female girda said: "Then you are not going to take me back to the desert to find yourself a beautiful young wife?" The young man laughed and said: "No, I am not. You, my kind girda girl, will stay here with me."

The young girda said: : Then there is something else that I have to say to you. Have you ever before known a girda that could talk?" The young man said: "No, I have never known such a thing before." The female girda said: "Having seen something so unusual with your own eyes, would you be prepared to believe me capable of other unaccustomed things?" The young man said: "Certainly, I would believe you to be capable of such things." The female girda said: "Then tomorrow at midday go to your father, the emir, and invite him to come and dine with you. Your father will find everything as good as it was in your brothers' houses." The young man said: "I will do as you say." The girda girl got up and went into her room to sleep on her angareb.

The young man remained sitting on his bed. He said: "This business with the girda girl is quite unlike anything I have ever heard of before." After a while the young man stole across to the other room to take another look at the remarkable girda girl. He went and stood beside her angareb.

A little moonlight was filtering in through a crack in the old wall. It fell on the girda girl who was lying asleep on the angareb with her face turned away from the light. Observing the girda girl, the young man saw that there was a slit in the monkey skin through which some locks of hair had spilled out. They were as soft as silk and bound with a thread of gold. The young man looked at the hair. He put out a hand and cautiously touched the hair. Then the girda girl sighed in her sleep and he stole quickly and silently back into his own room. In his room was the spear that he had thrown. He ran his hand over the spear, saying: "Old friend, you can travel well and fast and far, but you cannot speak. What might you not tell me about all this is only you could talk?"

The next day at noon the youngest son went to his father and said: "The day before yesterday, O father, you dined with your eldest son. Yesterday you dined with your second eldest son. Come today and dine with me, your third son."

The father said: "My unfortunate son, you are not married but have thrown away your good fortune and your comfort for a female girda. You will be even more painfully aware of this fact if I come to share a meal with you in your lonely lodging." The youngest son said: "Father, I beg you to visit me today." The emir said: "I will not refuse your request. I will come."

The father mounted his horse. He rode with his son to the latter's house.

When the two riders arrived outside the house they were met by a pair of magnificently clad slaves who came out of the house to hold their horses. Then two other servants unrolled a long, silk mat between the door and the gate. They helped the emir and his son out of the saddle and followed them as they walked towards the house over the silken materials.

On their arrival at the door the emir and his son were met by handsome boys bearing a bowl of water and towels so that they could wash away the dust. Others removed their shoes for them, so that they should not soil the beautiful carpets with which the floors were covered. The emir was the first to enter the room. He immediately said to his son: "Explain this, my son." The youngest son said: "I can give you no explanation at all, O father, for I do not even know whether or not I am in my own house. But pray take a seat on these cushions and accept my hospitality if, indeed, I have any right to call it my hospitality!" The emir sat down. The youngest son sat down. They both observed the carpets that lay on the floor and decked the walls. They looked at the kursi upon which had been placed a gold sinia bearing thirty different kinds of food.

When he ate the food, the emir found it more delicious than anything he had ever tasted before. But he said nothing, thinking to himself: "I will not ask my son about anything, for this whole affair of the female girda is nothing but a lie, and if I were to ask him he would only tell me further lies. But I will do what I can to show up his lies so that I can punish him for them."

When he ate the food, the youngest son found it more delicious than anything he had ever tasted before. But he said nothing, thinking to himself: "Ever since seeing the silken locks plaited with gold under my girda girl's monkey skin, all I can be sure of is that I know nothing at all about her and her doings. If I say anything to my father, he will not believe it but will think that I am a liar. But I shall take care to find out what else is concealed under my girda girl's monkey skin."

After the emir and his son had finished eating, the father rose and said: "I see to my joy, O my youngest son, that you are living in circumstances just as happy as those of your older brothers. Now I shall leave your house. Accompany me home and do not forget that I owe all three of you a meal in return for those prepared by your wives. Therefore I should like you and your three admirable wives to dine with me tomorrow evening." The son said: "Very well, I will come." The emir laughed and said: "But not alone. You must bring your wife who provided for me so splendidly today, for I wish to make her acquaintance. The son accompanied his father home. When the son returned to his own house it was as bare and dirty as it had been before. He crept into the other room where the girda girl was lying on her angareb. But there was no hair to be seen. Nor was there any moonlight coming in through the crack in the wall, but only sand blown by the wind, and it filled his eyes, chasing him back into his own room.

The following morning the young man went hurrying into the girda girl's room. Sitting down on the edge of the angareb he said to the girda girl: "When my father left yesterday he was very satisfied." The girda girl said: "I know." The young man said: "My father said that his three sons and their wives were to come and dine with him today." The girda girl said: "I know." The young man said: "But what am I to do?" The girda girl said: "You will have to go." The young man said: "But what wife can I take with me?" The girda girl said: "Take me back quickly into the desert and get yourself another wife. I will show her to you." The young man said: "And what would become of you?" The girda girl said: "As you already know, I would die." The young man said: "And as I have already told you, I do not want that." The girda girl said: "Then there is only one thing to do and that is for me to go as your wife to your father's feast!"

The young man was alarmed. He knew that his brothers wives were very beautiful. He did not want to take the shaggy female monkey with him as his wife. The young man remained silent. The girda girl said: "Your father has invited me as your wife this evening. Do as you choose. Either take me back into the desert and get yourself another wife or else let me go to your father's alone. I do not ask that you should go with me. But I myself shall go." The young man went out.

The young man lay down in the yard feeling very sad. At noon the girda girl came to him again and said: "Once again I put it to you: take me back into the desert and let me provide you with a beautiful wife." The young man said: "No, I will not let you die." The girda girl said: "But then I shall go to your father's feast." The young man said: "Very well, go. But you will have to go alone." Then the young man got up and saddled his horse. Having ridden away a short distance he stabled his horse at a friend's house and made his way across the roof tops to the spot where the moon had shone through the crack in the wall onto the girda girl's angareb.

When it grew dark he saw the girda girl get up from her angareb. The girda girl inserted her hand into the opening in the monkey skin and pulled out a diamond that glittered brighter than any flame. Next the girda girl pulled the monkey skin back off her head. The youngest son watched while her long silken locks came tumbling out till they were hanging down her back, and he saw that the heavy silken tresses were plaited with threads of gold. The girl passed her hand over a rough patch on the mud wall which instantly became a mirror. And now, as he looked in through the crack in the wall, the young man could see that the girda girl was exceedingly beautiful, so beautiful, indeed, that he began to tremble with excitement and nearly fell off the edge of the roof.

Then the young girda stripped the rest of the monkey skin off her body and limbs and he could see, beneath the fine linen in which she was swathed, a young and beautiful body, ivory limbs, and rounded breasts. When he saw the young girda standing there in the mud hut in front of her mirror looking so beautiful, the emir's youngest son was overcome with happiness and would have cried out had he not bitten into his own hand. To stifle his exclamation he bit deeply into his hand.

Meanwhile the girda girl was looking at herself in the mirror. She dressed her hair. From the monkey skin she extracted all kinds of ornaments. She put a golden necklace around her neck. She put gold bangles around her wrists and ankles. She threw the monkey skin onto the angareb, wrapped herself in a big shawl belonging to the young man, and left the house to go to her father-in-law's. As soon as the young man heard the girda girl go out, he climbed down from the roof and hurried into the house. He looked into the girda girl's room. He saw the monkey skin. He took the monkey skin and threw it into the fire. Then he sat down on the angareb and waited for the girl to return.

During this time the young girl had been on her way to

the emir's seriba. First she entered the house where the emir's wife was supervising the preparation of the food. When the old woman saw the veiled girl enter, she asked: "Who are you?" The girl said: "I am she whom your youngest son chose for his bride." The old woman said: "Show me your face!" The young girl threw back the shawl. After looking at her for a while the mother said: "Beware O my daughter, of your husband's father of my husband, the emir." The girl said: "I beg you, O mother, to give me a loaf." The old woman gave the girl a loaf. Putting the loaf under her arm, the girl left to go to the emir.

The two eldest sons and their wives had already arrived at the emir's house. The women were beautiful. They were richly clad and were adorned with valuable jewelry.

The emir was talking to his sons' wives. The emir said: "The wife chosen by my youngest son is also coming." The door-keeper came in and said: "A veiled woman is coming across the courtyard." The brothers' wives said: "That must be the monkey woman arriving. Do we have to eat out of the same dish as this creature?" The emir said to the door-keeper: "Show the woman in."

The door opened. The veiled woman came in and stood still. The emir said: "Who are you?" The veiled woman said: "I am the girl whom your youngest son chose for his wife." The emir said: "My other sons' wives are also here and they are not veiled. Let us see you. We shall not insult you." The veiled woman said: "As the father of the man who has desired me for his wife, why should you wish to insult me?" Then she let the long shawl fall away. At the same time the room grew very light, and the difference was as great as if the sun had suddenly risen where before it had been night.

The girl said: "Why should you insult me?"

The emir's two elder sons looked at the girl. The wives of the two sons looked at the girl. The emir looked at the girl and said to himself: "This girl shall be *my* wife. I will kill my son." From under her arm the girl took the loaf the emir's wife had given her. It had turned into a diamond. Handing the damond to the emir, the girl said: "Take this as a gift of greeting. I am not what you thought I was. I assumed the monkey skin to find out if your youngest son is as kind as he is handsome. My monkey skin has been a sore trial to him and now I shall go home to console him. For even when he was most sorely tried he did not want the wretched monkey girl to die, and so I am going to be a good wife to him and give him all that, as daughter of the King of Alledjenu, I am able to give." Having said this, the girl took up the shawl again and went. No one, however, had had time to say anything.

The youngest son sat on his angareb and waited. When he had been waiting for some time he noticed that the darkness outside was growing lighter. Then he heard footsteps and saw that his dwelling was lit by a number of lamps and torches. Wherever he looked he saw carpets and cushions appearing. The closer the footsteps approached, the loftier and larger the rooms became. He felt that his garments were changing, and outside he could hear the birds singing although it was still night. Then the door opened and the daughter of the King of Alledjenu came in. She let the shawl fall to the ground. The daughter of the King of Alledjenu came towards him, knelt down, and kissed the wound he had made when he bit his hand in order to suppress his first joyous excitement. And at once the wound was healed. The emir's son lifted the king's daughter to her feet. Then the two of them walked through the brilliantly lit rooms of the seraglio in which the youngest son and his beautiful wife were to live from then on.

All that night the emir lay considering how he might kill his son and marry his beautiful daughter-in-law. The following day he sent for his youngest son and said to him: "My son, I hear you are laying out a garden. If you can do that for yourself, no doubt you can do something of the same kind for your father. See to it, then, that by tomorrow afternoon there is a new vine growing in my garden. I have invited some guests for tomorrow evening and I want them to enjoy ripe grapes from this vine. If you fail to do what I ask, I shall have you put to death tomorrow evening."

Disconsolately, the son left. Disconsolately, he went into his seraglio. Disconsolately, he threw himself down on the cushions. After a while his beautiful wife came to him. She stroked his hair, saying: "Tell me what is troubling you!" Thereupon the emir's son told her about his father's demands. After hearing what he had to say, the daughter of the King of Alledjenu laughed and said: "If there is nothing more to it than that, then it is easily done!" Take this little bottle of water to your father's garden, use it to moisten a piece of ground, and plant a dry twig there. Then ask your father to say how many bunches of grapes he wants the grapevine to bear. The son took the bottle from his wife, mounted his horse, and rode to the garden. Having planted a dry twig in it, he went to his father and said: "Now all you need to do is to decide how many bunches of grapes you want the grapevine to bear. Then all will be as you wish." The emir's son rode away again. On the following day, when the emir's guests arrived and went out into the garden, the dry twig had grown into an enormous grapevine from which each guest was able to pick a large and perfect bunch of grapes.

But this only served to enrage the emir still further. The next morning he once again sent for his youngest son and said: "My son, see to it that this time tomorrow there is a garden beside my house. In it there must be water-melon plants covered in fruit. The son said: "And it must be in the place where now there is only sand?" The emir said: "Yes. By tomorrow evening there must be plenty of melons in that very place, for I am expecting numerous guests and each of them will want to take a melon away with him. If you do not do this by tomorrow evening, I shall have you put to death." The son went home. The emir's son went to find his wife and told her about the new demand made by his father and about the renewal of his threat. The daughter of the King of Alledjenu laughed and said: "That, too, is very simple. Take this water and these seeds and mix them with some of the sand where the garden is to be. Then throw the mixtures onto the stretch of sand." The emir's son did as his wife had told him. On the following day, when the emir looked out over the stretch of sand, he saw that it was covered with the vines of water-melon plants each of them bearing so much fruit that every man in the village could have picked one melon at the very least.

When the emir saw that his son had been able to accomplish this task also, he became exceedingly angry and in his rage he took one of his friends aside and said:

"Suggest something that I can order my son to do that is impossible so that his failure can provide me with a pretext for having him put to death." The friend said: "I suggest that you fill a house with bread and meat and demand that he eat it in the course of one night." The emir said: "That is an excellent idea."

The next day the emir sent for his youngest son and said: "Tonight I shall lock you into a house that will be filled with bread and meat. If it is not all eaten by the following morning, I shall have you put to death." The emir's son went home and told his wife about his father's fresh demand. But the daughter of the King of Alledjenu laughed and said: "Let yourself be locked in and do not worry. My people could clear several houses full of food in the twinkling of an eye." That evening the son went to the emir and allowed himself to be locked into the house filled with bread and meat. He lay down on the ground and slept. On the following day, when they opened the door and called to him to come out, so little was left of all the bread and meat that it would hardly have been enough to whet the appetite of a mouse.

The emir now decided to make a demand which could not conceivably be met, for with the passing of each day his longing to marry his daughter-in-law increased and with it his determination to see his son put to death. He therefore sent for his youngest son and said: "My son, this is the last order that I shall give you. I demand that a child born this evening shall be able to walk and talk by tomorrow morning. If you cannot bring this about you shall die." The emir's son went to his wife and told her about his father's fresh demand. The daughter of the King of Alledjenu said: "Now I realize that your father is determined to marry me and put you to death! Therefore you must assemble everyone in the place and demand that your father agree to the following terms. Should the newborn child he sends you this evening not be able to walk and talk by tomorrow morning, your father can have you put to death. But should the child be able to walk and talk, your father must give up both life and emirate in your favor. Now go and make this demand in front of everybody. This is the time when all of the notables will be with him."

The emir's son went to his father. All of the notables

were assembled around the emir. The son went up to his father and said: "You have demanded, O father, that this evening I should take a newborn child into my house and that by tomorrow morning that same child should be able to walk and talk. You have demanded this of me and said that you will have me put to death if I should fail. I now declare before all of these witnesses that I am prepared to do this on condition that, if I fulfill the impossible task that you have demanded of me under pain of death, you yourself should relinquish both life and emirate in my favor." The emir said: "I agree. For if, after this, you do not die, my own life will be of little worth to me." The son went away.

That evening a child was born in the town. It was taken to the youngest son's house. The daughter of the king of Alledjenu laid it on a mat. The emir's youngest son and his wife went to bed and slept. The following morning they were woken by a great hubbub. The emir was waiting outside the house with all of the notables. The emir was looking at the large, new house and grounds and everyone was uttering cries of admiration. In a loud voice the emir demanded to be let in.

Then the baby that had been born the previous day got up from the mat upon which it had been laid by the daughter of the King of Alledjenu. The child went across and opened the door. The little boy looked at the emir and the people of note standing around him. The emir said: "Is that not the little boy who was born yesterday?" The people said: "Yes, it is he!" The little boy said: "Yes, I am the boy who was born yesterday evening. I can walk and talk, as everyone here can witness, and therefor you have forfeited both your life and your emirate." When the boy finished speaking the emir dropped down dead.

Thereupon the youngest son became the country's overlord.

In Sadia there lived a king, Anko Gindo. Anko Gindo
had seventy wives. But none of these wives ever became
pregnant. No child was born to Anko Gindo of any of
these seventy wives. Thereupon he married an Urussu
woman and she at once became pregnant. On the same
day that King Anko's young wife gave birth to her child,
the wife of the king's musician also gave birth. Thus the
king's son and the musician's son were exactly the same
age. The king's son was named Badju. The musician's
son was named Gimmile.

Since Badju Gindo and Gimmile Drami had been born
on the same day, the king had them taken up into a high
tower on the city wall and there a dwelling was prepared
for them. If the babies cried and wanted to be fed, their
mothers had to climb up to the top of the tower and leave
again afterwards. And so it went on even after the children had been weaned. The two boys never came down
to the ground but always had to stay up in the tower.
They never saw the ground or the people on it otherwise
than from the top of their tower. And so it went on until
they were grown-up. After they had grown up, Gimmile
was the first to be allowed to descend. He went down and
while he was down there he saw a young wife of the king's
who was very beautiful. As soon as he saw her he fell
deeply in love with her. But she was the king's wife. Then
he was sad. He went back to the top of the tower and to
Badju, bound a cloth about his head, and lay down in a
corner. Badju said: "What is the matter with you, O
Gimmile?" Gimmile said: "Nothing very much. I have a
headache." Badju said: "If my friend Gimmile has a
headache, then I too have a headache.' 'He bound a cloth
about his head. Badju and Gimmile were such close
friends that they always had to share everything they did.

Later a woman came to the tower with food for the two
boys. Both of them were lying with their faces to the wall
and cloths bound about their heads and they would not
turn around. Badju said: "You can take the food away.

We are ill and do not want anything. Badju and Gimmile are ill." The woman took the food away again and gave it to Badju's mother, saying: "Badju and Gimmile are ill. They do not want anything to eat." Then Badju's mother took the dishes and climbed up into the tower. She said to Badju: "My Badju, what is wrong with you?" Badju said: "Gimmile went down to the ground and when he came back he had a headache. As you know, one of us cannot feel unwell without the other also feeling unwell. Now I too have a headache." His mother said: "Eat, all the same." Badju said: "I cannot. I have a headache. Gimmile is not eating, so I cannot eat either." Badju's mother went away.

When Badju's mother had gone away, Badju turned to Gimmile and said: "Gimmile, my friend, we were born in the same hour. Until now we have spent our lives in the tower. Neither of us ever saw anything without the other seeing it. Why will you not tell me today what it is that ails you?" Gimmile said: "I will tell you, Badju my friend. When I got down into the courtyard, I saw a beautiful young woman. I at once fell deeply in love with this woman, but I cannot woo her for the young woman is married to the king, your father." Badju said: "Is that all? It can be easily settled! Is that all?" Gimmile said: "Yes, that is all." Badju said: "Then you can remove the cloth from your head."

Badju in his turn went down from the tower into the courtyard. Badju looked for the dainty young wife of his father, the king, and said to her: "Yesterday my friend, Gimmile, came down out of the tower. He saw you and fell in love with you. Gimmile knows that you are the young wife of my father, the king. But Gimmile will die unless he can win your favors. Do not let that happen!" The young woman said: "This I can understand, for yesterday I too saw him for the first time and I too fell in love with him. This is the first time I have seen you as well. Tell Gimmile to come to me not during the day, but at night. And he must not come before midnight. He must look at the fur rug lying outside my house. If there are two cola nuts on it, he must not come in, but if he sees only one cola nut on the rug he will know that it is safe to enter. For then I shall be alone and expecting him." Badju said: "It is good."

178

Badju went back to the top of the tower and told Gimmile all that had happened. Gimmile said: "I thank you." At midnight Gimmile went down and looked for the young wife's house. He found the fur rug outside the door and on it there was one cola nut. He went inside. From then on he went down from the tower every night. If he found only one cola nut on the fur rug outside the door he would go in, but if he found two cola nuts on the fur rug outside the door he would turn around and go back to the top of the tower.

One night the young wife had placed two cola nuts on the fur rug outside her house. The king was with her. But the wind rose up and blew one of the two nuts away. Gimmile came along and looked at the fur rug. He found only one cola nut. He went into the house. He went towards the woman's bed. He ran his hand over the bed. But his hand was gripped by the powerful hand of a man. It was the king's hand. The king's hand grasped the ring which Gimmile wore on his little finger. Gimmile snatched his hand away, leaving the ring in the king's hand. Gimmile fled out of the house and up into the tower. When he reached the top he told Badju all that had happened. Badju said: "Do not worry. I will settle everything."

Very early the following morning Badju went to the overseer of the Urussus and asked him: "Is there anywhere in the neighbourhood where I can find a lioness with cubs?" The Urussu overseer said: "I do not know but I will ask the shepherd. He is bound to know." The shepherd was called. Badju asked: "Do you know anywhere in the neighbourhood where I can find a lioness with cubs?" The shepherd said: "Yes, I do know a place." Badju said: "Then take me there." The shepherd took Badju to the place. He said: 'The lioness and her cubs are there in the scrub." Badju went into the bush. The old lioness was away and only the cubs were there. There were four cubs. Badju took them. He gave the shepherd two of the cubs to carry. Two of them he carried himself. Then he set off and took them up into his tower.

On the day after following the night during which he had pulled off Gimmile's ring in his wife's house, King Anko had the public drum sounded and gave out an order for all the men in the town and in the villages round about to assemble before him. They all came together. When all of the men were there he took out the ring which he had pulled off Gimmile's hand the previous night and began to search for the man upon whose little finger the ring would fit. He tried the ring on the first man's finger but it would not even go over his nail. He tried it on a second man with little success. He tried it on one man after another. But it would fit none of them. The king himself said: "It cannot have been any of these people."

Then the king went back into his house and considered. All of his people had been assembled before him. The ring had fitted none of them. Then the thought suddenly occurred to him. "There are my two boys up in the tower." He called a woman and said: "Go and fetch Badju and Gimmile." The woman went. She returned with Badju and Gimmile. The king took the ring and put it on Gimmile's little finger. It fitted. The king asked: "Is this your ring?" Gimmile said: "Of course it is my ring." The king asked: "Did you come to me last night when I was with my wife?" Gimmile said: "Yes, I did come to you last night when you were with your wife. You took the ring off my finger."

Badju said: "May I tell you, O father, how this came about?" The king said: "Speak!" Badju said: "The night before last we had an argument about which of us was brave enough to do something that was really daring. I said that the more dangerous thing to do was to fetch a lioness's cubs out of the bush. Gimmile said: "It is more dangerous to visit the king at night when he is lying with one of his wives." Our argument was only about which of the two things was more dangerous, and we decided that each of us should carry out his own suggestion. That is why last night Gimmile came to visit you when you were with your wife and why this morning I went into the bush to visit the lioness." The king said: "I have Gimmile's ring here before me. And as for you, did you get the lion cubs?" Badju said: "They are up in the tower." The king said to his men: "Go up into the tower and fetch the lion cubs." The men went and fetched them. The king looked at them and was much pleased. He gave each of the two friends a young wife.

Ever since that time the Habbes and their musicians have been excellent friends. Their friendships are very close. But when the musicians visit the Habbes they no longer enter the house but wait outside the door.

AHUN PUTS THE KING'S NOSE OUT OF JOINT
Yoruba

There was a woman called Betjubetje. She was very beautiful. The osi[1] sent her a message, saying: "Sleep with me!" Betjubetje answered: "I will not sleep with you." Four times the osi sent messages to the woman, each time saying: "Sleep with me!" And always Betjubetje answered: "I will not sleep with you." Ahun heard this. He said to the osi: "You are an osi and yet you cannot get Betjubetje to sleep with you. I am only Ahun and yet a single exchange will be enough to make her take me." The osi said: "That remains to be seen!"

Ahun went into the bush. There he killed a snake. He carried the dead snake to the path leading to his farm. He laid the snake's body right across the path. After a while Betjubetje came along the path, which also led to her farm. She noticed the snake. She saw Ahun at work on his farm and called out: "Ahun! Come and kill the snake that is lying here across my path!" Ahun came, aimed a blow at the snake, but managed it in such a way that he struck not only the snake but his foot. Ahun cried out: "Oh, that is what comes of killing the snake for you, Betjubetje! I kill it for your sake and hurt myself! Oh, who is going to help me now?" Betjubetje said: "Climb onto my back and I will carry you. Where do you want to go?" Ahun said: "Carry me to your house!" Betjubetje carried Ahun home.

When Betjubetje had carried Ahun into her house she said: "Where shall I put you down?" Ahun said: "Let me spend the night on your bed." Betjubetje laid him down on her bed. When evening came she lay down beside him on the other side of the bed. During the night

[1] King.

Ahun took out a piece of redwood dye and, while Betjubetje lay asleep, drew a cross with it on her belly.

The next day Ahun went to the king and said: "Did
you not express disbelief yesterday when I said that, unlike you, I would have no difficulty in getting Betjubetje
to sleep with me?" The osi said: "That is so." Ahun said:
'Well, I have done it." The osi said: "How can you prove
that?" Ahun said: "If you examined Betjubetje's belly
you would find on it a cross made with redwood dye. It
was I who made it."

The osi sent for Betjubetje. They pulled up her dress.
They saw the mark. Overcome with shame, Betjubetje
ran into the bush.

THE HUNTER AND THE SNAKE WOMAN I
Yoruba

Every day a hunter used to go to his farm with his son.
When the father wanted to eat he would send the boy to
fetch fire. The track branched out in three directions.
One of the paths was well kept and along it lived a
woman who was the hunter's enemy. The second path was
overgrown with grass and along it lived a man with many
wounds. The third path was overgrown with scrub and
along it there was fire. Every time the hunter would say
to his son: "Go to the overgrown path and fetch me
some fire. But do not go along the path that has been
well cleared!"

One day it was raining. The hunter said to his son:
"Go and fetch me some fire. But go along the overgrown
path and not along the path that has been cleared." The
boy said: "I will do as you say." The boy went. It was
raining. The boy said to himself: "Why do I always have
to go along the bad, scrubby path. I will go along the
good path instead. There is bound to be some fire there."
The boy went along the good path. He arrived at the
woman's house. He went in. He saw the woman. She was
a very beautiful woman. The woman was boiling grain
in water. The woman said: "What do you want?" The

boy said: "My father has sent me to get fire." The woman said: "Did your father send you to me?" The boy said: "No, my father told me to take the other path, but it is raining and the other path is badly overgrown!" The woman said: "Here is fire for you. But do not tell your father that you got the fire from me." The boy said: "I will not tell my father where I got the fire." The boy took the firebrand and went.

After he had gone some distance with the firebrand the boy thought to himself: "This woman is very beautiful. I must look at her again." The boy put out the firebrand and went back. He again went into the woman's house. The woman asked: "What do you want?" The boy said: "I will not tell my father where I got the fire firebrand." The beautiful woman gave him another firebrand and said: "Here is some more fire for you. But do not tell your father that you got the fire from me." The boy said: "I will not tell my father where I got the fire from." The boy took the firebrand and left once more.

After he had gone some distance with the firebrand, the boy said to himself: "This woman is very beautiful. I must look at her again." The boy put out the firebrand and went back. He went into the woman's house. The woman asked: "What do you want?" The boy said: "The fire went out again. Give me another firebrand." The beautiful woman give him another firebrand and said: "Here is some more fire for you. But do not tell your father that you got the fire from me." The boy said: "I will not tell my father where I got the fire from." The boy took the firebrand and left once more.

After he had gone some distance with the firebrand, the boy said: "This woman is very beautiful. I must look at here again." The boy put out the fire and went back. He went into the woman's house. The woman asked: ' "What do you want?" The boy said: "The fire went out. Give me another firebrand." The beautiful woman said: "I will bring your father the fire myself. But do not tell him on which path you met me." The boy said: "No, I will not tell him." The woman took a firebrand and went with the boy to the hunter's farm.

The boy arrived at the hunter's farm with the woman. The woman was carrying the fire. The father saw her. The father saw that the woman was very beautiful. The father said to the boy: "Where did you meet this woman?" The boy said: "I met her on the overgrown path." The woman said: "Do not scold the boy. He met me. Here is the fire." The father took the fire. The father saw the woman. The woman was very beautiful. The father did not know that the beautiful woman was the irri or big snake, because he did not know that she had come from the good path. The beautiful woman said: "I will go to your house and sleep with you." The father said: "That is good. Come to my house and sleep with me."

The hunter went to his house with the beautiful woman. The hunter took her into his room and slept with her. The hunter made love with the beautiful woman. Afterwards the woman said: "I want to go. Accompany me through the bush." The hunter said: "I will do that." The hunter wished to take his gun. The woman said: "Do not take your gun or I shall be frightened of you." The hunter had three dogs. He wished to take them with him. The woman said: "Leave the three dogs at home. Shut them up. Otherwise I shall be frightened of them." The hunter shut up the three dogs. He accompanied the beautiful woman without either his dogs or his gun.

The beautiful woman walked with the hunter through the bush. After a while he said: "Now I shall go home." The beautiful woman said: "Not yet. Keep me company a little longer." Thereupon he accompanied the woman a good distance further. After a while he said: "Now I shall go home." The beautiful woman said: "Not yet. Keep me company a little longer." After a little while he said again: "Now I shall return home." The beautiful woman said: "Not yet. Keep me company a little longer." Thereupon he accompanied the woman a good distance further.

After a while the beautiful woman said: "Look at the fruit on that tree! Go and fetch me some of the fruit. Climb the tree and pick me some of the fruit." It was a very tall tree. But the hunter climbed it. The hunter climbed up very high and threw fruit down to the woman. The man climbed higher and higher and when he had reached the very top of the tree the woman below called up to him: "You can try, if you want, to climb right up to the sky. You can try, if you want, to escape by way of the ground. Whichever way you choose, I shall devour you this day." The hunter looked down. He saw that the woman had changed into an irri, a truly fearsome snake, and had wound herself round the base of the tree.

The hunter saw this. He shouted. He shouted the names of his dogs. The names of his three dogs were Oke Makeren (he who cuts), Osoquako Gwenini (he who snaps), and Ogballe Gbarawe (he who cleans). When the hunter shouted, the three dogs were shut up at home. When the hunter shouted, Oke Makeren began to cut his way through the house door. All three dogs ran through the bush as fast as they could. They arrived at the tree in which the hunter was sitting. Osoquako Gwenini at once flung himself upon the irri, bit off its head and swallowed it. The snake was dead. Thereupon Oke Makeren began cutting the snake into pieces and Ogballe Gbarawe separated the flesh from the bones. Then he cleansed the place of blood.

The hunter came down from the tree. The first thing he did was to thank the dogs. Then the hunter looked at the meat and said: "So much meat! Who can possibly carry it home for me?" The three dogs said: "Promise us that you will not say a word to anyone and we will carry the meat home. But you must not even tell your wife about it!" The hunter said: "I promise you that I will not tell anyone, not even my wife." Then the three dogs went into the bush and fetched some palm leaves. They wrapped up the meat into three packages. They picked up the packages and stood upright. All three had turned into men. In the form of men they carried the meat home and put it in the agballa at the back of the hunter's house. They went into the house by the back entrance while the hunter went in by the front.

Having set the meat down in the agballa the three men changed back into dogs again. The hunter went in through the front entrance. As he entered he met his wife and said to her: "Go and look at the meat I have had put in the agballa for you!" The wife said: "You have had meat put in the agballa for me? Who brought it? Who did you send with it?" The hunter said: "The men have already gone away again. I met them on my way here. I do not know who they are. They must be strangers." The woman went into the agballa and saw the pile of meat. The woman said: 'They must have been three strong men!" The next day the woman went to a babalawo and asked him: "What kind of men were they who brought the meat home for my husband yesterday?" The balbawo said: "Buy some emu[1] and some ogoro[2] and cook a good meal. But all this in front of your husband, and then you will find out." The hunter's wife went home. The woman bought some emu and some ogoro. She prepared a good meal. She put the meal in front of her husband. When he had eaten, she gave him the emu and the ogoro. The husband drank them both. The husband became drunk. The wife asked her husband: "Now tell me who it was brought the meat here the other day?" The hunter said: "I should not tell anyone. But you are my wife. You will not talk about it. I will tell you. My dogs brought the meat home for me. The three dogs changed into men. But do not tell anyone." The wife said: "I will keep it to myself."

Every morning the dogs would lie outside the hunter's room. The following morning the wife wanted to do some sweeping there. She chased away the dogs saying: "Get out of my way, you who are neither proper dogs nor proper men!" When the dogs heard this, they said to each other: "The hunter has been chattering to his wife!" Thereupon the dogs ran into the bush.

The hunter's wife was pregnant at the time. Three months later she gave birth to a child. The child could not hear, the child could not speak. The hunter consulted all the orisas and all the ada-ushis. None of them could make the child speak. The child remained dumb. The hunter paid much money for help but no one could do anything. One day, however, Akuko, the domestic cock, came to them and said: "Would you not like me to teach your child to talk?" The mother said: "We would give you a great deal of money!" The hunter said: "We would give you a great deal of money." Akuko said: "Let the child's father, the hunter, bring me one hundred whips. Take the whips into the bush. Take the child into the bush." Akuko went into the bush and they brought

1 Palm wine.
2 Bamboo wine.

him the child and a hundred whips. Akuko said to the boy: "Wait. I will bring you some honey." He went away, came back, put down an empty gourd beside the boy, and said: "Do not touch it. I am going to fetch some more." He went. Akuko came back. He looked into the gourd and shouted at the boy: "Why have you eaten up all the honey? Then he began to beat the boy with the hundred whips. When the boy had been beaten with ninety-seven of the whips he began to shout at the top of his voice. When he had been beaten with all hundred whips he said: "You are a liar!"

The cock said: "You see! You can talk now!" From then on the boy could talk. The cock took him home. The mother gave everything she possessed to the cock. The father gave everything he possessed to the cock. That is why, among backyard fowls, the cock is the first to speak and that is why he wears a large comb upon his head.

THE HUNTER AND THE SNAKE WOMAN II
Togo-Tim

One day a hunter went into the bush to hunt. On the same day a lion went into the bush to hunt. On the same day Dom, the snake, went into the bush to hunt. Each went his own way. None of them knew the others were there. They came to a place where a female antelope was standing. The hunter took his bow and was about to fit an arrow to it when he saw Dom strike and kill the antelope.

The lion also saw Dom strike at the antelope and kill it. The lion came out of the bush and said to Dom: "I was stalking this antelope. Give it to me. It is mine. I ran it down." Dom said: "The antelope's mine, for I made the kill." The lion said: "Let us ask some one else's opinion. Dom said: "I agree. Let us ask somone else's opinion."

The hunter thought: "If I decide in favor of the snake the lion will bite me." Now Dom had the gift of knowing everything that other people were thinking. Dom said: "Let us ask the hunter who is standing behind that tree." Dom said to the hunter: "You can come out and tell us what you think. We will not hurt you." The lion said: "No, we will not hurt you if you tell us what you think." Then the hunter came out from behind his tree.

The hunter said: "The lion's claim is not a just one. For it was the snake, not the lion, who made the kill. If several hunters are following a quarry which they kill, the quarry is shared between the man who first wounds it and the man who makes the kill. Thus Dom has first claim on the antelope. But I think that in this case we should have little difficulty in reaching an agreement. We can share out the antelope between us."

Dom said: "I agree to that. We will divide the antelope into three. One share for the hunter as judge, one share for the lion, and one for me." The lion said: "Very well, I am content." Then they divided up the antelope. They heaped up the meat in three portions. The lion took his share and went away.

Dom said to the hunter. "Pick up my share. Come with me and carry my share to my house." The hunter thought to himself: "Once he has got me in his house the snake will kill me." Dom knew at once what the hunter was thinking and said: "You managed that business with the rapacious lion very well. So do not be afraid. I will not harm you."

They continued on their way. After they had gone a considerable distance they came to a great river. Dom said: "My town lies beneath this river. Follow me into the river." The hunter said: "The water will drown me." Dom said: "You will not drown. You will be all right if you come." They went into the water. They went below the surface of the water. Under the water there was a big town. Dom's farm was in that town.

They arrived at Dom's farm. The hunter put down the meat. Dom's wife and his two children picked it up and placed it to one side. One of Dom's two children was a very beautiful girl. When the hunter saw the girl he thought to himself: "I would like very much to sleep with that girl. Then I would gladly die." Dom, who never had any difficulty in reading other people's thoughts, said: "The girl is my daughter. Sleep with here as much as you like. But you will not have to die because of it."

The hunter thought to himself: "How can Dom possibly know all that I am thinking?" Dom said: "God tells me. God tells me everything." Dom gave the hunter a big house. Then Dom called his daughter. His daughter's name was If-you-serve-the-man-well-God-will-not-punish-you. Dom's daughter came. Dom said to his daughter: "Clean up the house for the hunter." The girl did so.

That evening the woman prepared a tasty meal. The girl brought a dish full of good food into the hunter's house. The hunter ate. The girl stayed with him. He slept with the girl. The hunter remained in Dom's house for six days.

Then the hunter went to Dom and said: "Now I must go home. I beg you to give me some of the medicine which enables you to tell what other people are thinking." Dom said: "I will give you some of the medicine and I will also give you my daughter for your wife." Dom went and fetched the medicine. Dom said: "Here is the medicine. When you get home, put it on your food. But do not chase away the goats if they also want to eat some of your meal." The hunter said: "Very well."

The hunter took the medicine and Dom's daughter and left the place. With his wife he came out of the river and made for the village where he lived. On arriving home he decided to try the medicine at once. Having taken out the medicine, he was about to put it on his food and eat it when the goats came crowding around. The hunter tried to hit the goats. But as a result he dropped the medicine which chanced to fall on his penis.

That is why the ability to read the thoughts of others was acquired, not by the hunter's head, but by his penis. And ever since that time, whenever a woman has entertained loving thoughts about a man, his penis has known immediately. And ever since that time his penis has risen.

SURRO SANKE   *Mande*

In Kaarta a man grew friendly with a king's son. They were very close friends until the day the king died and his son succeeded him. Then the friendship was over and the young king was at pains to get rid of his former friend.

Though he persecuted him in all kinds of ways, the king could not get the better of Surro Sanke. Then Surro Sanke said: "It is quite simple. You want to kill me. You therefore kill me if you ever find me jealous, and by that I mean if you catch me being jealous of my wife. Or you may also kill me if I lie in any way or say something that is untrue. Or you may also kill me if you can ever prove that I have acted like a coward." The king said: "Very well. I will abide by that."

The king decided to take immediate steps. He therefore sent for a Dugutigi whose village was a short day's march away and said to him: "Tomorrow morning I shall send Surro Sanke to you. He will tell you to come to me at once. You must agree to come and then begin to saddle your horse. Send him on ahead, saying that you will easily catch him up since you will be on horseback, but when he has gone unsaddle your horse again and do not come. Surro Sanke, when he arrives back here, will tell me that you are coming and will thereby tell an untruth." The chieftain said: "I will do as you say."

Then the king sent for a hundred soldiers and said: "Tomorrow I shall be sending Surro Sanke along such and such a road to see such and such a chieftain. Take powder but no bullets. When Surro Sanke comes along unsuspecting, use the powder to give him a thorough fright, but do not fire bullets at him." The hundred soldiers said: "We will do as you say."

Then the king sent for three men and said to them: "Early tomorrow I shall be sending Surro Sanke to such and such a chieftain. Surro Sanke has three wives. As soon as he is gone I want each of you to go to one of Surro Sanke's wives and to sleep with her. You must each remain with one of the wives until Surro Sanke comes in. Then make sure that Surro Sanke knows exactly what you have been doing with his wives. This will make Surro Sanke jealous." The three men said: "We will do as you say."

The following morning the king sent for Surro Sanke and said to him: "Go along such and such a road to such and such a chieftain and tell him to come to me at once." Surro Sanke said: "Very well." He went away. He had gone some little distance when the hundred men who were lying in wait for him began to fire at him with the powder. At once Surro Sanke stood still. With him he had brought a bow and three arrows. As soon as one soldier came into view, he let fly with his bow. The man fell dead on the spot. Thereupon he shot and killed another soldier and yet a third so that the remainder took fright and returned to the town. The ninety-seven soldiers went to the king and said: "This man, Surro Sanke, has killed three of our number. When we fired he showed no fear whatever. You may kill him, but you will never be able to make him afraid."

Meanwhile Surro Sanke went to the chieftain and said: "The king has sent me to tell you to go to him at once." The chieftain said: "It shall be done." He saddled his horse. He put a foot into the right hand stirrup, but before his other foot was in the other stirrup he said: "You go on ahead. For you are on foot and I can easily catch up to you. Surro Sanke said: "Very well," and left. Then the chieftain dismounted again, unsaddled his horse, and remained where he was. Surro Sanke went to the king. The king asked: "Is the chieftain coming?" Surro Sanke said: "I do not know." The king said: "How is it that you do not know? Did you not give him my message?" Surro Sanke said: "Of course I gave him your message. But I cannot tell whether he is really coming. Perhaps if he placed his left foot into the stirrup, as he had already placed his right, he may be coming. But when I last saw him the chieftain was only half in the saddle." The king said: "Very well, then. Go home."

Surro Sanke arrived at his farm. He went up to his first wife's house, opened the door, and saw, beside his wife, a man who was just pulling on his trousers. Thereupon Surro Sanke calmly shut the door and went towards his second wife's house. As he was about to open the door, another man came out, went past him, squatted down, and made water. Thereupon Surro Sanke closed that door also, went across to his third wife's house, and opened the door. But when he tried to go in he met another man who was just about to come out. Thereupon he closed this door as well.

Going into the middle of the courtyard, he called out: "Does anyone have a meal ready for me? If so, will they tell me where I can find my portion?" Then all of his three wives came out bearing gourds full of food and beside each of them walked her paramour. The three men made as if to go but Surro Sanke exclaimed: 'Surely you do not intend lo go off just like that? I hope that my wives have prepared enough food for all four of us. Come, then, and eat with me." The three men went and washed their hands, after which all four sat down to their meal. The four men ate together.

When the three men rose to go, Surro Sanke said: "Wait. I will come with you." He accompanied them as far as the gate and beyond, to the place where all three were to take different paths. Surro Sanke offered each of them snuff and gave them some cola nuts to refresh them on their way. Then, having shaken each of them by the hand, he went home again. The men did not separate, however, but went to the king and said: 'You may kill Surro Sanke, but you cannot make him jealous." The next day the king sent for Surro Sanke's three wives and asked: 'Did your husband, Surro Sanke, scold you at all yesterday after finding the three men with you?" All the wives said: "He neither said nor did anything at all." The king said: "It is impossible to make him jealous."

The king sent for Surro Sanke. When he came, the king said: "What you told me was true. You are not afraid, you are not jealous, and you do not lie."

Surro Sanke said: "I can tell you how that is."

Surro Sanke said: "I was once fighting in a war. We were not doing well. In one affray all of my friends were killed. I alone was left. I felt extremely thirsty. I thought I was going to die of thirst. Then I came to some water in which many caymans were lying side by side. The water was full of caymans. I thought that if I ran past and quickly dipped in my hand I would be able to get away unscathed. I tried to do this but a big cayman lashed out at me with its tail, knocking me into the water. At once all of the caymans came after me, lashing out with their tails and trying to bite me. But the cayman which had been the first to strike me sheltered me under its belly and protected me from the others. Then it put me in its cave from the surface of the water. And so I sat where the cayman had left me. The entrance to the cave was guarded by other caymans. I did not know how to get out. Then a herd of large antelopes went galloping overhead. One of them put its hoof through the top of the cave, so that I could see daylight above me. I knew then that I was quite near the surface of the ground. I worked away at the small hole that the antelope had made until I was able to crawl out. And since that day I have been impervious to fear.'"

Surro Sanke said: "One day I and some good friends of mine went out raiding. There were thirty of us. For three months we wandered about without obtaining any prizes. Nothing seemed to succeed. Three months we spent in the plain without seeing a woman. Then one day we managed to get hold of a woman and so lustful had we become that all thirty of us raped her one after the other. Thus we continued for another three months, each of us making love with this woman every night. Then, having succeeded in ravishing another woman, we decided that fifteen of us should have one of the women and fifteen the other. We told the woman what we had decided. Then both women went to draw water. When they came to the well, the woman who had already spent three months with us pushed the new woman into it, crying: 'What? I am to have only fifteen men to sleep with? I will not stand for that!' And since that time I have never been jealous."

Surro Sanke said: "One day when I was on my travels I came upon a human skull. I said: "How did a human skull come to be here, so far away from any village?" The skull said: "Because I talked too much." I asked: "Why?" The skull said: "Because I talked too much." I asked: "Why?" the skull said: "Because I talked too much." Three times the skull spoke to me. Then I went on my way. Having arrived at the nearest village, I told the Duguti: "Between your village and the previous one there is a talking skull." The Duguti said: "You are lying!" I said: "No, I am telling the truth." The Duguti said: "You are lying!" I said: "No. I am not lying, and if you will not believe me, I will take two men along with me and then they can hear it speak for themselves." The Duguti said: "Very well. Let two men go with him. If it turns out to be true that the skull can talk, well and good. Otherwise this man must be beheaded on account of the lies that he has told." I went to the place with the two men. When we had come to the skull I asked it: "Why are you lying here on the ground?" The skull did not answer. Three times I asked it, but still it did not answer.

Then the two men bound me as they had been told to do. One of them had already raised his sword to cut off my head when I exclaimed: "Ah, why, if you spoke yesterday, will you not speak today?" Then all at once the skull said: "Nda. Nda."[1]

My companions said: "Yes, it can talk." They untied my bonds. They led me back to the Duguti and said: "It is true, the skull does talk." And ever since that time I have said: "Of the two openings in the human body from which badness comes forth, the mouth is the more dangerous by far. And since that time I have never told a lie."

The King said: "Very well. I cannot kill you."

Surro Sanke said: "There is another way you can kill me. I have three hairs on my head, each of which has its own name. If you can find out what these names are, then you can kill me." The King said: "It is good."

The King was so angry at having been unable to kill Surre Sanke that he was determined to leave no stone unturned in an attempt to find out the secret of the three hairs. He therefore sent for Surro Sanke's first wife and asked her: "You are the wife of a man who is not rich. If you tell me what your husband's three hairs are called, I will make you my wife and give you many cows." The woman said: "I am not able to tell you, since I do not know." The King sent for Surro Sanke's second wife and said to her: "You are the wife of a man who is not rich. I will make you my wife and heap riches upon you, but in return you must tell me the names of the three hairs that grow on your husband's head." The woman said: "I am my husband's favorite wife. My husband loves me better than all his other wives. I cannot tell you." The King said "I will give you much cattle and jewellery." The woman said: "Would you take me for your wife?" The King said: "I will grant anything you care to ask." The woman said: "The hair on the right hand side is called walli-di-tege-mogo-dinje (not even a friend's son can be a substitute for your own). The small hair on the left hand side is called kani-kono-fo-mussue (never discuss your affairs with women). The thick hair in the middle is called kekorro-ba-kanji-kaphula (it is well if there is an old man

[1] Mouth.

194

among the company). Those are the names of the three hairs on my husband's head."

When the king had learned what he wanted to know he was jubilant. He said to his men: "Go and fetch Surro Sanke." The messengers went to Surro Sanke and summoned him. Just then it happened that he was at work and hence had no cloak with him. But a boy was there whom one of his wives had brought with her into marriage. Hurriedly Surro Sanke took the lad's cloak, small though it was, and went to the king. Immediately the king said to him: "The small hair on the right hand side is called wallidi-tege-mogo-dinje. The small hair on the left hand side is called kani-kono-fo-mussue. The thick hair in the middle is called kekorro-ba-kanji-kaphula. Is that not right?" Surro Sanke said: "Now you can kill me."

Surro Sanke was led out. The executioner walked beside him carrying the sword. The king walked behind. Then Surro Sanke's stepson came running and as he ran he shouted: "Oh, my cloak! Oh, my cloak! Now it will get covered in blood!" The boy had no thought to spare for his father's execution, but was concerned only for his cloak. Then Surro Sanke's true son came running and as he ran he cried: "Oh, my poor father! Oh, my poor father! Here is my cloak. Wear it, for your last walk. Oh, my father! Oh, my poor father!" Then Surro Sanke changed cloaks, and in the place of his stepson's small cloak he put on the small cloak of his genuine son.

When they reached the place, Surro Sanke knelt down. The executioner raised his sword. Surro Sanke bowed his head. Just then an old man shuffled forward on his knees and in a low voice said to Surro Sanke: "Greet my old father for me! Greet my old mother for me!" On seeing this the king exclaimed: "Someone is trying to send a message about me into the next world! You want to complain about me there! Well, if that is the case, then I will not allow this man to be put to death." Then they untied the bonds with which Surro Sanke was bound.

The king said: "Now, tell me why you have given your three hairs these names." Surro Sanke said: "Just now you saw how much concern my stepson showed for his cloak though he spared no thought for me. That is the reason for the name of the small hair on the left hand side. You were told the names of the hairs by the wife whom I love best, and that is the reason for the name of the small hair on the right hand side. If the old man had not been of this company you would have had me put to death. And that is the reason for the name of the hair that grows in the middle of my head."

MUSSA'S GRATITUDE   *Kordofan*

There was once a man called Mussa who was extremely rich and who, because of his wealth, was renowned throughout the land. For miles arouond there was no one who possessed so many slaves or such large herds of cattle, nor anyone whose influence in the country was as great as Mussa's. Moreover, Mussa was also exceedingly strong. When he was out hunting in the desert and came upon a hyena, a lion, or some such wild animal, he would leap out of the saddle and attack the creature with his bare hands. Having overpowered the animal he would tie it up and take it home. In his seriba he would allow the beasts to roam free in a special compound, where he would feed them. At last he was harbouring so many animals from the desert that the people of the village where he lived began to be afraid. After a time they came to him and said: "Friend Mussa, while it is true that you are very rich and very strong, and while it is true that you are richer and stronger than all of us put together, you now have so many wild animals in your seriba that we have grown afraid. Hence we beg you to look for another place and, having found it, to remove your seriba to that place along with the wild animals." Thereupon Mussa got ready, loaded his camels, oxen and horses, and went to a place far out in the desert. Mussa had seven sons whom he loved dearly. These sons helped him when he moved into the desert.

One day, after Mussa had set up his seriba, he ordered his horse to be saddled, took up his spear, and said: "My seven sons, I am going out hunting. Keep watch over the seriba." Then he rode away. But he had not been gone very long when some robbers arrived. They crept up to the seriba, forced their way in, murdered Mussa's seven sons, and drove away all of the cattle, leaving nothing behind them, so that when Mussa returned from the chase, he found the compound silent and deserted. Mussa was very surprised at the silence and said: "I can hear no sound, either of horse, donkey, camel, cattle, sheep, or any of my sons." Mussa tethered his horse to a stake outside and went into his seriba. Mussa went into the seriba and found that all of the cattle-pens were empty. Mussa came upon the bodies of his sons. Mussa was filled with fury. He called out the name of his first wife. But his first wife, who was then with child, had taken refuge in her hut where she was cowering on the floor. She did not dare answer. Mussa once again called out the name of his first wife and when she did not answer, his rage increased and he thrust his spear through the hut wall.

Inside the woman screamed. The spear had pierced her belly and killed the child. Both woman and child died at the very moment Mussa opened the door. In mortal terror, however, the woman hurled a log at the intruder, for she was no longer able to recognize Mussa. The log hit Mussa in the face, destroying one of his eyes. Mussa withdrew and went to his second wife's house. He found her and summoned her, meaning to leave the place with this second wife. He made for the entrance of the seriba, outside which he had tethered his horse to a stake.

Meanwhile, however, a lion had slunk up to the seriba, attracted there by the smell of the murdered sons' blood. Thus the lion found the horse. It sprang on the horse and killed it. Just at that moment, Mussa came along. Mussa and his wife made off as fast as they could. They both began to climb a tree. But the lion caught the woman by the leg, pulled her down, and killed her. And while Mussa sat in the branches of the tree, the lion devoured his wife beneath it. The lion remained under the tree the whole night. Only when morning came was Mussa able to come down out of the tree and go on his way. When Mussa set out, he had nothing left but the clothes that he was wearing and those were tattered and torn.

As Mussa continued on his way, he came to an elephant trap. Branches had been laid across it and, stepping on them, Mussa fell in. When Mussa had been at the bottom of the pit for a little while, some elephants came that way and one of them fell into the trap on top of Mussa, pinning him down so that he was helpless. Mussa lay thus the whole night. But the next morning the men who had laid the trap arrived. Seeing that there was an elephant there they climbed down, cut up the animal, and carried the meat up out of the pit. When they took out the last piece, they discovered a man lying underneath the elephant skin. They pulled him out and carried him up out of the pit. The man stood before them in the bright sunlight. He was clad in rags, filthy and bedraggled from head to foot, battered and scratched by roots and stones, with one eye gone and his limbs covered in wounds. They looked at him and exclaimed: "Is this not Mussa? Is this not the rich, strong, fortunate Mussa?" Some of the men said: "Look how wretched he is now!" One man said: "This man Mussa once killed one of my relations. At that time Mussa was rich and I could not take my revenge. But now that he is poor and miserable, I shall kill him in return. I demand Mussa of you as my prisoner!" The other men turned away, saying: "Take him prisoner if you want. We will not try to prevent you."

The man took Mussa home with him. When they got there the man bound Mussa with chains and fettered him by the ankle to another prisoner. The man said to Mussa: "Today you shall live like a slave in chains, but tomorrow I am going to kill you." When night fell the other prisoner said to Mussa: "Come, let us flee together!" Mussa said: "No. I have never yet run away. I will not flee." The other prisoner said: "Since my foot is fettered to yours I cannot escape alone. So you must flee with me!" Mussa said: "No, I will not flee. If I made an attempt to run away, life would no longer be worth living." Then the other prisoner fell silent. But when Mussa was asleep, the other prisoner fell upon him, bound his hands together, and gagged him so that he could not cry out. Now Mussa, being weak with hunger and thirst and loss of blood, was unable to resist. The other prisoner picked him up and staggered away with him. When they had covered some distance in this fashion a lioness and her young came out of the bush and sprang at the two fettered captives. They were beside a tree but the other prisoner could not climb it first without first wedging Mussa in among the lower branches. Then he climbed up after him. The lioness, however, caught hold of the other prisoner and began tearing off his arms and head and other parts of his body. At last nothing was left of Mussa's fellow prisoner but the foot that had been fettered to his own. Then the lioness went off with her cubs. Each of them carried in its mouth a piece of the other prisoner.

When Mussa was at last alone, he began to fray through the cords with which the other prisoner had bound his hands by rubbing them against the tree. As soon as he had freed his hands, he took the gag out of his mouth, removed himself from the branches into which he had been wedged, climbed down, and set off with his dismembered companion's foot still firmly attached to his own. At last he came to a village that was governed by a prosperous and much respected Arab.

Now Mussa possessed nothing at all. He had lost everything he had. Every member of his family was dead. His name was dishonoured and around his ankle he still wore the iron shackle that denoted captivity. Mussa went to the Arab and said: "I beg you to take me on as a guard and servant for your cattle. I will guard them faithfully and give you untiring service." The Arab looked at Mussa. He did not know Mussa, but he took him into his service and entrusted him with his cattle. The Arab saw that Mussa carried out his duties faithfully and honestly, and that he guarded the cattle with care. Having observed this, the Arab called Mussa to him one day and said to him: "Mussa, you do your work so well that I can see you must have possessed great herds of your own in the past." The Arab paused, but Mussa too remained silent and did not speak. The Arab went on: "There are two people who are dear to my heart. One of them is my son who at present is far away from here; the other is my sister. I will give you my sister in marriage, so that she can bear you children." Thus the Arab gave Mussa his sister in marriage, and Mussa took her to him and slept with her so that she soon became pregnant.

But one dark night not long after Mussa's marriage to the Arab's sister, the Arab's son, returning from his travels, came back to the village where his father lived. In the darkness of the night he guided himself by the noises the cattle were making out in the bush and he came quite close to the cattle. Then Mussa, their guard, who could not have known the Arab's son, noticed that a stranger was approaching the place where he kept the cattle. Believing the stranger to be a cattle thief, Mussa threw his spear at him. Gravely wounded, the Arab's son managed to stumble a short distance further. Then he fell down dead.

The next morning the villagers found the dead Arab. They lifted him up and carried him into his father's house. They said to the Arab: "Here is your son whom we found dead out there." But the Arab said to the villagers: "That is not true! My son was not dead when you found him. It was you who murdered him." The villagers said: "No, we did nothing of the sort. Someone else must have done it." A fierce argument ensued. The Arab wanted to put two of the villagers to death. But the villagers said: "Do not kill anyone. Though we were not responsible for your son's death, we would sooner pay blood-money than that there should be any bloodshed. Only tell us what you want." The Arab said: "You must pay be a hundred cows." The men said: "For the sake of peace we will pay you a hundred cows." The Arab having consented, the men paid him a hundred cows. Then the Arab sent for Mussa and said to him: "You, my friend and my sister's husband, take your wife, take the hundred head of cattle, and everything else that I have given you, and go with them to some other place. Set up your own seriba and see what you can do for yourself."

Then Mussa packed together everything that the generous Arab had given him. He left the village with his wife, the Arab's sister, and with all of his cattle, and built a seriba of his own. Now in due course his wife gave birth to a son. Moreover, Mussa's stock throve and multiplied so that he grew wealthier day by day and month by month. The small son who had been born to Mussa by his wife, the Arab's sister, grew up to be a fine, strapping youth.

Now Mussa watched over his son, noting his age and the progress of his growth. When he was as tall and as old as the Arab's son whom he, Mussa, had killed one night long since, his father wrote a letter, saying: "One night I accidentally killed your son. Then he was tall and strong just as the lad who brings you this letter is tall and strong. At that time you had already given me your sister in marriage in order that she should bear me children. My wife had since borne me a son who has grown to be as tall and strong as your son used to be. I am therefore sending you this youth, with the request that you should kill my son as I once killed yours." Having written this letter, Mussa called his son and said to him: "Now go and carry this letter to the Arab who is your mother's brother." The youth took the letter and carried it to his uncle.

After greeting his nephew, the Arab took the letter and read it. Thereupon he called all the people of the place together and said: "Listen to this letter!" Then he read Mussa's letter aloud to them. When he had finished he said: "This letter was written by Mussa to whom I once gave my sister in marriage. Now I know who it was that killed my son, although by accident. Tell me then what I should do. Shall I or shall not kill the son of my sister and of my brother-in-law, Mussa?" To this the villagers replied: "Listen, O Hammad Abu Kallam. This affair concerns you alone and therefore the decision rests with you and with you alone. But remember that if you kill this lad who is your sister's child, it would be almost as though you were killing your own child." The Arab, Hammad Abu Kallam, having listened to and pondered their reply said: "I think as you do. Instead of killing the son of my sister and of Mussa, I will give him my own daughter in marriage."

Then the Arab ordered a sheep to be killed. He sent for Mussa's son and welcomed him with kind words. He gave Mussa's son his own daughter in marriage, made him gifts of money and sheep, and said: "Now go back to your father, taking with you all that I have given you. My greetings to your father and to my sister, your mother. Tell them that I hope very soon to visit them myself and to spend a few days enjoying the sight of their prosperity." Thus Mussa's son returned home. Instead of having been killed he had been given a wife and valuable possessions. He was followed a day or two later by the Arab, Hammad Abu Kallam, who set up camp near Mussa. He greeted Mussa and, at nightfall, lay down on the ground beside his horse outside the seriba.

Before going to sleep, Hammad Abu Kallam played his rababa for a while. Then he lay down and fell asleep. Meanwhile two thieves had come creeping up. One of them stood holding his spear over the Arab's head. He said: "If he moves, I will kill him." The Arab woke up. He saw what was happening. The Arab said: "I will not call for help. I only want to play my rababa." While one of the thieves unhobbled the horse and the other continued to hold his spear over the Arab's head, Hammad Abu Kallam played his rababa and said: "O sister Sherifa! O sister Sherifa! A thief is standing beside my head, holding his spear above it, and he is going to kill me. And another thief is unbuckling my horse's girths in order to steal it. Hear me, O sister Sherifa!"

The thieves did not understanding the meaning of the song that the Arab was singing to his rababa. But Sherifa, Hammad Abu Kallam's sister, understood his song. She woke Mussa, her husband, and said: "Wake up, Mussa my husband! There is a thief outside trying to steal my brother's horse, and there is another thief holding a spear above his head, ready to kill him if he moves." Mussa rose. He took his spear. He threw it at the man who was trying to steal the horse, so that the thief fell down dead. Then the other man, who had been threatening Hammad Abu Kallam with his spear, took fright and ran away.

When the thief had gone, Mussa said: "How did these men get here? There have never been thieves in this region before! Such a thing has never happened here before!" Hammad Abu Kallam said: "They were horse thieves. Horse thieves roam all over the country." Mussa said: "It is well that one of them was killed." Hammad Abu Kallam said: "Yes. It was lucky for me! You saved my life which I should otherwise have forfeited to those dogs. But tomorrow I shall depart from here."

The following morning Hammad Abu Kallam took leave of his sisters, his daughter, Mussa, and Mussa's son, and left to return home to his village.

Now when the Arab had ridden away, Mussa said to himself: "I was destitute and utterly cast down. Then this Arab, Hammad Abu Kallam, made me wealthy again and gave me his sister in marriage. When he had thus restored both my reputation and my happiness, I killed his son. But instead of retribution, I was given an abundance of riches which once again enabled me to become master of my own village. When my son had grown big enough I sent him to Hammad Abu Kallam so that the Arab might kill him, as once I had killed his own son. But instead of doing so he bestowed rich gifts upon me. And to my son he gave his own daughter in marriage before taking leave of him as of his own child. In return for the injury I did him he has never done me anything but good. Now I am at a loss what to do. I cannot allow him to remain alive. I can only follow him and kill him."

Mussa mounted his horse. Mussa took his spear. Mussa rode after Hammad Abu Kallam. As Mussa caught up with Hammad Abu Kallam, he called out to him, saying: "Now hear me! Wait for me! You have done me so many favors that I cannot allow you to remain alive. I must kill you!" Hammad Abu Kallam said: "Why should you want to kill me when I have never done you any harm?" Mussa said: "No, you have never done me any harm! From you I have never had anything but favors. Indeed, you have done me so many favors that I could never pay them back even if I were to work as your bondsman for the rest of my life. Therefore I can no longer tolerate your existence. Hence I shall have to kill you." And taking his spear, Mussa hurled it at Hammad Abu Kallam. But the latter leaned to one side and the spear missed him and buried itself in a patch of scrub. Hammad Abu Kallam retrieved the spear. He handed it back to Mussa, saying: "Here is your spear, but do not kill me, for I have never injured you, nor have I any desire to injure you." Mussa said: "I cannot allow you to remain alive, for you have already done me too many favors!" When Hammad Abu Kallam heard this he pulled his horse around and fled, so taking himself out of range of Mussa's spear.

Hammad Abu Kallam came to his village. Calling the villagers together, he said: "That man Mussa who killed my son, and to whose own son I nevertheless gave my daughter in marriage, today sought to kill me because he finds it intolerable that I should remain alive any longer. But I was able to escape him." When the villagers heard this they said to the Arab: "Then we must all take up arms. Then we must all go and take this Mussa prisoner!" The villagers dispersed and each man fetched his spear. Then they reassembled and set off for Mussa's seriba. They arrived there during the night. They surrounded the seriba. They forced their way in. They captured Mussa and bound him hand and foot. Thus bound, they took him to Hammad Abu Kallam. Mussa's wife followed the band of men and their captive.

When Mussa was brought before Hammad Abu Kallam, the latter said: "Is this how we have to meet again? Have I not done you every imaginable favor? And what do I get in return?" Mussa said: "You have done far too much for me. You have done me so many favors that it is beyond all bearing. Unless you kill me, I shall have to kill you!" Hammad Abu Kallam said: "I, too, have realized this. Therefore I shall keep you prisoner in this room for tonight and tomorrow I shall kill you!" Mussa said: "It is well." When Hammad Abu Kallam left the room, however, he was followed by Sherifa, his sister who was also Mussa's wife. Outside she threw herself down at her brother's feet, wept, and said: "I beseech you, O brother, to spare my husband's life!" Hammad Abu Kallam said: "No, Sherifa, my sister! I have done your husband too many favors. Am I now to die because they were so many?" But Sherifa wept even more bitterly, saying: "No, brother, that is not what I meant. I do not want you to die. But nor do I want my husband to die, for he is the father of my children." Thereupon Hammad Abu Kallam raised his sister to her feet, saying: "Do not weep, O sister. But unless there is a death, we shall be unable to live in peace. It is better that only one man should die than that two or more should be destroyed. Therefore I shall have to kill your husband, unless you want the worse alternative." Then Hammad Abu Kallam veiled his face and went into his house. He sat down on the angareb.

Sherifa went out into the desert. She wept and wept. But at nightfall she returned to the seriba and went into the room where her husband lay in bonds. Sherifa cut through all the bonds with which Mussa's hands and feet were tied. Then she said to him: "Now hurry, Mussa, and escape with me!" Mussa said: "I have never yet fled, O wife! I am incapable of flight, whether my companion in chains is being devoured by lions, or whether I am destined to be transfixed by your brother's spears! I can neither flee nor leave this place without first killing your brother, for he has done me so many favors that I cannot allow him to remain alive."

Once again Sherifa threw herself weeping to the ground. Over and over again she besought her husband: "Mussa, O valiant man! Mussa, O slayer of lions! Mussa, O father of my children! Mussa, O my Mussa! I beseech you, come away with me. That would not be flight! See how many they are in this village, and you are alone against them all. Mussa do not court death! Your mare and your stallion, your dogs and your animals will give tongue. The lions will leap into the compound and strike down the calves. Your huts and your house will fall into ruins. Your children will be deprived of father and land because you, O Mussa, O my husband, will have chosen to die here before your time!"

Mussa said: "Stand up, Sherifa! When your brother is dead, no one will carry on the quarrel. And if I have to die and everything that is mine goes to rack and ruin, it will not be because I am wicked, but because custom demands it and because your brother has been too kind. Therefore, stand up!" Sherifa stood up. Sherifa said: "Then wait here. I will fetch my brother. You can settle your affair together." Sherifa went. She went into the house where Hammad Abu Kallam was sitting on his angareb. She said: "I would beg you, O my brother, to come with me. Mussa desires to speak with you." Hammad Abu Kallam rose. He sighed and went out. Hammad Abu Kallam said: "What does he want to speak to me about?" Sherifa said: "I do not know!" Hammad Abu Kallam said: "Now you are lying, O my sister!" Then Hammad Abu Kallam went over to the house. Sherifa cast herself upon the ground and wept. As Hammad Abu Kallam was about to enter the house, Mussa plunged a spear into his breast.

The following day the villagers came and put Mussa to death. They took all of the herds and everything else that Mussa and Hammad Abu Kallam had owned. Mussa's children were sold. Sherifa, however, clothed herself in rags and from that day until her death she remained a beggar, for ever wandering from place to place.

THE YOUNG GIRL AND HER VISITOR

Togo-Tim

A man married a woman. The woman bore him a child. The child was a girl, a very pretty girl. A young man asked for the girl's hand. Her father agreed. The father said: "When the girl is old enough, you can marry her." The father kept the girl locked up so as to prevent her meeting any other men. Every day the mother took food to the confined girl. The girl was never allowed to leave the hut during the daytime.

One night the young girl went outside in order to make water. As she was going back into the house she was seen by a young man. The young man at once fell in love with the young girl. He went to his friends and said: "Who is the young girl who was going into this house by night?" His friends said: "Her father has promised her to a young man and now she is never allowed out of the house." The young man said: "No matter. I have got to possess the girl. I cannot live without her." His friends said: "That is impossible. No one is allowed out of this house and no one is allowed into this house. She is always kept locked up."

Thereupon the youth said to his friends: "You must wrap me up well in pieces of cloth so that no one could possibly know that I am a man. Then carry me to the girl's father and say: "Here is a cushion for your beautiful daughter to put under her head, so that she may rest more comfortably." His friends did as he asked. The youth was well wrapped up in pieces of cloth. His friends carried the package to the father. The father took it in. The mother carried it to the girl and said: "This is a pillow sent to you by the young men of the village so that you have something soft to rest your head on."

Then the mother went out, leaving the girl alone with the pillow. When the mother had gone out, the girl lay down on the pillow. The girl unwound one piece of cloth and then another and then another. She pushed her hand in between the pieces of cloth to see if the pillow was all made of cloth. She reached the inside. Her hand happened to grasp the young man's penis. The young girl said: "What is that?" She felt further down and took hold of his testicles. She said: "What is that?" She pressed his testicles, whereupon the young man's penis became erect.

The young girl pulled the pieces of cloth apart. She saw that there was someone inside. The young girl was alarmed, for she had never seen a man before. But the young man took the girl in his arms. She lay still. The young girl pointed to the young man's penis and asked: "What is that for?"

Then the young man made love to the young girl. The following morning he said: "Now wrap me up again in the pieces of cloth so that your mother does not see me." The young girl did so. But in the evening she again pulled the pieces of cloth apart and let the young man sleep with her.

After a few months had gone by the young girl's mother said to her husband: "Our daughter's belly is growing big. She must be pregnant!" The father sent for his daughter and asked her: "Who has got you with child?" The young girl said: "The pillow mother brought me."

That is why today young girls are not kept under lock and key. For after all there is nothing to be done when young people really fall in love with one another.

SPINNE WINS THE HAND OF URO'S DAUGHTER
Togo-Tim

In a village there lived a chief who possessed a growing daughter. Uro's daughter grew up and became ripe for marriage. The chief summoned all of his people and said to them: "I want a stalwart husband for my daughter and one who had given her real satisfaction. He must be a man with a stout penis. I will give my daughter's hand to the man who is able to cut off with his penis those seven fruits at the top of the fanpalm yonder. He and none other shall have her for his wife." The men listened to him. None of those who heard him made the attempt. They all went away, each man to his own homestead.

Among those present was Spinne's wife. She too went home. Later, when Spinne came in from the fields his wife said to him: "Uro called everyone together and said: 'I will give my daughter's hand to a man with a very strong penis, a penis with which he can cut off the seven fruits growing on the fanpalm.'"

Spinne waited until it had grown dark. As soon as it was dark Spinne took a hatchet and a small gourd full of redwood water. Thus equipped, Spinne set out through the darkness to the fan-palm. He climbed up the fan-palm. With his hatchet he cut nearly all the way through the stalks of all seven fruits so that the slightest touch would be enough to bring them down. Then he concealed the small gourd containing the redwood water among the leaves. Having done these things he climbed down again and went home.

The next day Spinne went to Uro and said: "Yesterday when I came in from the fields my wife told me that Uro had called everyone together and said: "I will give my daughter in marriage to a man with a very strong penis, a penis with which he can cut off the seven fruits growing on the fan-palm.' Now call everyone together, let them come. I am going to cut down the seven fruits with my penis and then you must give me your daughter." Uro said: "Very well."

Uro called everyone together. They all came and stood underneath the tall fan-palm. Spinne arrived and climbed up into the fan-palm. When Spinne had reached the top, he began sawing with his penis. He went on sawing away at the stalks with his penis, screaming horribly the while. And all the time Spinne kept dribbling redwood water out of the gourd onto his legs. The people said: "Look! That is blood dripping down! Listen! He is screaming with pain! Spinne will die, but Spinne will get the girl."

Spinne sawed, Spinne screamed, Spinne dribbled blood out of the gourd. At last one fruit fell to the ground. Spinne sawed, Spinne screamed, Spinne dribbled blood out of the gourd. At last the second fruit fell to the ground. Spinne sawed, Spinne screamed, Spinne dribbled blood out of the gourd. At last the fifth fruit fell to the ground. Spinne sawed, Spinne screamed, Spinne dribbled blood out of the gourd. At last the sixth fruit fell to the ground. Spinne sawed, Spinne screamed, Spinne dribbled blood out of the gourd. At last the seventh fruit fell to the ground.

Then Spinne climbed down out of the tree. All of the seven fruits were lying on the ground. Groaning, Spinne crossed the market-place with legs astraddle as though unable to walk in any other fashion. Everyone said: "I would never endure as much pain just for the sake of a girl!" But the chief said: "I promised my daughter in marriage to the man who could cut off the seven fruits of the fan-palm with his penis. Take my daughter, therefore." Then Spinne took Uro's daughter and went with her to his farmstead.

Some time later Spinne went out into his fields to work, accompanied by Uro's daughter, his new wife. When he had been working for a while he said to his wife: "Go and get me some water from the river. I am thirsty." The wife said: "I have nothing to draw it with. Give me a gourd!" Spinne said: "I have no gourd." Spinne's wife said: "How then am I to fetch water if I have nothing to fetch it in?" Spinne said: "Use your vagina to fetch water." Spinne's wife said: "But how can I do that?" Spinne said: "Just lie down in the water wait till it has filled your vagina, and then bring the water back here. That is easier than sawing off fruit with one's penis."

Spinne's wife went. She went to the water and lay down in it. She let the water run into her vagina. But when she stood up again the water ran out. She lay for a second time and let the water run into her vagina. But when she stood up the water still ran out. She lay down for the third time. The same thing happened. The water still ran out. The wife jumped out of the water. She hurried away.

In tears, she came to her father, saying: 'Spinne wants me to take him water in my vagina. But every time I fill it the water runs out again. Spinne says it is easier than sawing fruit from trees with his penis. But I cannot do it." Then Uro understood what Spinne had meant. He said: "It is not right for a man to choose his son-in-law on the strength of his penis, or to ask him to use his penis to cut off the fruits of the fan-palm. Every father should give his daughter in marriage to the man who loves her."

THE WHORE'S REVENGE *Mande*

The whore lived in a town that is about the same distance from Bamako as Bamako is from Mecca. She would never go out into the streets but would receive all her friends at home in the evenings, and her assemblies were always lively and enjoyable. Now this whore had a younger brother of whom one day it was rumored that he had prostituted himself to a woman. And although the rumor could not be substantiated, since there was in fact no truth in it, the judge nevertheless sentenced the youth to one hundred strokes of the lash. The mayor, to whom the youth appealed, confirmed the verdict, as did the almami.[1] Thereupon the whore went to the court of justice and said: "There is no truth whatever in the rumor and you have sentenced my brother unjustly. But in order to spare him the dishonor, I am prepared to pay a fine instead." To this they replied: "Even though you were prepared to pay your brother's weight in gold, we must still have to have him beaten!" So the youth received his hundred lashes.

When it was over, the whore said to her brother: "You were sentenced by all three of them. I shall find a way of having each of them given a hundred strokes of the lash." Three days later the whore put on her finest clothes and went to the place where the almami was. She walked past him. The almami said: "What, no greeting?" She said: "I did greet you, but you did not hear me." The almami said: "Out for a walk? It is not often that we see you out of doors!" The whore said: "Why should you be surprised by an exception, being, as you are, an exception yourself in never coming to visit me like all of the other men in this town?" The almami said: "I would

[1] Chief priest.

like to come. But there are always so many other people there." The whore said: "Is that the only reason? Well, no one else will be there at half past six this evening." The almami said: "Really?" The whore said: "By your justice I swear it!" The almami said: "Then I will come to you at half past six this evening."

The whore continued on her way. She came to the judge's house. He asked her the same question as the almami. They exchanged just the same remarks and ended up by arranging that, since the judge would find her alone at eight o'clock, she swore he would, he too should pay her a visit that evening.

The whore continued on her way. She walked past the mayor's house. He asked her the same question as the almami and the judge. They exchanged just the same remarks and ended up by arranging that, since the mayor would find her alone at midnight, as she swore he would, he too should come to visit her that night.

Then the whore went to find her younger brother and said to him: "Come to see me after midnight when you will have an opportunity of settling accounts with the men who sentenced you to a hundred strokes of the lash."

Hardly had the almami concluded the prayer that he was intoning before the congregation that he went hurrying to the whore's house without so much as stopping to take a meal. He flung his brightly colored clothes into a corner and joined the whore on her bed. The whore dallied with him without, however, allowing him full satisfaction, continuing thus until eight o'clock, when there was a sound of footsteps outside the door. In alarm the almami asked: "Is someone coming?" The whore said: "It is eight o'clock already? Then it must be the judge." The almami asked: "Does he often visit you?" The whore said: "No, to-day is the first time." The almami cried: "Oh, he must not find me here! Hide me!" There were three large chests in the room. Opening one of them, the whore said: "Get in there!" Naked as he was, the almami hastily climbed into the chest. The whore locked it, removing the key which she pocketed.

The judge came in. He threw his official robes hastily into a corner and joined the whore on her bed. The whore dallied with him without, however, allowing him full satisfaction, and continued this game until midnight when there was a sound of footsteps outside the door. In alarm the judge asked: "Is someone coming?" The whore said: "Is it midnight already? Then it must be the mayor!" The judge asked: "Does he often visit you?" The whore said: "No, today is the first time." The judge cried: "Oh, he must not find me here! Hide me!" At this the whore put another chest on top of the first one in which the almami was already hiding. She said: "Get in here!" Naked as he was, the judge climbed into the chest. The whore locked it and removed the key which she pocketed.

The mayor came in. Leaning his spear against the wall, he hurriedly threw his clothes into a corner and joined the whore on her bed. The whore dallied with him without, allowing him full satisfaction, and continued this game until there was a sound of footsteps outside. In alarm the mayor asked: "Is someone coming?" The whore said: "It must be my younger brother!" The mayor said: "The one we sentenced to a hundred strokes of the lash?" The whore said: "The same!" The mayor said: "Oh, he must not find me here! Hide me!" At this the whore placed a third chest on top of the two that already contained the almami and the judge. She said: "Get in here!" Naked as he was, the mayor climbed into the chest. The whore locked it, and removed the key which she pocketed along with the others.

The whore called her brother in. She said: "I promised you that I would place at your mercy the three men who sentenced you to a punishment that was as shameful as it was undeserved. In the corners of this room you can see those men's clothes and their badges of office. Against that wall you can see the mayor's spear. The three chests here contain the three men themselves. Here are the keys to those chests." Her brother said: "The chests are too heavy to be dragged away, but I will take the clothes and the keys and lodge a complaint before the judge in the neighboring town."

He took all the things and went away.

The following morning the congregation of the faithful waited for the almami to intone his prayers. But they waited in vain. Then the people grew uneasy and said: "We will go to the judge and ask him to organize a search

for the almami." The whole crowd went streaming to the
the judge's house. The judge's servants said: "The judge
has not been seen since last night." Thereupon the
crowd, which by now had been joined by many others,
made its way to the mayor's quarters. As they went, they
shouted: "The mayor must see to this business! The
mayor must organize a search for the almami and the
judge!" In the mayor's compound they found only his
wives. The women grumbled: "Last night he did not
come to either of us!" On hearing this, the multitude
became anxious.

In the meantime the mayor, who was lodged in the
topmost chest in the whore's house, could no longer resist the call of nature, having drunk a great deal. He
therefore began to piss copiously, his water trickling
down through the cracks in the chest onto the judge
below, who cried: "Desist, O mayor!" The mayor recognized the judge's voice and said: "Are you here, too?"
Then the judge, in his turn unable to resist the call of
nature, emptied his bladder, so giving the almami in the
chest below him a showerbath. The almami cried: "Desist, O judge! I, the almami, am here beneath you!"
Thereupon the mayor said: "Since all three of us are
here, we may as well shout!" From his chest, the mayor
let out a yell. Their clamor penetrated to the crowd of
people anxiously hurrying about the streets of the town.
Some of them said: "Come! There is a fight going on
in the whore's house!" Everyone came running. They
could see no one in the house, but there were pools of
urine beside the chests from which groans and shouts
were coming.

The people broke open the three chests and from them
emerged the mayor, the judge, and the almami, all three
of them naked.

CLEVER HATUMATA DJAORA   *Sahel*

Once upon a time there was a woman in Wagadu who
was wondrously beautiful . She was even more beautiful
than Sia Jatta Bari and her name was Hautumata Djaora,

for she was a member of the Djaoro family. She was the most beautiful woman throughout the land and her father said: "I do not want you to marry a man you have not yourself chosen. I will not compel you to marry anyone. Your choice must be free." Hatumata said: "If a man is rich, if he has great herds and many horses, I will not marry him because of that, for I am not fond of rich men. I prefer clever ones." Hatumata's father built a fine dwelling in which she lived with her mother. The dwelling had three gatehouses. Each gatehouse was guarded by one or two prisoners and a dog.

So beautiful was Hatumata that many suitors came asking for her hand. Whoever had one ox would offer that ox. Whoever had two oxen would offer two oxen. Whoever had ten oxen would offer ten oxen. Whoever had twenty oxen would offer twenty oxen. But always Hatumata answered: "I will never marry a man for his oxen, but only for his brains and his wits." The father had an old bondsman by the name of Alanj. Every one of Hatumata's suitors was required to lodge in this man's house. Hatumata's father said: "Stay with Alanj. My daughter will supply you with food." Hatumata would send a little slave with the food. She said to the slave: "Note carefully how the people eat the food that I send them. Take note of what they say. Afterwards take away the empty gourds and bring them back to me." The food Hatumata sent consisted of a bowl of porridge, on top of which she had set a bone with very little meat on it and four red cola nuts. The little slave went across with the food. He sat down apart from the strangers, who without saying a word, dipped their hands in the bowl and ate all that was in them. Then the little slave got up, removed the empty gourds, and carried them to his mistress. Hatumata asked: "What happened?" The little slave said: "They ate everything up without saying a word." Hatumata said: "Tell the men to go away. Such people are not the kind for me." The boy told them. The men left. The same thing happened with numerous suitors. Each time Hatumata's reply was: "I will not marry such a man."

In the country of Wagadu there lived a man whose

name was Kide Djaora which meant that he belonged to the same tribe as Hatumata. Kide said: "If Hatumata says that she is not to be won by oxen but by wits and cleverness, then I shall see if I can make her my bride, since few would seem as suitable to marry her as I." With two companions, one young and one old, he set off for the capital. He went to Hatumata's father. He said: "I wish to marry your daughter." The father said: "You must go and lodge with my old bondsman, Alanj. My daughter will supply you with food there." Thus the three men, like all the others before them, went to stay with Alanj.

Meanwhile Hatumata prepared bowls of porridge upon which she laid four red cola nuts and a bone with very little meat on it. She said to the little slave "Take this to Kide and his companions. Mark well how they eat the food and when you return the gourds, tell me what you have seen." The little slave took the food to the three visitors in Alanj's house and carefully noted all that happened. Kide looked at the bowls. Taking the bone with little meat on it, he set it aside saying: "Maybe in the place where the gourds came from, there is someone pining for this." Then he laid the four red cola nuts on one side and he and his companions began to eat the porridge. Finally he put the red cola nuts back into the empty gourds which he handed to the little slave to be returned to Hatumata. Hatumata took the gourds with the four red cola nuts inside. She asked: "What happened?" The slave said: "Kide put the bone with little meat on it on one side, saying: 'Maybe in the place the gourds came from, there is someone pining for this.' Then he put the red cola nuts on one side, and when he and his companions had eaten the porridge, he put the four cola nuts back into the gourds." Hatumata said: "Kide can stay until tomorrow. These people are of a different kind." The little slave went to the men and said: "You can stay until tomorrow."

The next day Hatumata sent a bowl of porridge on which she had laid two red cola nuts, two white cola nuts, and a bone with very little meat on it. Kide considered the dish. He laid the bone with little meat on one side, saying: "Maybe in the place where the gourds came from, there is someone pining for this." Then he put the two red cola nuts on one side also and ate what remained in the dish, including the two white cola nuts. Finally he put the red cola nuts back in the gourds and returned the empty bowls to Hatumata. Hatumata took the gourds with the two red cola nuts and asked: "What happened?" The slave said: "Kide put the bone with little meat on it on one side, saying: 'Maybe in the place where the gourds came from there is someone pining for this.' Next he set the red cola nuts on one side, and when he and his companions had eaten the white cola nuts and the porridge, he sent me back with the empty gourds and the two red cola nuts." Hatumata said: "Kide can stay until tomorrow. He is a man of a different kind."

On the third day Hatumata sent a dishful of porridge upon which she had laid four white cola nuts, a bone with very little meat on it, a wisp of straw, a cotton seed, and a grain of tommono. Moreover, the lid of the basket was arranged in such a way that only half the contents was covered. When she had despatched the food, Hatumata said to her servants: "You must set my chamber and my bed in good order, for it is likely that something will happen today." Meanwhile the bowls containing the food had been taken to Kide. Kide removed the bone, laid it on one side, and said: "Maybe in the place where the gourds came from there is someone pining for this." He further removed the wisp of straw, the cotton seed, and the grain of tommono, put them into his wallet, and said: "Today we shall eat all four cola nuts as well as the porridge." He ate everything up before giving the completely empty gourds back to the boy. The little slave took them to Hatumata. Hatumata asked: "What happened?" The little slave said: "Kide took the bone and set it on one side, saying: 'Maybe in the place where the gourds came from there is someone pining for this.' Then he put the wisp of straw, the cotton seed, and the grain of tommono in his wallet, with the words: 'Today we shall eat all four cola nuts as well as the porridge.' They ate everything up and gave me back the empty dishes." Hatumata said: "This is the right man. See that my bed chamber and my bed are properly prepared." Next Hatumata went to the slaves who watched the gates, presented them with a sheep, and said: "You need not keep watch tonight. Take this sheep, eat it, and hold your celebrations elsewhere." On her way back, where the path forked just beyond the third gatehouse, Hatumata strewed some grains of tommono on the lefthand fork. When she returned to her house she said to the little slave: "Bring me a large and very white cotton seed." The boy brought her one. When evening came she laid the cotton seed in front of her door and, instead of closing the wooden door, hung a straw mat over the entrance, but in such a way that only half the opening was covered.

Towards midnight Kide rose from his bed in Alanj's house, shook his sleeping companions, and said: "Wake up!" His two companions rose. The older one said: "What is it?" Kide said: "I am going to marry Hatumata." The old man said: "There is something strange happening! No one else has been allowed to stay here longer than a day. But you have already been here three days. And now you say that you are going to marry Hatumata this very night!" Kide said: "I am very partial to Hatumata!" The old man said: "Do you want us two to stay awake?" Kide said: "No. There is no need." The old man said: "Then I will seek out some other lodging. This seems to me a very risky business." The old man then left Alanj's house and went to find an acquaintance to whom he said: "Kide intends to sleep with Hatumata tonight. I have come to you so that later on you will be able to bear me out when I say that, although I came here with Kide, all this has nothing to do with me." The old man stayed with his friend.

Kide set out to find Hatumata. In the first gatehouse there were no sentinels, but only a dog. The dog was about to set on him when he threw it one of the three bones. This satisfied the dog. In the second gatehouse he again found no sentinels but only a dog. The dog was about to set on him when he threw it a bone. This satisfied the dog. In the third gatehouse, as before, there were no sentinels but only a dog. The dog was about to set on him. He threw it the third and last bone. Beyond the gateway the path forced to the left and to the right. Kide scrutinized it closely. There were some grains of tommono on the lefthand fork. From his wallet he drew the grain of tommono that he had removed from the third dish of food, laid it beside the other grains, and, having compared it with them to his satisfaction, took the lefthand fork. This led him to an open space where there were four houses in a row, each having one door. He noticed that three of these were wooden doors and that they were closed, but that the entrance to the fourth house was only partially covered with a straw mat. In front of the straw curtain lay a shining white cotton seed. Kide took from his wallet the cotton seed and the wisp of straw, both of which he had removed from the food sent by Hatumata. Next he compared the cotton seed with the white fluffy seed on the ground, and the wisp of straw with the curtain over the entrance.

Then he went in through the half opened doorway. At that moment Hatumata braced her body, breaking the fastenings that retained her shift. The shift fell to the floor. Kide advanced towards her. Hatumata said: "What have you come for?" Kide said: "On the first day you sent me a dish with four red cola nuts. Now cola nuts are not usually served with porridge. This struck me all the more in that all four nuts were red and that with them there was a bone with insufficient meat on it to satisfy a man. From this I concluded that you were having your period, since all four of the nuts were red, and that I should not come to you. The bone, however, I thought to be intended for the watch dog in your gatehouse. On the second day you sent me two white and two red cola nuts, meaning that your period was nearly over. And once again there was a bone, from which I concluded that there was another dog to be overcome in the second gatehouse. On the third day I found four white cola nuts and I knew that your sickness was over. Moreover, I noted that the lid of the basket only half covered the food, thus indicating that your door would likewise only be half closed and that you would be waiting for me tonight. The bone led me to suppose that there was yet a third gateway guarded by a dog. The wisp of straw, the grain of tommono, and the cotton seed were obviously signs to help me find my way, and hence I put them in my wallet. In the course of the night I set out. As I had supposed, there were three gatehouses one after the other, in each of which there was a dog to be placated. I gave them each a bone and was thus not tempted to deviate either to the right or to the left of my proper course. Beyond the gatehouses the path forked, but I knew at once which way to go because of the grains of tommono I found there. This led me to an open space with four houses each having one door. Here I could not go wrong, for three of the houses were closed with wooden doors and only one had a straw curtain. I knew that you must live there and be waiting for me, because you had sent me a wisp of straw, and because of the shining white lint of the cotton seed visible even in the darkness outside your door, and lastly because the straw curtain only half covered the entrance, just as the food this morning had been only half covered. So I thought to myself that I might come in. That I had interpreted correctly I knew when, upon my entering, you braced your body, breaking the fastenings of your shift so that it fell to the ground, thus enabling you to welcome me in all your beauty."

Thereupon Hatumata Djaora said: "Come!"

That night Kide made love to Hatumata. The next morning he left, saying to his wife: "I will go back to my village and inform my father that I have got married. Then, all being well, I will return." Having taken his leave, he set out. The prosperous men of Wagadu were enraged that Kide, who was not even from the capital, should have succeeded in winning Hatumata Djaora, and they determined to seek their revenge. They heard that Kide was leaving for his village in order to bring news of his marriage to his father. Seven armed men therefore set out to lie in wait for him and kill him. They concealed themselves in the bush.

Presently Kide came along. The seven murderers surrounded him and said: "We are going to kill you for taking the woman that none of us have ever been able to get! Now we shall kill you!" Realizing that death was inevitable, Kide said: "I will tell you how you can get the gold that I left with Hatumata."

The murderers said: "Speak!" Kide said: "Tell my wife, Hatumata, that I have sent you to collect the gold from under her bed, the gold that covers me from head to foot. If she refuses to believe you and asks for further indentification, tell her the following: 'My long-trousered companion is with me from morning until night. My old companion with the questing head is with me from dusk until dawn, and I am expecting a companion who has neither hands nor feet.' If you tell this to Hatumata, she will know just what my intention is and will see to it that you get the gold that I owe you." The murderers said: "Now we know how to get your money, but nevertheless you will have to die!" Then the seven murderers killed him.

Immediately afterwards the seven murderers returned to the town and went to Hatumata. Outside Hatumata's compound they said: "We bring tidings from Kide Djaora for Hatumata Djaora." A messenger went in and called Hatumata out into the courtyard, where she awaited them. She asked: "What tidings has my husband sent me?" The seven murderers answered: "Your husband said you are to give us the money that he left under your bed and which covers him from head to foot." Hatumata said: "Wait. I will send for my father to be a witness to the just execution of my husband's wishes." The seven murderers waited. Hatumata's father was called. He entered the courtyard with his slaves.

Hatumata said: "Now repeat the whole message given you by my husband." The seven murderers repeated Kide's words, saying: "Your husband told us: 'Tell my wife, Hatumata, that I have sent you to collect the gold from under her bed, the gold that covers me from head to foot. If she refuses to believe you and asks for further identification, tell her the following: My long-trousered companion is with me from morning until night. My old companion with the questing head is with me from dusk until dawn, and I am expecting a companion who has neither hands nor feet. If you tell this to Hatumata, she will know just what my intention is and will see to it that you get the gold I owe you.' That is what your husband said to us. Now give us the gold."

Hatumata said: "Father, you heard everything. You know these men. They are people who sued for my hand and were rejected. Hence their intentions towards Kide, of whom they were envious, cannot have been good, nor are they likely to have done him any service in return for which he could have owed them so much gold. The mes sage he has sent me from the bush by way of these men here has another meaning. The gold that covers him from head to foot is the blood that flows over the murdered man from head to foot. The companion who is with him from morning until night, the long-trousered companion, is the vulture whose feathers wholly cover its legs. It pecks away all day at his body. The companion that stays with him from dusk until dawn, the old companion with the questing head, is the jackal which tears at his flesh by night. The companion he is expecting, the companion with neither hands nor feet, are the worms that will infest and destroy the corpse. Kide's intention is perfectly clear when he says that these seven murderers are to be given the gold that he owes them. This means that I am to shed their blood as they have shed Kide's. That is the gold that I shall give them. But first we must follow the track leading to the village where Kide's father lives in order to find Kide's body and bring it back for burial. For he was a clever man and deserves to be buried honorably."

Hatumata's father's bondsmen bound the seven murderers and afterwards went to seek Kide's body, which they found. When Kide had been buried, the blood of the seven murderers was made to flow above his burial mound.

And ever since that time it has been considered wiser not to seek wealth in marriage, but rather to look for a clever wife or a clever husband.

THE CHIEFTAIN'S SONS   *Togo-Bassari*

There was once a very rich and important chieftain who had six wives each of whom had borne him a son. He also had a young and very beautiful wife. The chieftain's six sons were already grown up. Every day they went to look after the chieftain's cows and oxen. One day they were tending the cows out in the fields. They had eaten yams. They were talking together.

The eldest son said: "For six days I would like to own all of my father's cows. Then, every day, I would have them led past me. Every day I would have one slaughtered, I would share out the meat, and use everything up. Then, for all I care, I could die on the seventh day. But during the first six days I would like to do exactly as I pleased."

The second son said: "For six days I would like to own all of my father's corn and yams. Then every day I would summon all of the women from all the villages and every day I would order them to make food and brew beer and so use everything up in six days. Then, for all I care, I could die on the seventh day. But during the first six days I would like to do exactly as I pleased."

The third son said: "For six days I'd like to occupy my father's leather seat. I would summon all of the people, I would distribute gifts, I would have all disputes brought up before me, I would kill people and deal with everything in a manner such as in my opinion befits an important chieftain. I would ride, make war, and take prisoners. Then, for all I care, I could die on the seventh day. But during the first six days I would like to do exactly as I please."

The fourth son said: "For six days I would like to have all of the meat that my father's village could provide. During these six days, I would have everything slaughtered, cooked, and shared out. I would eat what I liked and make free with everything. Then, for all I care, I could die on the seventh day. But during the first six days, I would like to do exactly as I please."

The fifth son said: "For six days I would like to be in command of all of my father's young men. I would send for some of them and order them to dance. Some of them I would send hunting. Some of them I would send to work in the fields. Some of them I would send to war. Some of them I would sell, and anyone I did not fancy I would have put to death. Then, for all I care, I could die on the seventh day. But during the first six days I would like to do exactly as I please."

The sixth man said: "For six days I would like to live in a hut with my father's young wife. I would sleep with her in the morning, I would sleep with her in the afternoon, I would sleep with her at night. I would never let her out of my arms, even if it killed her. Then, for all I care, I could die on the seventh day. But during the first six days I would like to make love to this wife so often that I would not have any strength left."

A man had overheard all that the six brothers had been saying. He went and told the chieftain what he had learned. The chieftain sent for his sons and said to the eldest: "Take all of my cows." To the second he said: "Take all my corn and my yams." To the third he said: "Take my place on the leather seat." To the fourth he said: "Take all the meat there is." To the fifth he said: "Take all the young men." To the sixth he said: "Take my young wife."

The six sons took everything that their father had given them in response to their wishes. For six days each son lived in accordance with his heart's desire. All of the chieftain's cows and oxen were slaughtered, all of his corn and yams were used up, all of his meat was boiled or roasted, all of his beer was drunk, all of his men were sent fighting, hunting, and dancing. Many of them were killed, sold, or driven away. Everything was turned upside down. The sixth son, however, shut himself up with the chieftain's young wife whom he held constantly embraced, while the young wife kept repeating: "Your penis is sweet! Your penis is sweet! Your penis is sweet!"

At the end of six days all of the chieftain's possessions had been destroyed, all of his forces dispersed, and his peaceful relations with his neighbors disrupted. But meanwhile the chieftain had obtained six lions. He placed one lion outside each son's dwelling. The six lions were put there so that they might devour the six sons when they came out on the seventh day. When the six days were over, the eldest son came out and was devoured. When the six days were over, the second son came out and was devoured. When the six days were over, the third son came out and was devoured. When the six days were over, the fourth son came out and was devoured. When the six days were over, the fifth son came out and was devoured.

On the seventh day the sixth son, too, said: "Today is the seventh day. Today I shall die." The young wife said: "No, you must not die. We will escape. I will show you the way." The young wife went to the far end of the hut where she lifted the straw thatch off the top of the wall. She said: "Come out with me this way." The young man climbed out with the young woman. The young man and the young woman walked for some distance. The young woman said: "Now we must kill a cow and cut off its four legs. They may well be of use to us." The young man killed a cow. They cut off the legs and went off with them.

When the fugitives had gone some way further the lion came up behind them. The lion had almost caught up with them. Then the fugitives threw it a cow's leg. The lion flung itself on the cow's leg and began to crunch it up. Meanwhile the fugitives hastened on their way. But as soon as the lion had finished eating the cow's leg, it set off in pursuit until it had almost caught up with them. Then the fugitives threw it the second cow's leg. The lion flung itself on the cow's leg and began to crunch it up. Meanwhile the fugitives hastened on their way. But as soon as the lion had finished eating the second cow's leg, it set off in hot pursuit until it had almost caught up with them. Then the fugitives threw it the third cow's leg. The lion flung itself on the cow's leg and began to crunch it up. Meanwhile the fugitives hastened on their way. But as soon as the lion had finished eating the third cow's leg, it set off in hot pursuit until it had almost caught up with them. The fugitives threw it the fourth cow's leg. The lion flung itself on the fourth cow's leg and began to crunch it up.

Meanwhile the fugitives had come to a river that could not be crossed, for it was wide and deep and there were no boats. But a young girl was walking on the far bank. She was Unji-bugara's daughter. The girl shouted across the river to the young man: "You cannot get across this river. But if you will marry me I will help you." The young man said: "Yes, I will marry you." The girl hurried away. She came back with her uncle whose beard was huge and long. The man threw the end of his beard across. The young man caught the end of the beard. The young man and the young wife that he abducted from his father's house got to the other side. Hardly had they got across than the young man's father arrived with his men. He had gone forth himself on hearing that his son and his young wife had succeeded in escaping the lion. But now the young man and the young woman had got across to the other side, and his father and the men he had with them could do nothing.

When the young man had reached the other side with the help of the old man's beard, the young girl said to him: "You promised that you would marry me." The young man said: "I shall gladly do so." The girl said: "Then I will take you to my father's farm. My father is a very important chieftain. He often kills people. Therefore you must remember what I tell you. My father's name is Unji-bugara. He has ten wives, nine of whom are good. Unjankann, however, is bad. My father always asks people which of his wives is the bad one. If you can point her out and say her name you will no longer be in danger." The young man arrived at the farm. The young girl pointed to a woman saying: "Look, that is Unjankann, my father's bad wife."

They appeared before Unji-bugara. Unji-bugara ordered food and drink to be brought and a hut to be prepared for them. Later he sent a message to the young man, saying "We will play jworra¹ together." The young man came and played with Unji-bugara. Unji-bugara said: "I have ten wives one of whom is bad. If you cannot single her out I will have you beheaded. But if you succeed, you may slit my throat." The young man said: "I agree." Unji-bugara said: "Let all of my wives assemble." The ten wives came. Unji-bugara said: "Tell me which of them she is." After looking at each wife in turn, the young man pointed to the tenth and said: "This is the bad one amongst your wives and her name is Unjankann." Unji-bugara said: "You are right. Slit my throat." The young man slit Unji-bugara's throat.

The young man fulfilled his promise and married Unji-bugara's daughter. In addition he inherited all ten of Unji-bugara's wives and Unji-bugara's thousand cows. He was now a rich man and a very important chieftain. His cows were very large and white. Amongst them was one

¹ A game played on a board.

cow that was large as a hill and completely white all over.

Unji-bugara's daughter became pregnant and bore her husband a son. The young man's first wife also became pregnant and gave birth to a child. Both the children grew and learned to walk. They played together. Unji-bugara's daughter's child said: "The white cow's tail belongs to me!" The other child said: "Why do you say that? I want the tail." The first child said: "No, the tail is mine!"

The children's father heard this exchange. He gave orders that the big white cow should be slaughtered. He had its tail cut off. He had the severed end bound with brightly colored leather, in the style of the Dagomba leather workers. Then he took it and called the two children to him. He said to them: "You were quarrelling about the white cow's tail. You must not quarrel. Now I am going to throw the tail into the air and whoever catches it when it comes down can keep it." The two children stood there ready to jump or run after it. The father threw the tail of the large cow that was completely white all over high up into the air. Up and up went the tail. The tail turned into the moon and its hairs turned into stars.

And since that time cows have never been as big as they once used to be.

A BOY WHOM THE GIRLS LOVED   *Muntshi*

A man married a woman. The woman bore two children. One was a girl and the other a boy. The children grew and throve. When the girl was fully grown, the father lay with his own daughter. When the boy was fully grown he gave him a wife.

The man had a big farm. His son and his slave worked on the farm. A small boy hiding nearby overheard what the two were saying. The youth and the slave did not know it. The youth had had nothing to eat. He said to the slave: "I am hungry. I would like a dish of beans today." The slave, too, had had nothing to eat. He said to the youth: "I am hungry. I would like a dish of chicken today." The boy had heard what they said. He ran to the house of the youth's father and said: "Your son has said that he would like a dish of beans. Your slave has said that he would like a dish of chicken." The father said: "Very well." The father ordered a dish of beans and a dish of chicken to be prepared.

When the youth and the slave had finished working on the farm they set off for home. They found the man at home. In front of the man were two covered gourds. The man asked his son: "What would you like to eat today?" The son said: "Today I would like a dish of beans." The father gave his son a gourd. The son took off the cover. There were beans inside. The man asked the slave: "What would you like to eat today?" The slave said: "Today I would like a dish of chicken." The man gave the slave the other gourd. The slave took off the cover. There was chicken inside.

The youth said to the man: "O father, as you are granting every wish today, there is something else that I want." The father asked: "What is it?" The youth said: "I want to lie with my sister!" The father said: "But that is not done! You cannot lie with your own sister!" The youth said: "There are other things that are not usually done. You lie with your own daughter." The father said: "I will not permit you to lie with your sister!" The son said: "But I want to lie with my sister!"

The father said: "That you will not do!" Taking hold of the youth, his father led him into a house. The father locked the door behind him. On his way back to his own house, the father met his daughter. The daughter said: "Father, I would like to sleep with my brother!" The father said: "I will not permit my son to sleep with my daughter!" The daughter said: "But I want to sleep with my brother!"

The father said: "In that case I shall shut you both up in the same house." Then the father took hold of his daughter and led her to the house where his son was already confined. He locked both of his children in together.

Now the son had a friend called Hingaga. Hingaga

came to visit his friend. Hingaga searched the whole farmstead but could not find his friend. Hingaga went to the youth's father and asked him: "Where is my friend? I have been looking for him and cannot find him." The father said: "I have locked up your friend together with his sister in that house." Hingaga said: "Can I perhaps visit my friend?" The father said: "You may visit him just once more." The father ordered the door to be unlocked for Hingaga. Hingaga went inside.

Hingaga asked his friend: "What is wrong?" The youth said: "I wanted to lie with my sister. My sister wanted to sleep with me. I told my father. My father locked us up in here. Tomorrow my father will put us to death." Hingaga said: "I do not think that you will have to die. I will show you how you can get away with your sister." Hingaga began digging inside the hut. First Hingaga dug a shaft. Then Hingaga dug an underground passage that led right under the village, only coming to the suurface on the far side of it.

When Hingaga had finished the tunnel he hurried back along it to the hut where the youth and his sister were confined. Hingaga said to the youth: "Come with me. Now we can all leave together. I will go ahead. You and your sister can follow me." Hingaga went down the shaft and then along the underground passage. The youth and his sister followed after him. Beyond the village Hingaga emerged from the tunnel. Beyond the village the youth and his sister emerged from the tunnel.

The youth and his sister hurried away as fast as they were able. When they had been walking through the bush for some time the youth was bitten by a snake. He fell down dead. The girl screamed and wept. Presently a Jukum girl came through the bush. She asked the sister: "Why are you crying? Why are you screaming?" The sister said: "My husband and I were walking through the bush. My husband was bitten by a snake and now he is dead!" The Jukum girl said: "I have medicine with me. I can restore the young man to life and health. But when I have done so he will have to take me with him as his wife." The first wife said: "Bring him back to life and health and then he will do as you wish." The Jukum brought out her medicine. She put the medicine under the young man's nose.

The young man woke up. He looked about him. The young man said: "What is happening?" His first wife said: "You were bitten by a snake. You were dead. I was sitting here and crying. Then this Jukum girl came along. The Jukum girl had medicine with her. The Jukum girl said: 'I can restore the young man to life and health. But when I have done so he will have to take me with him as his wife.' Then she brought you back to life and health." The young man said: "Very well. I will continue on my way with two wives."

The youth set out with his two wives. With the two of them he went further and further into the bush. They walked a great distance. They came to a river. They could not find any place where they could cross the river. They went up and down the river bank. At last the Jukum woman caught sight of a fishing boat. There was a girl in it. The Jukum woman said: "Take us across to the other side." The fisher girl brought her boat closer to them and said: "Who am I to take across?" The Jukum woman said: "There are three of us; the young man here and we, his wives." The fisher girl looked at the young man. The fisher girl said: "I will ferry you across, but when I have done so, this young man here must take me with him as his wife." The young man said: "Very well. Then I shall continue on my way with three wives!"

The fisher girl ferried the young man and his two wives across the river. When she had done so, the young man went on his way with his three wives. When they had covered a very great distance they came to a big city. The toro[1] of the city saw the young man and his three wives. The toro said to his servants: "This young man has three beautiful young wives. I will take them all away from him." The toro said: "Take a big crock of beer for the young man's wives and a small one for the young man. You must poison the beer in the small crock." The servants did as he had told them. The servants brought the big crock containing good beer to the young man's wives. They brought the small crock with the poisoned beer to the young man himself. When the beer arrived, the

[1] King.

Jukum woman tasted the beer in the big crock. The Jukum woman said: "This beer is good." The Jukum woman tasted the beer in the small crock. She spat it out, saying: "This beer is poisoned. The toro of this city is trying to poison our husband. Let us drink the beer from the big crock." Thereupon she emptied the beer out of the small crock and they all four drank out of the big one. When the servants returned to the king, they said: "The wives have thrown the poisoned beer away. They and their husband are drinking the good beer."

The next day the toro sent for the young man and said to him: "If you can tell me which is my first wife, I will not kill you. But if you fail to do so, than I shall kill you." When all of the people were assembled, the toro sent for his wives. The toro's wives were all lined up in a long row. When all of the people and all of the wives were there, the toro said: "Now, which is my first wife? Can you tell me or can you not?" The young man looked along the row of women. He did not know which of them was the first wife. The king's first wife, however, was thinking to herself: 'The toro must be wanting to kill this young man. I would rather be his wife than the toro's wife. I will give the young man a sign." The toro's first wife signalled with her hand. The young man saw it. The young man went up to the first wife and said: "This is the toro's first wife."

Everybody began to shout: "The young man is right! The young man is right! Do not kill the young man! Kill the toro, for he is wicked!" Everybody ran towards the toro. They caught hold of him. They took him into the bush. They killed the toro.

Then they made the young man their king.

THE MOTHER'S BOY   *Muntshi*

A man married. His wife became pregnant. His wife bore a child and the child was a boy. The wife took the child out to the farm with her. The child grew up on the farm. He always worked alongside his mother. The child grew into a strapping youth. The youth's mother always cooked his meals for him and the youth himself always worked on the farm. The youth grew big and strong and his mother went on cooking for him and he went on working on his mother's farm.

Some people came to the farm. The people saw the youth. The people said: "That is a fine, strapping youth!" The people asked the youth: "Do you not want to take a wife?" The youth said: "No. All I want is my food, and what my mother gives me is both good and ample."

One day the father came to the farm where the youth was living with his mother. The father said to the youth: "Do you not want to take a wife so that you can beget a son? Come back with me now to the village!" The father took the youth back with him to his village. The father shaved his son's head. When he had finished, he gave him many beautiful beads. He put strings of beads around his neck. He wound strings of beads around his toes and ankles. He put fine bracelets on his arms. He rubbed his body with red dye. He gave him a new loin-cloth. Then his father said: "Now go and look for a wife with whom you can beget a child."

The youth went. The youth walked about the place and looked at the girls. He took a girl and brought her home to his father. He said to his father: "I want to marry this girl." His father said: "That is good." The father led his son and the girl to a hut. The father said: "Go in there with the girl and lie with her so that she becomes pregnant." The youth went into the hut with the girl. But when he had laid the girl down on the bed, he came out again and hurried back to his mother's farm. He said to his mother: "Mother, I am hungry. Cook me a good meal." The mother cooked a meal for the youth. Then he stayed with her.

The newly married girl ran out of the hut. The girl went hurrying to the youth's father and said: "Your son did not lie with me. He took me into the hut and then he hurried out again." The father got up and went. He went to his wife's farm. He said to his wife: "Is my son here?" The mother said: "Yes, your son is here. Last night he came and said: 'Mother, I am hungry. Cook me a good meal!' Then I cooked him a good meal. He ate it and stayed here."

The father said: "My son got married yesterday. But he did not lie with his wife last night. He came running to you and asked for food. Something must be done. I think that the next time he asks for food you must give him terrible food or none at all. Then he will go hurrying back to his wife." The mother said: "I will do as you say." The father went back to town.

Presently the youth came to his mother and said: "Mother, I am hungry. Cook me a good meal!" The mother said: "Did you not marry a wife yesterday?" The youth said: "Yes, I did marry a wife yesterday." The mother said: "If you married a wife yesterday, then go to her and ask her to prepare you a meal." The youth went. The youth went to his father and said: "My mother will not give me food any more." The father said: "Did you not get married yesterday? Did you lie with your wife?" The youth said: "No, I did not lie with my wife." The father said: "Then go to your wife and lie with her. Then tell her to cook a good meal for you. Then your wife, too, will be able to satisfy your appetite."

The youth went. He lay with his wife. Afterwards his wife washed herself and cooked him a a good meal. The youth watched her at her work. The young wife brought him food. The youth ate it. When he had eaten enough he said to his wife: "Come indoors. I want to lie with you again!" Not long afterwards the young wife became pregnant. She gave birth to a son.

A father should bring his son up to be a man and a husband, for if he stays with his mother he will only learn to eat.

JEALOUSY PUNISHED — *Muntshi*

A man married a wife. The wife was very beautiful. The husband could not bear any other man to look at his wife. The husband always remained near her in an attempt to prevent other men from looking at her. The husband said: "Something must be done about this. All of the men keep looking at my wife. I shall go with my wife into the bush where no man ever comes, and there I shall build myself a house and start a farm." The husband said to his wife: "Pack your things. We are going into the bush together." The wife packed her things.

The husband went into the bush with his wife. In the bush he built himself a house. In the bush he started a farm. He said: "Here no man will be able to look at my wife. Here I shall have her all to myself. I can go out and work without any worry." Taking his mattock, the man went out into the fields.

His wife was sitting outside the house door. Hardly had the husband gone away than a male antelope passed nearby. When the antelope was quite close to the house the woman called: "Where are you going?" The antelope replied: "Just down the track to make sure that no one is coming." The woman said: "That is good. When you have had a look you can come back this way."

The male antelope went down the track to see if anyone was coming. Having made sure that no one was coming the antelope returned. As the antelope approached the hut the woman's kurru[1] said: "O antelope, why not make love to me now?" The antelope said: "I will gladly do so." The woman's kurru said: "Make haste, then, and come into the hut!" The antelope went into the hut. Inside the hut he made love with the woman's kurru. When he had finished he hurried out again. The woman called after the antelope: "Where are you going?" The antelope said: "Just down the track to make sure that no one is coming." The woman said: "That is good. When you have had a look you can come back this way."

The male antelope went down the track to see if anyone was coming. Having made sure that no one was coming, the antelope returned. As the antelope again approached the hut, the woman's kurru said: "O male antelope, why not make love to me again?" The antelope said: "I will gladly do so!" The kurru said: "Make haste, then, and come into the hut!" The antelope went into the hut.

[1] Vagina.

Inside the hut he made love with the woman's kurru.
When he had finished he hurried out again.

Once more the woman asked the antelope where he
was going. Once more the kurru invited him in and asked
him to make love. In this way the kurru persuaded the
male antelope to make love five times. When the male
antelope had made love with the woman's kurru five
times he hurried out again, saying: "Let me go, now. I
am tired!" Thereupon the antelope trotted back into
the forest and lay down to sleep.

After a while the husband returned home from the
fields. He ate his supper. Then he lay down on the bed.
His wife lay down beside him. During the night his wife's
kurru said to him: "A male antelope came here today.
I persuaded him to make love with me five times." On
hearing this, the husband leapt up from the bed. Waking
his wife, he said to her: "Get up, O wife! Pack all your
things. We are going back to the village where we will
have people around us. If a man makes love to you there,
then I can at least give him a good hiding!"

Thus the husband and wife returned to their village.

THE SISTER WITH A PENIS
Muntshi

A toro[1] had a daughter. The daughter had a lover.
Every night he would come to her mother's house and
spend the night with her. Suitors arrived, wanting to
marry the girl. The girl said: "I do not want to marry."
The girl did not want to take a husband. But the father
said to the girl: "I want you to get married!"

Then a man came whose name was Bogo. Bogo said to
the toro: "I want to marry your daughter." The father
asked his daughter: "Are you going to refuse this man
Bogo as well?" The girl said: "No. I will marry Bogo."
Bogo married the girl and took her to his village. When

[1] King.

234

the young wife had lived with Bogo in his village for a while she said to herself: "My husband is not at all like my lover. How I should like to sleep with my lover once more!"

The young wife went to Bogo and said: "I would like to go and visit my mother." Bogo said: "No, stay here and do your work." The young wife said: "I would like to go there for just one night." Bogo said: "No. For the time being you must stay here. You have everything that you want."

The young wife's lover said to himself: "I would like to know how my girl is getting on. How I should like to sleep with her again!" The young wife's lover said: "I shall go to Bogo's village. Perhaps I shall be able to speak to my girl." The lover set off. He arrived in Bogo's village. The lover bided his time until Bogo went out.

When Bogo left the house to go out into the fields, the lover went to the young wife and greeted her. The young wife said to him: "I was longing to sleep with you again. I told my husband I wanted to see my mother again. My husband told me I must remain with him and do my work." The lover said: "Ask your husband once more. Perhaps he will let you go this time." The young wife said: "Very well, I will ask my husband once more." The lover went away.

The next day the young wife said to her husband: "O my Bogo, I should like to visit my mother again!" Bogo said: "No, stay here!" The young wife said: "I would like to go there for just one night!" Bogo said: "No, you will stay here. You have only to look about you, and you will find everything that you need as a wife."

A few days later the young wife's lover returned again to Bogo's village. He waited until Bogo left the house. When Bogo had left the house the lover went to the young wife and greeted her. The young wife said: "I was longing to sleep with you again in my mother's house. Once again I asked my husband if I could go and see my mother. My husband said I must stay here where I only had to look about me to find everything I needed as a wife." The lover said: "Ask your husband yet again. Perhaps he will let you go this time!" The young wife

said: "Very well, I will ask my husband once again."
The lover went away.

The next day the young wife said to her husband: "O my Bogo, I beseech you to let me visit my mother!" Bogo said: "No, you will stay here!" The young wife said: "I would like to go there for just one night!" Bogo said: "No, you will stay here! Do not think about your mother so much. You must try to become a mother yourself."

A few days later the young wife's lover once again came to Bogo's village. He waited until Bogo had left the house, the lover went to the young wife and greeted her. The young wife said to him: "I was longing to sleep with you again in my mother's house. Once more I told my husband I wanted to go and see my mother. My husband said I must stay with him and do my best to become a mother myself." The lover said: "I will see if I can do something about this. Wait one more day and then I will come and fetch you." The lover went away.

The lover went away. The lover dressed himself up as a woman. He put on a head-cloth. The lover tied some pretty beads around his neck. Then the lover went back to Bogo's village. Disguised as a woman, the lover went to Bogo. He greeted Bogo and said: "I am your wife's sister. I have come to fetch your wife and take her to a festival in our mother's village. An ox is to be killed. If we leave at once, you can spend tonight at my house and we will arrive at our mother's house tomorrow." Bogo said: "Very well." Bogo got himself ready. His wife got herself ready. They set off

When it was dark they arrived at the lover's village. The lover led them to his own house and said: "There is only one bed in this house. Do you want to find somewhere else to sleep." Bogo said: "No. You two sisters can sleep on the bed. I myself will lie outside the door. I shall sleep outside the door and then I can be sure that no man can get in to you." The lover and the young wife thereupon went into the house. They lay down together on the bed. Bogo lay outside the door.

Now when the lover and the young wife thought that Bogo had gone to sleep, the lover rose and placed himself between the young woman's legs. Then he did as he had always been wont to do in former days when the young wife had been living with her mother. Recalling her earlier raptures and feeling that this particular bout was nearing its end, the young wife moaned out loud saying: "Ah, this is better than Bogo! Ah, this is better than Bogo! Ah, this is better than Bogo!" Then the lover let go of the young wife and lay down at her side.

Bogo, who was lying asleep outside the door, woke up on hearing his wife moan and speak his name. He raised himself on his elbow and, without opening the door, said: "What was that you were saying, O my young wife?" The young wife said: "I was dreaming. In my dream I said: 'I will do my work well, O Bogo! I will do my work well, O Bogo! I will do my work well, O Bogo!'" Bogo said: "Sleep and do not fret. If you work when you are at home in the village, that is enough." Then Bogo turned over, lay down, and went to sleep again.

Now when the lover and the young wife thought that Bogo had once more gone to sleep, the lover rose and placed himself between the young woman's legs. Then he did as he had always been wont to do in former days, when the young wife had been living with her mother. Recalling her earlier raptures and feeling that this particular bout was nearing its end, the young wife moaned out loud, saying: "Ah, if only my Bogo could do it like this! Ah, if only my Bogo could do it like this! Ah, if only my Bogo could do it like this!" Then the lover let go of the young wife and lay down again at her side.

Bogo, who had fallen asleep again outside the door, woke up on hearing his wife moan and speak his name. He raised himself on his elbow and, without opening the door, said: "What was that you were saying, O my young wife?" The young wife said: "I was dreaming. In my dream I said: 'O my Bogo, I will try to find everything that I need as a wife! O my Bogo, I will try to find everything that I need as a wife! O my Bogo, I will try to find everything that I need as a wife!'" Bogo said: "Sleep and do not fret. If, when you are at home in my village, you manage to find everything you need as a wife, then that is enough." Then Bogo turned over, lay down, and went to sleep again.

Now when the lover and the young wife thought that Bogo had once more gone to sleep, the lover rose and placed himself between the young woman's legs. Then he did as he had always wont to do in former days, when the young wife had been living with her mother. Recalling her earlier raptures and feeling that this particular bout was nearing its end, the young wife moaned out loud, saying: "Bogo is weak but you are strong! Bogo is weak but you are strong! Bogo is weak but you are strong!" Then the lover let go of the young wife and lay down again at her side.

Bogo, who had fallen asleep again outside the door, woke up on hearing his wife moan and speak his name. He raised himself on one elbow and, without opening the door, said: "What was that you were saying, O my young wife?" The young wife said: "I was dreaming. In my dream I said: 'O my Bogo, I will do my best to become a mother very soon; O my Bogo, I will do my best to become a mother very soon! O my Bogo, I will do my best to become a mother very soon!'" Bogo said: "Sleep and do not fret, O my young wife. You will become a mother soon enough!" The young wife said: "Yes, now I think so too!" Then Bogo turned over, lay down and went to sleep again.

When it was almost morning the young wife got up. Her lover was still asleep. Taking a crock, the young wife opened the door, stepped over Bogo, and went to the brook to wash herself and fetch water. While she was away, Bogo woke up. Seeing the door open, Bogo looked into the house. Bogo saw that there was only one person lying on the bed. Bogo went into the house.

The lover's gown had fallen off while he was asleep, exposing his djoa.[1] Bogo looked at the penis. Bogo said: "This sister has got a penis! What shall I do to this penis?" Bogo pulled out his knife. Bogo said: "Shall I cut off this sister's penis?" Bogo said: "I will wait until there is more light." Bogo went out of the house. He put his knife away again.

Bogo sat in front of the house, saying: "I must cut off the sister's penis!" Bogo said: "No, I must kill the

[1] Penis.

sister!" Bogo drew out his knife again. Bogo went up to the lover. Bogo said: "'I must kill this sister!" Bogo considered the lover and said: "I must wait until there is more light!" Bogo left the house. When he was outside he put his knife away again.

Presently the young wife returned from the brook. Bogo went to meet his wife, saying: "Your sister has got a penis!" The young wife gave a scream. The young wife cried: "What is that you say? You say my sister has got a penis? I have never seen such a thing before! I have never heard of such a thing before!" The young wife flung down the jar of water. She screamed. Everyone came out of their houses. The young wife shouted: "Just listen! I have got a sister with a penis." Everyone said: "It is not pleasant that your sister should have a penis. Send her away!" Others said: "Well, there are women who have those things, but they cannot do anything with them."

The lover was now awake. He had put on his dress. Bogo asked him: "Tell me, O sister-in-law, can you do anything with your penis?" The lover said: "No, I cannot do anything with this penis, for it never grows strong." Bogo said: "Then all is well. Then we can continue on our way."

The lover visited the young wife often. Soon afterwards the young wife gave birth to two children. One was a boy and the other was a girl.

THE LOVE BETWEEN BLOOD   *Nupe*

A young woman became pregnant. She gave birth to a son. At his birth he was already a grown man. The son said to his mother: "Take these three thousand cowries. Go out and fetch me a wife so that I can sleep with her." The mother took the three thousand cowries. She went out to fetch a wife. She met a man. She owed the man three thousand cowries. The man saw the money in her hand. The man took the three thousand cowries away from her, saying: You owe me these three thousand cowries. I will take the money." The woman said: "Do not take the money. Leave me the money. The money does not belong to me. It belongs to my son. My son sent me out to fetch a wife for him to sleep with." The man said: "That is nothing to me!" The man kept the money. The man went off with the money.

The mother went home. The son asked her: "Have you brought me a wife?" The mother said: "In five days' time a wife will be here to sleep with you." When five days had gone by the son asked: "Where is the wife that is going to sleep with me?" The mother said: "The wife will come to you tonight." Now the mother had just been having her period. That evening the mother washed herself thoroughly. She put on freshly laundered clothes. In the evening the son lay down on his bed. When it was dark the mother went in to him. The man asked: "Who is there?" The mother did not answer. The son wanted to blow on the embers of his fire. Seizing the water pot, the mother poured water on the fire. Then the mother lay down on a mat near the door.

When it was past midnight the son rose and went over to the woman who was lying near the door of his house. He lay with the woman. He lay with his mother. Then he went back and lay down again on his bed. Towards morning the woman got up. She left the house. She went out. The son followed her. The woman did not know it. The woman went towards her hut. The son saw that it was his mother's hut. The son called out: "Mother! Mother!" The woman screamed. The son saw that it was his mother. The son said: "I have lain with my own mother!"

When day came the son went to see his friend. He said to his friend: "I gave my mother three thousand cowries. My mother was to find me a wife to sleep with. My mother did not bring me a wife. I grew impatient. Yesterday I asked my mother what had happened to the wife I wanted to sleep with. My mother said I should have her that night. During the night a woman came to me. The woman did not speak. She poured water on the embers of my fire. She slept in my house. Towards morning I lay with her. When it was almost dawn the woman went out. I followed her. The woman went towards my mother's hut. I called after the woman. She ran away. I saw that it was my mother. I have lain with my own mother. Do not tell anyone. You are my friend. I had to tell you about it. Do not tell anyone. Nobody must know." The friend said: "I will not tell anyone."

The son had lain with his mother just after her period was over. The mother became pregnant and at the end of three months her belly grew big. People said: "The woman is pregnant. Who did she sleep with?" People asked the man's friend. They said: "The woman is pregnant. Who did she sleep with?" The friend said: "The son lay with his mother. You must not tell anyone." A few days later the son was walking through the town. He met a man. The man said: "Go away from here! You have lain with your own mother!" The son went on his way. He passed another man. The man said: "Go away from here! You have lain with your own mother!" The son hurried back to his house. He packed up his things. He ran out of the house. He ran out of the town. The son ran through the Nupe country. The son ran through the Hausa country. The son came to Kano. In Kano the son went to a mallem. The son said to the mallem: "Be my father and my mother, I beseech you! Let me stay with you!" The mallem said: "Very well." The mallem said to his first wife: "This youth has asked me to be father and mother to him. Look after him!" The wife said: "Very well." The son remained with the mallem.

Nine months after the son had lain with his mother, the mother gave birth to a child. The child was a girl. The child grew and throve. The girl played with other children. When the girl was grown up, the other girls said to her: "Go away! Before you were born, your brother lay with your mother!" The girl was ashamed. The next day the other girls said to her: "Go away! Before you were born your brother lay with your mother!" The girl was ashamed. The next day the other girls said to her: "Go away! Before you were born your brother lay with your mother!" The girl was ashamed. The girl packed up her things. The girl left home.

The girl wandered through the Hausa country. The girl came to Kano. The girl came to Kano marketplace.

In the marketplace was the wife of the mallem who had taken the mother's son into his house. The girl said to the mallem's wife: "Will you be my mother?" The woman said to the girl: "What has happened to you?" The girl said: "When my mother gave birth to my brother he was already fullgrown. My mother had no wife for him. My mother's son gave her three thousand cowries with which to get him a wife. He wanted to sleep with a woman. The mother went off with the money. She met a man to whom she owed three thousand cowries. The man took the money away from her. My brother grew impatient. My mother went to my brother in the night. The son lay down with his mother. The mother had just had her period. The mother became pregnant. I was born. All the other girls shouted after me: 'Go away! Before you were born your brother lay with your mother!' I was ashamed. I packed up my things. I ran away. I came here. I beseech you to be my mother!" The mallem's wife took the girl home with her. She said to the mallem: "Today a young girl came to me. The girl asked me to be her mother. I took the girl with me." The mallem said: "Very well."

After a time the mallem said to his wife: "Now, I have this young man who once upon a time asked me to be both a father and mother to him. And you have the girl who asked you to be a mother to her. I have no wife for this man. You have no husband for the girl. Should we not marry them to each other?" The wife said: "As you wish." Thereupon the mallem and his wife married the mother's son to the girl.

Two months after the mother's son and the girl had got married, the mother's son said to the girl: "When my mother bore me I was already fullgrown. My mother had no wife for me. I gave my mother three thousand cowries with which to get a wife. I wanted to sleep with a woman. My mother went out with the money. She met a man to whom she owed three thousand cowries. The man took the money away from her. I grew impatient. My mother came to me during the night. I lay with my mother. My mother had just had her period. My mother became pregnant. Everyone called out after me: 'Go away! You have lain with your own mother!' Then I was ashamed and ran away. Then I came here. I asked the mallem to be both father and mother to me. The mallem took me in. The mallem gave you to me as my wife. That is how it was."

The young wife said: "When my mother gave birth to my brother he was already fullgrown. My mother had no wife for him. My mother's son gave her three thousand cowries with which to get him a wife. He wanted to sleep with a woman. The mother went out with the money. She met a man to whom she owed three thousand cowries. The man took the money away from her. My brother grew impatient. My mother went to my brother in the night. The son lay with his mother. The mother had just had her period. The mother became pregnant. I was born. All the other girls shouted after me: 'Go away! Before you were born your brother lay with your mother!' I was ashamed. I packed up my things. I ran away. I came here. I met the mallem's wife. I asked the mallem's wife to be a mother to me. The mallem's wife took me in. The mallem gave me to you as your wife. That is how it was."

The mother's son asked his wife: "What town did you come from?" The wife told him the name of the town. It was the town from which he himself had come. Then the mother's son knew that he had married his mother's daughter. The mother's son knew that he had married his own daughter. His wife fell asleep. The mother's son packed up all his things. The mother's son quietly opened the door. The mother's son hastened away.

The mother's son went a long way away. He went further and further. The mother's son arrived in Mecca. The mother's son hurried to the imam. The mother's son said to the chief imam: "I was a grown man when my mother bore me. I gave my mother money to fetch me a wife. A man took the money away from my mother. My mother came into my house in the night. I lay with my mother. I saw that I had lain with my mother. I told my friend. The people heard that I had lain with my mother. The people hurled insults at me. I was ashamed. I ran away. I fled to Kano and took refuge with a mallem. I had lain with my mother just after her period. My mother became pregnant. She gave birth to a daughter. The girl grew up. The people hurled insults at the girl. The girl was ashamed. The girl ran away. The girl fled to Kano and took refuge with the mallem's wife. The mallem gave me the girl as my wife. I married the girl. I have lain with my mother. I have lain with my mother's daughter. What will become of me?"

The chiem imam said: "Nothing can be done to help you. When you come to die the great fire awaits you." The mother's son said: "Can nothing at all be done to help me?" The chief imam said: "No, nothing at all can be done to help you." The mother's son said: "Is there no chance that it might be otherwise?" The chief imam said: "Should an old, dead branch which has not borne a single leaf for three whole years once again bring forth leaves and twigs, then it will be otherwise." The mother's son heard what he said. The mother's son went away.

The mother's son said to himself: "When I die the great fire awaits me. It cannot be otherwise. A branch that has borne no leaves for three whole years cannot bring forth twigs and leaves. It will never be otherwise." The mother's son went into the bush. The mother's son cut himself a staff. Its wood was hard and dry. The mother's son went along the road that leads from Kano to Mecca. The mother's son lay in wait beside the road. A merchant came along it, carrying goods from Kano to Mecca. The mother's son leapt out and killed the man with his staff. The mother's son took the murdered man's load and carried it to his house. The mother's son went back to the road. He lay in wait beside the road. He killed many people who were travelling with their loads from Kano to Mecca. The mother's son took all their goods to his house. For three years the mother's son lived beside the road from Kano to Mecca. For three years he murdered the merchants who travelled along it by striking them dead with his staff.

In Kano there was a rich Madugu. He had a beautiful young wife. The Madugu wanted to go to Mecca with his wares. A young man in Kano saw his wife. He wanted to possess the wife. He went to the Madugu and said: "Have you any need of a porter to carry your load to

Mecca?" The Madugu said: "Certainly I would have use for a porter to carry my load to Mecca." The young man said: "I will go with you as porter." The Madugu said: "Very well."

The Madugu, his beautiful young wife, and the porter set off for Mecca. They reached the spot at which the mother's son was lying in wait with his staff. At this spot the Madugu's beautiful young wife fell to the ground. She was dead. The Madugu said to the porter: "Carry my load as far as the next village. Then come back here and help me bury my young wife. I will stay with her in the meantime." The young man said: "I only became your porter so that I could be with your beautiful young wife. Now you can carry your load yourself. I will go no further with you. I shall stay with the corpse." The Madugu said: "I beseech you to carry my load to the nearest village and then come back and help me." The porter said: "No, I will not! I do not want to have anything more to do with you!" The Madugu said: "Many have already been robbed of their loads in this part of the bush. Help me to carry my load away!" The young man said: "Help yourself!" The Madugu put the load on his head. He hurried with his load to the nearest village.

When the Madugu had gone away with his load, the young man threw himself down beside the corpse of the beautiful woman. He flung himself on top of the beautiful young woman. He made love to her. The young man made love to the corpse of the beautiful woman. The mother's son was lying in the bush with his staff. The mother's son leapt out of the bush. The mother's son leapt out upon the young man. The mother's son cried: "How can you make love to the corpse of a dead woman?" Seizing his staff, the mother's son killed the young man. Then the mother's son buried the corpse of the beautiful young wife. He did not bury the corpse of the young man.

The mother's son went back to his house. He lay down in his house. He went to sleep. While he was asleep the people from all around came to the spot. They entered the house. They went up to the mother's son. They said: "This is the man who murders people on their way from

Kano to Mecca. Let us take him prisoner. They took him to Mecca. They brought him before the chief imam.

The chief imam saw the mother's son. The chief imam said: "This man lay with his own mother. This man married his mother's daughter. This man married his own daughter. This man has murdered and robbed many people seeking to travel between Kano and Mecca. Put him to death!" The chief imam had spoken. Men came to put the mother's son to death. Then a leaf fluttered down out of the sky. The leaf came to rest at the imam's feet. The imam picked up the leaf. There was writing on the leaf. The imam read what was written on the leaf. The writing on the leaf said: "The mother's son lay with his mother. The mother's son did not know that it was his mother. The mother's son fled. The mother's son married his mother's daughter. The mother's son did not know that it was his mother's daughter. The mother's son married his own daughter. He lay with his own daughter. He did not know that it was his own daughter. The mother's son fled. The mother's son came to Mecca. The mother's son came to the chief imam. The chief imam said to him: 'Nothing can be done to help you. When you come to die the great fire awaits you.' The mother's son said: 'Is there no chance that it might be otherwise?' The chief imam said: 'Should an old, dead branch which has not borne a single leaf for three whole years once again bring forth leaves and twigs, then it will be otherwise.' The mother's son went into the bush. He cut himself a staff. Its wood was hard and dry. The mother's son went along the road that leads from Kano to Mecca. He killed many people with his staff. He buried them. A young man came along and made love to the corpse of a young woman lying in the road. The mother's son killed him. The mother's son buried the young woman's corpse. Go and look at his staff which for three years has borne no leaves."

The people hastened to the place. On the staff there were leaves and twigs. The chief imam said: "Help has come for the mother's son." The mother's son was set free. Everyone congratulated the mother's son. The mother's son remained in Mecca. Three months later the chief imam died. Then the people made the mother's son chief imam.

THE BLIND MAN WHO SAW   *Nupe*

One clever man said to another: "All wives deceive their husbands and sleep with other men." The second clever man said: "All other wives do so, perhaps. But not my wife." The first clever man said: "Just you put her to the test some time and see!" The second clever man said: "I will put her to the test some time!"

The man gummed up his eyes in such a way that people thought that he was unable to see, though in fact he could see perfectly well.

Then he came home at midday and said to his wife: "Wife, my eyes are paining me exceedingly and I cannot see." His wife said: "How can that be? You could see perfectly well this morning." The husband said: "It must have happened while I was out working in the fields." The wife guided her husband to his mat.

The man sat on his mat. The woman hurried quickly away. The woman hurried to her njetshi[1] She said to her lover: "My husband has gone blind. Come and have supper with me this evening." The lover said: "I will come along at once." The lover accompanied the woman. The woman cooked a meal. The lover passed very close in front of the husband. The husband said nothing. The woman put food down in front of her husband. The husband put his hand into the dish and took some food. The lover reached out his hand and took some of the food from the dish. The husband said nothing. The lover thought to himself: "The husband is completely blind." The lover shared his meal. Then the husband's hand touched the hand of the lover. The husband said: "Usuma, my wife, come and chase away this dog. My sight is already so bad that I cannot even prevent dogs coming in from the streets and eating out of my bowl!"

[1] Paramour.

247

The next day the wife went out. For Usuma did not have just one lover. Usuma had two lovers. Usuma went to the second lover and said: "My husband is completely blind. Climb over the wall into the wash-yard tonight. Then I will come out and fetch you. If my husband happens to come out, say nothing and do not move. My husband cannot see anything now." The lover said: "I will come." The paramour went to the wall and climbed over it into the yard used for washing and urinating where he stood and waited. From the sauri the husband watched all this through his gummed-up eyes. The husband got up, felt his way out into the wash-yard, and relieved himself there. The lover stood motionless, one hand on the wall. When the husband got up again, he touched the lover's hand with his own. The husband called out: "Usuma, my wife, come and chase the chickens back to their run. They are roosting on the wall. I felt one of them, though I could not see it." The next evening the man said to his wife: "I have been to see the boshi.[1] The boshi told me I should have the thigh bone of a large ox laid on top of my food. He said that if I kept it my me all day until the evening meal, my blindness would probably be cured within a year." The woman bought a large bone and that evening she laid it on top of her husband's supper. The man removed the bone. Then he ate. When he had eaten the husband again went out into the wash-yard, carrying the thigh bone under his arm. Once again the lover was standing in the wash-yard waiting until the wife should call him in. The husband made as if to squat down and piss. But instead he seized hold of the thigh bone and smote the lover. The blow killed the lover. The lover fell down dead.

Thereupon the man went back into the house with the thigh bone. The other lover had just arrived and was in the house. The lover pressed himself against the wall. The husband felt his way along to him. He took firm hold of the bone and, when he was close beside the lover, he raised it and brought it down on the lover's skull. The man made off with a broken head. The husband waited until it had grown very late and then, under cover of

[1] Soothsayer.

night, he lifted up the lover that he had killed and carried the corpse to the market place. Having left the corpse in the market place, he went home again.

The next day some people found the corpse in the market place. Everyone foregathered in the market place. Some of them ran to the king and told him: "A dead man has been found in the market place. His skull has been smashed in." The king sent for all the people. The king questioned them all. No one could offer any explanation. An old man said: "Close by there lives a man who has been blind for the past few days. The man is in such great pain that he cannot sleep at night. If anyone heard anything, it would be this man." The king sent for the husband. The blind husband was led before him. The king asked: "Did you hear anyone shouting during the night?" The blind husband said: "Last night I heard a man shouting. He was saying: 'You have wounded me in the head. Now I am going to kill you!' Then I heard someone fall. Now if somebody has been killed in this town, you should look for a man with a wound on his head." The king said: "Very well." The king ordered all the people of the town to assemble. The king said: "Take off your caps." Everyone removed their caps. Only one man refused to take off his cap. It was the wife's lover. The king said: "Why will the man not take off his cap?" He ordered it to be removed. The man's cap was taken off. They saw that he was wounded.

The king said: "This is the man who committed the murder put him to death." Thus the second lover too was killed.

A few days later the husband said to his wife: "The thigh bone of the ox has cured me. Now I can see again." A few days after that the first clever man came to see the second clever man and said: "I have heard that you were blind." The clever husband answered: "Yes, I have been blind, but now I can see more clearly than before."

A man married a woman. He did not wish his wife ever to look at another man. He therefore took his wife and concealed her in a hut out on his farm. The wife was never allowed to leave the farm and go into the town.

Before her marriage the wife had had a man friend. This friend said: "I should like to talk to my girl again. If her husband tries to stop me, then I will make him suffer for it." The friend took the fruit of a baobab tree. Making a little hole where the eye was, he removed all of the seeds. Next he filled the fruit with small cowrie shells, and closed up the hole with a little wooden peg. Then, under the cover of night, he went to the farm owned by his girl's husband. On this farm there grew a baobab tree so tall that it was almost unclimbable. He hid the fruit that he had hollowed out and filled with cowries amongst the bushes at the foot of the baobab tree. Then he went home again.

The next day he went back to the form owned by his girl's husband. The husband called out: "What do you want here? What are you doing here?" The friend said: "I have come from afar and lost my way. I have been walking for a very long time. Can I go to the hut over there for some water?" The husband said: "Certainly not. I will go myself and fetch you some water. Stay where you are!" The husband went and fetched some water. The friend drank. The husband said: "Now, be off with you!" The friend said: "Could your wife not prepare some food for us?" The husband said: "No. Be off with you! I do not want to see you on my farm again. This is not a pathway. I want to be left in peace here!" The man said: "Just one more request before I go. Give me one of the fruits of this baobab here." The husband said: "The tree is too tall. It cannot be climbed. And anyway, what do you want the fruit for?" The friend said: "I will tell you. Instead of seed, the fruits of this baobab contain cowrie shells. Some of them have two hundred inside. Some of them have three hundred inside." The husband said: "You are lying." The friend said: "What reason would I have to lie? Let us see if any of the fruit has fallen down amongst these bushes. Then you can cut one open and find out for yourself." The friend went searching about amongst the bushes. He said: "I have found a fruit." He picked up the fruit and took it to the husband. It was the fruit that he himself had placed there during the night. The husband took the fruit. He flung it down on the ground. The fruit burst open, scattering cowries on all sides.

The husband looked at the cowries. The husband said: "It is true. I have a lot of money on my farm. But it was you who first showed it to me." The husband picked up some of the cowries. He said: "These are cowries!" The husband examined the cowries. Then he said to the friend: "Stay here under the tree. I must go to the barn to fetch a ladder." The husband went into the barn. He fetched a ladder. The friend stayed under the tree. The husband came back with the ladder. The husband leaned the ladder against the tree. The friend said: "I will go up and do the picking." The husband said: "No, I will climb the tree and do the picking!" The friend said: "Let me climb the tree!" The husband said: "Now I know what you have come for! You wanted to steal my fruit with the cowries inside! No. It is I who will go up!" The husband climbed the ladder and went up into the top of the tree.

The tree swayed. The husband climbed about among the branches. The branches trembled. Several fruits fell down. The friend picked them up and looked at them. The husband saw him. The husband yelled: "Wife, wife! Come out! Keep an eye on the friend. If there is no one to keep an eye on him, he will gather up the fruit and run away." The wife heard him. The wife called out: "Did you say I was to come out to the friend?" The friend lay down on the ground. The husband yelled: "Wife, come out, lie down beside the friend and stay with him to see that he does not run away with any of the fruit." The wife came out. She brought a mat with her and said: "I am to lie down with the friend?" The husband yelled: "Yes, go on! Take hold of him!" The

251

woman put the mat down beside the friend. The friend pushed the ladder with his foot. The ladder fell down. The friend lay down on the mat. The friend said to the woman: "Now take hold of me!" Then he made love with her.

The husband saw the ladder fall down. The husband saw the friend on the mat. The husband could not get down out of the tree. The husband yelled: "God help me! God help me! God help me!" The friend made love with the wife five times. Then he said to her: "All I wanted was to come and have a talk with you. The rest was arranged by your husband!"

A woman should not be kept shut up as though she were a dog.

A WARNING TO A WAYWARD WIFE   *Nupe*

A husband thought: "My wife has a lover. I shall put a stop to this adultery." The man came to his wife and said: "I am going out into the fields for three days." The man went out of the sauri. Presently he saw his wife come out. When the wife had gone away, the husband crept back into the compound and hid himself in his wife's hut on top of the sinsarra.[1]

After a while the wife returned. The wife had told her lover that her husband was going out onto the farm. Soon after the wife had come in, her lover arrived. The wife said: "What is your desire, O my lover?" The lover said: "First I want some water to drink. Then I would like to eat. After that I will enter your sussoko three times." Is that what you would like?" The wife said: "Yes, that is what I would like." The lover was given the water and drank it. The lover was given the food and ate it. The wife lay down. The lover made love with her three times. The wife said: "O my lover, what is your

[1] A cupboard for storing pots and pans.

252

desire?" The lover said: "I want to wash and then I will go home." The wife gave the lover water. The lover washed. The lover went away. The wife went outside with the lover. The husband came down off the sinsarra and went away.

On the evening the the third day the husband came home. The husband ate his supper. Then the husband went to bed. The wife, too, went to bed. During the night the wife heard her husband's voice. The husband was saying: Well, first the wife asked: 'What is your desire, O my lover,' and then the lover said: 'First I want some water to drink, then I would like to eat. After that I will enter your sussoko three times. Is that what you would like?' She said: 'Yes, that is what I would like.' Then the lover was given water and drank it. Then he was given food and ate it. Well, what next? After that the wife lay down. Is that so? It is so. How often? What? He came into you three times? Three times!"

The wife heard what her husband was saying. The wife began to be afraid. The wife said: "O my husband, who is that you are talking to?" The husband said: "I am talking to your sussoko. Your sussoko is telling me tales."

After that the wife never took a lover again. And ever since that time, when men have tried to start an affair with the women in the market place, the women have replied: "I will not! My sussoko might tell my husband about it!"

THE TEACHER   *Nupe*

A man married a woman. The woman gave birth to a child. It was a boy. The boy throve and grew. The boy grew tall. When the boy was grown up his father said to him: "I will give you a girl to be your wife. You are now of an age to marry." The youth said: "I do not want to marry!" The father said: "You are old enough for it!" Then the youth took his bow and arrow and went away. He went into the bush. He went to another country. For five years he remained in the bush and there he became a hunter.

At the end of five years the father and mother went into the town. They asked everyone they met: "Who will go into the bush and fetch our son back? Who will go into the bush and fetch our son back?" A woman came and said: "Why has your son ran away into the bush?" The father said: "My son ran away into the bush because I was going to give him a young girl to be his wife." The woman asked: "Was that all?" The father said: "Yes, that was all." The woman said: "Then I will go and look for him."

The woman took off her feminine clothing. She put on trousers and a long burnous. She slung a bag over her shoulder and took a bow and arrow. She went into the bush, to the place where the youth was living. She found the youth. The youth looked at her. He did not know that she was a woman. He took her for a man. The woman made friends with the youth. They went hunting together.

They were out hunting together. The woman cried: "I have shot at an eja buffalo!" The youth came and said: "You say you have shot at an eja?" The woman said: "Yes." The youth said: "Then we must follow it. You go to the left and I will go to the right." The woman went to the left. The youth went to the right. After a time the woman cried: "The eja has knocked me over! Help, help!" The woman threw off her clothes, threw the bag on top of them, and lay down a short distance away, naked and with legs apart. She screamed. The youth came to her. He said: "What is wrong?" The woman said: "The eja has butted me very hard." The youth asked: "What part of you did it butt?" The woman said: "It did not butt my head. It did not butt this arm. It did not butt that arm. It did not butt this leg. It did not butt that leg. I butted me in between. Everything has been pushed up inside." The youth saw that this part of the woman was not as it was with him. He said: "That is bad!" The woman said: "Go and get the bag over there. In it you'll find a bottle of tshigbe.[1] Rub the place with it." The youth fetched the bottle. The bottle contained oil. He took some oil. He rubbed that part of the woman with it. The woman said: "If the medicine is any good, that part of you will begin to rise up before mine does!" The youth rubbed that part of the woman. Then his member began to swell. The woman said: "Has it any effect on you?" The youth said: "Yes, it has had an effect on me." The woman said: "Then go on rubbing. If the treatment succeeds then what has been pushed in will come out again."

Then the boy lay on top of the woman. He put his member inside of her. For almost five minutes he went on enjoying her. At last he asked the woman: "Where are you from?" The woman said: "I belong here in the bush." The youth said: "Well and good. But if you go anywhere else I shall have to go with you so that I can go on giving you medicine." The woman said: "I have to go away. I must go to the town." The youth said: "Do you not want me to give you medicine any more?" The woman said: "I must go to the town." The youth said: "In that case I will follow you." The woman went on ahead. She went to the town. She went to the youth's father and said: "Good day." The father said: "I thank you! Good day!" The woman said: "Your son will soon be here. He is following behind me." The father was very pleased. He said: "Accept my thanks!" The woman said: "Well and good. But as soon as your son arrives you must give him a wife, or else he will run off into the bush again to look for medicine." The father said: "I shall do as you say."

The youth came. His father as once gave him a young wife. The youth was very happy and from then on he remained at home.

---

1 Medicine.

A man came to Edegi and said: "Give me a wife!"
Edegi asked him: "Are you clever?" The man said:
"Try me out and see!" Edsu Edegi said: "If you can
stir up a contention seven times without being punished
for it then I will give you a wife." The man said: "Very
well. I will see what I can do."

The man set off for Lapai. Beside the river just outside
Lapai he met a woman. She was selling snuff. The man
said: "Can I have a little snuff?" The woman said:
"Take what you want!" The man said: "I am not going
to take any. I would be grateful if you would hand it to
me!" The woman handed him the snuff. The man took
a pinch and put the rest in his pocket. He said: "Thank
you." Then he went on to Lapai. The woman followed
him into the town. She went to the edsu and said: "The
man took away my tobacco without paying for it." The
king sent for him and said: "You are a thief. You took
this woman's tobacco!" The man said: "No, I am not
a thief. First the woman told me to take the tobacco. I
refused to take it. Then she handed me the tobacco herself. After taking a pinch, I put the rest in my pocket."
The king asked the woman: "Was it thus?" The woman
said: "It was thus." The king said to the man: "I cannot
find that you have done anything wrong. You may go."

The man went on his way. He took the road to Agaye.
On the road to Agaye he met three girls who were carrying water. The man said to one of the girls: "Give me
a little water to drink!" The girl gave him some. The
man took it. He drank. He continued on his way. When
he had drawn a little way ahead, the girl called him
back and said: "Come here a moment!" The man turned
around and went back. He said: "What do you want?"
The girl said: "On my back there is a nasty fly. Swat it!"
The man said: "Look! I am wearing a ring on my
finger. If I strike you on the back with it maybe it would

kill you. So it would be better if I did not do it. Just chase the fly away." The girl said: "No. You owe me a favour in return for the water I gave you. Now, swat the fly on my back!" The man said: "If you insist, this is your own affair!" The man swatted the fly. It fell down dead. But the girl, too, fell down dead. Thereupon the two other girls hurried to Agaye. They went to the king and said: "Down by the river a stranger has just murdered a girl." The king sent for the man. The king said: "This man has murdered a girl. Put him to death." The man said: "Do not put me to death. First hear me!" The king said: "Then speak!" The man said: "Beside the river I met three girls. I was thirsty. The girls had just drawn water. I asked for water. One of the girls gave me water. I thanked her and continued on my way. The girl called me back. She asked me to kill a fly on her back. I told her she might herself be killed because of the ring I was wearing on my finger. The girl said I owed her a favour because she had given me water. She insisted that I kill the fly. Having told the girl that in that case it was her own affair, I swatted the fly and killed it. Like the fly, the girl also fell down dead." The king asked the other two girls: "Was it thus?" The girls said: "It was thus!" The king said to the man: "I cannot find that you have done anything wrong. You may go."

The man continued on his way. He came to Bida. He went to one of the king's sons who had two pretty wives. The king's son gave him a house. When evening came the man went to the king's son and said: "Give me a strong string." The king's son said: "I have not got any string. What do you want with string?" The man said: "I want to bind my penis. For during the night my penis insists on wandering around the compound in search of beautiful women. In order that nothing wrong will happen I therefore wish to tie it down." The king's son said: "I cannot go looking for string now! You must manage without it tonight." The man went away. When night came the king's son went into the house of one of the wives in order to sleep with her. Immediately afterwards the man also went into the house. He said: "You see! This is what comes of not tying up my penis! Now it is stirring up trouble. It is your fault!" The king's son leapt up intending to strike the man. But the man seized hold of the king's son and cast him out of the house. Then he made love with the beauiful young wife. The next morning the king sent for the man and asked him: "What wickedness was it that you did last night?" The man said: "Your son is to blame for any wickedness that there may have been. He gave me lodging. In the evening I went to him and asked him for some string so that I could tie down my penis. My penis has the habit of roving around any compound where there are pretty women. Your son refused to give me some string. He said I must manage without it for the night. Then, during the night, my penis went roving and made love with a woman. It was not my fault. That is the whole story." The king asked his son: "Was it thus?" The king's son said: "It was thus." The king said to the man: "I cannot find that you have done anything wrong. You may go."

The man continued on his way. He went towards Lafiagi. Just outside Lafiagi he met a horseman. The horseman dismounted, saying: "Ladogo-bagoa!" meaning that the men should hold his horse, though the phrase could also mean "cut my horse." The man said: "No, I cannot do that! I shall get into trouble if I do." The horseman said: "Come hold the horse for me! I want to piss." The man said: "If you insist!" The horseman said: "It is necessary." The man said: "Very well." The horseman handed him the reins and went into the bush. As soon as the horseman had gone into the bush, the man drew out his knife and cut off all four of the horse's feet. The horseman returned. He saw his multilated horse. He set upon the man. The man hit him back. More people arrived on the scene. They dragged the man to the town and took him before the king. The horseman said: "This man has cut off my horse's feet!" The king said: "What have you to say to this?" The man said: "The horseman himself asked me to do it. He said: 'Ladoga-bagoa!' I refused because I did not want to get into trouble. Then he insisted, saying: 'It is essential.'" The king asked the horseman: "Was it thus?" The horseman answered: "It was thus." The king said to the man: "I cannot find that you have done anything wrong. You may go."

The man continued on his way. He made towards the town of Zunga. Outside the town he came to a river where he caught an eshi, a kind of water rat. He put the eshi in his wallet. Then he went into the town and asked the king for hospitality. The king gave him a house in his compound. The king said to one of his wives: "Go and take the stranger a bowl of food." The wife prepared some food. Then she took a bowl of food to the man's house. She placed the bowl in front of him. The man asked the woman: "Have you any use for an eshi?" The woman, thinking he was using the word in the other sense of 'making love', said: "Do not let the king hear you say that! If he heard you say such a word he would have you put to death!" The man said: "I do not understand. I do not know what you mean. And you still have not told me whether you have any use for an eshi. I could let you have it at once, here in this very house. Do you want it?" The woman gave a scream. She ran out of the house. She ran to the king. She said to the king: "Just now the stranger to whom you have given hospitality asked me whether I wanted to lie with him!" The king said to his servants: "Bring the man before me!" The servants went and fetched the man. The king said to him: "Just now you tried to seduce my wife!" The man said: "I know nothing about that. It must have been someone else. On my way to Zunga I caught an eshi in the river. When your wife came to my lodging, I asked her whether she had any use for an eshi. I said that I could let her have it. The woman did not understand me. Here is the eshi!" With that the man took the eshi out of his wallet and laid it in front of the king. The king said to the man: "There has been a misunderstanding. Take your eshi. I cannot find that you have done anything wrong. You may go."

The man continued on his way. He made towards the town of Illorin. He came to a farm on which men were digging yams. He said to the men: "Could you give me a few of those yams you have there?" The men gave him five tubers. The man thanked them, saying: "What can I use to make a fire for baking my yams?" The men said: "Take anything that is lying about the farm to make your fire with." The man said: "Thank you." The man went to the edge of the fields where the men had left their shoes. He took the shoes. The men had also taken off their clothes. He took the clothes. The men had also taken off their hats. He took the hats. The men had left their mattocks there. He took the mattocks. The men had also left their baskets there. He took the baskets. The men had also left their gourds there. He took the gourds. The men who had left their sticks there. He took the sticks, The man had a great heap of all the shoes, clothes, hats, mattocks, baskets, gourds and sticks. He set fire to them and placed his yams on top. He baked the yams. The men working in the fields said: "What is that smell?" They went to find out. They saw all their shoes, clothes, hats, mattocks, baskets, gourds and sticks had been burned. The man was sitting beside the charred remains eating his baked yams. The people seized him and took him to the town. They led him before the king and said: "We gave this man five yam tubers. He thereupon took all our shoes, clothes, hats, mattocks, baskets, gourds and sticks and burned them." The king said: "What do you say to that?" The man said: "These men had given me five tubers. I asked them: "What can I use to make a fire for baking my yams?" The men said: "Take anything that is lying about the farm to make your fire with." So I collected together all the shoes, clothes, hats, mattocks, baskets, gourds and sticks and built a fire of them. It would have been much easier for me to use fire wood." The king asked the men: "Was it thus?" The men said: "It was thus." The king said to the man: "I cannot find that you have done anything wrong. You may go."

The man continued on his way. He made towards the town of Saragi. He arrived in Saragi. He went to the market place and bought a hundred cowries worth of yams from a woman there. Then he went to another woman who was offering for sale a big jar full of oil. The man wanted to buy some oil to go with his yams. The man asked the woman: "Can I have some oil? Will you sell me some oil to go with my yams?" The woman was standing in front of the big oil jar. She said: 'Elolishi!" meaning that she would sell either the whole jar or nothing at all. The man, however, chose to understand her as saying: "Get inside it!" He said: "What?

You really mean eloloshi?" The woman said: "Yes. Eloloshi!" The man said: "Well, so be it!" He took off his clothes, laid them on one side, and, in one bound, leaped right into the jar of oil. The jar burst and its contents went pouring out in all directions. The woman screamed. The woman at once ran to the king and said: "A strange man was in the market place just now. He jumped right into my jar of oil, breaking it and spilling all of the contents." The king sent for the man. He said to the man: This woman has told me that you broke her oil jar and spilled her oil." The man said: "I did nothing wrong. I did what the woman asked me to do, that is all. I was hungry. I went to the market. I paid a woman a hundred cowries for some yams. Then I went on to this woman wanting to buy a little oil. I asked the woman if she would sell me some soil. She told me to get inside the jar. I asked her if she really meant that. Again she said: 'Eloloshi!' Then I took off my clothes and in one bound I jumped into the jar. If this has meant a loss to her, then she only has herself to blame." The king asked the woman: "Was it thus?" The woman said: "It was thus." The king said to the man: "I cannot find that you have done anything wrong. You may go."

The man went. He went to Edegi's town. He went to Edsu Edegi and said: "You once said to me: 'If you can stir up contention seven times without being punished for it, then I will give you a wife.' I went to Lapai where I cheated a woman out of her tobacco. The king declared me innocent. I went to Agaye where I killed a young girl. The king declared me innocent. I went to Bida where I cast the king's son out of his own house and then lay with his wife. The king declared me innocent. I went to Lafiagi where I cut the feet off another man's horse. The king declared me innocent. I went to Zunga where I spoke to one of the king's wives and offered to lay with her. The king declared me innocent. I went to Illoria where I burned all of the shoes, clothes, hats, mattocks, baskets and gourds and sticks belonging to some farm workers. The king declared me innocent. I went to Saragi where, in the middle of the market place, I jumped into a woman's big oil jar, breaking it and spilling all of its contents. The king declared me innocent. Thus I have stirred up contention seven times without being punished for it. But before I ask you for my reward, I will go into the Hausa country just once more and start some trouble there."

The man went. He went into the Hausa country. On the road he met several Hausa. They gave him the Hausa greeting: "Sanu! Sanu!" which, besides meaning "blessings be upon you," can also mean "slow and leisurely." Striding up to the Hausa, the man exclaimed: "What? Are you calling me a sluggard? Are you trying to insult me?" The Hausa cried: "Sanu! Sanu!" Thereupon the man took his stick and started beating the Hausa with it. The Hausa hurried to the town and said to the king: "We have just been attacked by a Nupe man!" The Hausa king sent for the man and said to him: "You have been picking a quarrel with my people!" The man said: "What? They told you that I picked a quarrel with them? Did they not call me a sluggard? And when I warned them, did they not repeat the insult, calling out 'Sanu! Sanu?' But I am not lazy. I am a hard-working man. I refuse to take the insult and be called a sluggard! That is why I was angry because they called me a sluggard." The king asked the men: "Was it thus?" The Hausa said: "All we did was to shout 'Sanu! Sanu!'" The man said: "Yes, they did call me a sluggard!" The king said: "I cannot find that this man has done anything wrong. There has been a misunderstanding. The man may go."

The man went to Edsu Edegi. Edsu Edegi said to him: "Truly you are a clever man. I will give you a wife." Edsu Edegi gave the man a girl and said: "Take her, but do not go with her to the Sauadji country. For if you go there you will only have yourself to blame should someone else make love to her or take her away from you. The man said: "Very well." The man married the girl.

The man went with his wife to the town of Sauadji. The men of Sauadji were always on the look-out for more women. They could never get enough of them. When the man arrived they gave him a house of his own, but they sent his wife to the sonja.[1] The next day the

___
[1] A kind of chaperone.

man went bathing with the young men of the place. He returned to his wife. The woman said: "Why did you go away? Why did you not sleep with me?" The man said: "I wanted to have a look at the young men's members. So I went bathing with them. Each of them possesses not just one member but seven, and each of those seven is as sharp as a knife. That is what kills so many of their women and that is also why they are constantly searching for more."

The king's heir, the saba, had seen the man's wife. The Saba said to his men: "See if you can procure for me the young woman who has come from Edegi's town. I want to sleep with her." The young men came to the man. The man said to them: "You see my wife over there. She has already had five husbands and I am the sixth. She cut off the penis and scrotum of all her first five husbands with a single stroke of the hand." When the young men heard this they were afraid. They went to the saba and told him about it. But the saba said: "I must have this woman before she leaves, even if she cuts off all that I have!" The saba took seven thousand cowries and sent them to the woman with a message saying that he desired to possess her. The woman said to the messenger: "I am willing. But my husband is bad. He is always picking quarrels with people. So before our encounter you will have to give my husband plenty of palm wine. The saba sent plenty of palm wine. The man became drunk. Then the men picked him up, carried him into the house, and locked him in.

The saba summoned the woman to come to him. The woman went. The saba said to her: "Sit down." The woman sat down. The woman recalled what she had heard about the seven members that were as sharp as knives. She was afraid. The saba went out and called four segi.[1] The saba said to them: "Two of you are to stand outside each of my doors. If you her me shout, come in and drag the woman off me to prevent her cutting off my penis and scrotum." Then the saba went back into the room again.

[1] Pages, said by the Nupe to have been assigned to the edsu as sleeping partners. According to the Hausa, this is no longer the custom in the Koara country, though it is still prevalent in Bornu.

The woman and the saba were both lying on the bed. The saba thought: "Is it true about the stroke of the hand?" the woman thought: "Is it true about the members that are as sharp as knives?" The woman thought the saba was asleep. The woman thought: "I will feel him and find out." She put out her hand and touched the saba. The saba felt her touch him. The saba thought: "Now she is going to start cutting!" The saba shouted. The four segi came in, dragged the woman off the bed and flung her out through the door.

The men went and unlocked the house where the man was lying. They carried him out. The next morning he came to himself. He went to his wife and said: "Pack up our things. Now we can go away again." They went. In every street through which they walked, the young men ran away. The man laughed.

The man went back to Edsu Edegi. Edsu Edegi said: "So you have come back with your wife? Tell me about it!" The man told him everything. Edsu Edegi made him a present of two slaves and two horses in order that he should remain with him. Edsu Edegi said: "I thank you for having given me the opportunity of meeting a man as clever as yourself!"

AINICHTHEM[1]   *Kabyle*

This is what is told of Simoa, the son of Abid. It is held to be true.

It is said of Simoa, the son of Abid, that at eighteen years of age he was more handsome than any other man. Up to that age he remained at home. He was quite inexperienced and had no inkling of the inexhaustible potency of his sexual parts. But when Simoa was eighteen years old he said: "Now I am going to set out on my travels." Simoa ben Abid therefore took his leave and departed from his village.

[1] What he has done.

Simoa set out on his travels. On the first evening, when he was preparing to lie down to sleep at the wayside, he heard the sound of music. The music was coming from a town very close by. When Simoa realized this he did not lie down but went on into the town.

Simoa arrived in the town which was celebrating a festival. People were dancing. Simoa joined the dancers. All of the others stopped dancing and stepped aside. No one in the town had ever before seen so comely a man dance so exquisitely. The girls giggled and nudged one another with their elbows. The young men whispered to each other: "If only we could sleep with him!" The old women said to themselves: "If only we were not so old!"

Simoa went on dancing. Everybody shouted: "Do not stop! Keep on dancing!" Simoa said: "Then bring me an anklet for my foot, bring me braclets for my arms. Bring me a head ornament for my forehead. Bring me a chest ornament for my chest. Bring me women's garments made of silk. If you clothe me in all these things I will dance a dance for you such as you have never seen before."

The people brought him women's garments made of silk. They brought him ornaments for his chest, his forehead, his arms, his ankles. Simoa ben Abid put on the clothes. Simoa chose the most beautiful ornaments. The young women gazed at him. The old women came close up to him and nudged him with their elbows. Simoa ben Abid was more comely that any of the women who lived in that town.

Simoa ben Abid called out: "I am ready. Now you must play my own tune, you must sing my own song. Sing: 'Simoa ben Abid is running away. May God bless Simoa ben Abid for that!'" The fiddlers fiddled, the drummers struck their tambourines. The people stood round in a ring, singing: "Simoa ben Abid is running away! May God bless Simoa ben Abid for that! Simoa ben Abid is running away! May God bless Simoa ben Abid for that!"

Simoa ben Abid danced. Simoa danced to the right. Simoa danced to the left. Simoa danced. The women called out to him in shrill voices. The young girls tapped their feet on the ground and pressed their hands together. The young wives pressed their legs together and their hands against their breasts. The old women waggled their buttocks. Everyone watched Simoa ben Abid and sang: "Simoa ben Abid is running away! May God bless Simoa ben Abid for that!"

Simoa danced. Simoa leapt in the air. Simoa went leaping through the streets and out into the bush. Simoa gathered up his dress and said to himself: "My running away has everyone's blessing. God grant that I can run fast enough to enable me to keep all this fine jewelry." The people ran after Simoa They lost sight of him in the bush. The people said to one another: "If we cannot catch up with him on the open road and while we are on the open road and while we are still quite fresh, we cannot possible do so in the bush." The people gave up their pursuit and went back into the town.

Simoa ben Abid continued on his way. Simoa arrived at another town. He walked through the streets. Everyone, men and women alike, looked at Simoa. All of the men said: "Never have I seen such a beautiful woman!" All of the women said: "Never have I seen such a beautiful woman!" Simoa walked through the town. It was raining. Simoa felt cold. Simoa began to look for shelter. He came to a big house. Several girls of great beauty were looking out through a barred window in the house. The girls looked down at Simoa. Simoa looked up at the girls. Simoa stood there. Simoa sat down on the doorstep of the house.

The house was that of the town cadi. After a while the cadi came out of his house. The cadi saw Simoa ben Abid sitting on his doorstep clad in women's garments and richly bejewelled. The cadi said to himself: "Never before have I seen so beautiful a woman!" The cadi asked Simoa ben Abid: "What are you doing there? What is it you want, O young woman?" Simoa said: "O cadi, I am a newlywed wife. I was married the day before yesterday. But yesterday my husband beat me. Then I ran away. For I do not want to stay with him and yet I am ashamed to go home to my own parents." The cadi said: "Such being the case, O young woman, we must ponder the matter. I will see if I can help you."

To himself, however, the cadi said: "I would like to lie with this young woman." The cadi was too ashamed to say so out loud. The cadi said: I have a wife and seven daughters. Are you willing to remain in my house as maid-servant to my wife and daughters?" Simoa said: "I am willing. I will remain in your house as maid-servant to your wife and daughters." The cadi said: "Follow me. I will take you to my wife." The cadi led the way and Simoa followed behind him.

The cadi took Simoa ben Abid to his wife and said: "I have taken on this young woman to be a maid-servant to my seven daughters. Make sure that my daughters are kind to her, for this young wife has been unfortunate in her husband and she is deserving of our pity." The cadi's wife said: "I will see to it that the young woman is given a kindly welcome." The cadi left. The cadi's wife said to Simoa ben Abid: "Come with me to my daughter's rooms. This is the way, along the passage."

The cadi's wife pressed Simoa's hand, saying: "Even though you are a woman, I nevertheless feel an urge to sleep with you. I have never been able to understand how men could lie with other men, but today I can sense how it is that one woman can have pleasure with another woman." The cadi's wife pressed Simoa to her. The cadi's wife began to run her hands over Simoa's body. Simoa became excited. But Simoa said: "Do not do that. But tell me, how can one man enjoy another man?" The cadi's wife laughed and said: "If he turns the other man around, it is easy for him to imagine that he has also changed the other's sex and that before him he has the natural gateway to the paradise that is the female body. Men are very lucky, for in that way they can even transform a donkey into a woman. But we women have no such opportunities." Simoa said: "Such a thing had never occurred to me. But tell me, what is so good and desirable about all this?" The cadi's wife said: "Are you not married, then? I thought that you were a married woman!" Simoa said: "As yet I have known no such joys." The cadi's wife said: "Your husband must be a bad teacher then! Beware of my husband, who is a very good one. But it is all to the good that you should be so ignorant, for it means that you will not corrupt my daughters."

The cadi's wife led Simoa to the eldest daughter's chamber. The eldest daughter was very beautiful. The eldest daughter greeted Simoa and asked him to sit down beside her. The mother went out. The eldest daughter seized Simoa by the hand, saying: "You are a woman and yet I feel a longing for you." Simoa looked at the eldest daughter and saw that she was very beautiful. Simoa remembered all that the cadi's wife had told him. Simoa said: "Come onto the bed." The cadi's eldest daughter lay down on the bed with Simoa. The cadi's eldest daughter and Simoa embraced one another.

The cadi's eldest daughter began feeling Simoa's body. Simoa uncovered the girl's breasts. The girl cried: "What have you got here? It is something that I have not got! Quick! Show me!" Simoa said: "I too have found something that I did not know existed. Your mother has been telling me many things. Come. Let us start!" The girl cried out. Simoa said: "Do you want me to stop?" The girl said: "No. Go on. It is delicious!" Simoa went on. The girl said: "It is getting better and better!" Simoa went on. The girl said: "Oh young wife, ah my friend, this is more delicious than any food I have ever tasted!" Simoa said: "Yes, your mother has shown me the way to delectable things!" Simoa went on. The girl sighed and said: "Ah, if only I could keep you with me always! But I will not be greedy. I have six other sisters. You can spend one day with each of them in turn."

The cadi's eldest daughter took Simoa ben Abid by the hand and led him into the neighbouring room. She called her sisters. The six sisters came in. Each was more beautiful than the rest. The eldest daughter said: "Here, O sisters, is a young woman our kind father has sent to be our maid-servant. This young woman possesses something that we have not got. Our mother has taught her how to use it and she has already given me greater delight than any food I have ever tasted. She is going to remain with me today, but tomorrow she will come to you, the second eldest, and the next day to you, the third eldest. Each day of the week one of us will enjoy what this young woman has to give and so experience the same raptures."

All seven of the girls now surrounded Simoa ben Abid. They all stared at him and felt him. They all exclaimed:

"She is in truth a most lovely young woman!" The eldest sister went back to lie with Simoa on her bed, enjoying with him the delights of their disparity until the following morning. The next day Simoa went to the chamber of the cadi's second daughter and lay with her until the next day dawned. The cadi's second daughter said: "My sister spoke of the joys that you, O young woman, had given her. But she should have told us much more about them. There is nothing between heaven and earth to equal such raptures." On the third day Simoa went to the cadi's third daughter, on the fourth day to the fourth daughter, on the fifth day to the fifth daughter, on the sixth day to the sixth daughter and on the seventh day to the cadi's seventh daughter. Each daughter was more beautiful than the last, each was more enraptured than her sister.

Every day the cadi sent to Simoa, saying: "Come to me. I want to marry you!" And each time the cadi's daughter with whom Simoa happened to be that day would tell the messenger: "Today the young woman must stay with me. I have grown very fond of her. Each of us sisters wants to enjoy her company in turn for one whole day. We have all grown very fond of her. When the week is over, we will allow the young woman to go to our father and speak with him."

When Simoa had spent the seventh day with the seventh sister, he called all of the cadi's daughters together. They all embraced him saying: "Come back soon. You are our delight." After embracing all seven sisters, Simoa went to the cadi.

The cadi greeted Simoa ben Abid and said to him: "Ever since I first set eyes on you, O young woman, your beauty has constantly preoccupied my thoughts. During the whole of these seven days I have not slept because I could not put you out of my mind. Now I beseech you not to deny my love. I beg you to become my wife. I will make your life a happy one." Simoa said: "I am willing to become your wife. But as you know, my first husband beat me as soon as he had enjoyed my love. Now I am afraid that all men are equally brutal and unkind. I therefore insist that each time you want to lie with me, you allow me to tie your hand and foot, your bonds then being made fast to that wooden post. Only in this way could I feel safe. If you will include this condition in our marriage contract, I am willing to marry you." The cadi said: "Since your past experience has been so disagreeable, I am prepared to agree to this condition." Simoa said: "Then draw up the contract and arrange for the wedding feast."

The cadi drew up the contract and arranged for the wedding feast. Meanwhile Simoa remained in the chambers of the cadi's daughters, sleeping with each in turn for one whole day and one whole night. Then the wedding feast began. An the seventh day Simoa was led to the cadi.

The cadi embraced Simoa and said: "Now lie with me." Simoa said: "Wait until tomorrow. I am so tired." The cadi said: "Very well." At first light the cadi said: "Now come and lie with me!" Simoa said: "I am willing. But first there are the conditions of the contract to be fulfilled." The cadi said: "If you are intent upon it, I am willing." Simoa took some strong rope. He bound the cadi hand and foot. He fastened the ropes to the post. The cadi could not stir from the spot. Simoa turned the cadi over so that he was lying on his stomach. The cadi said: "What are you doing, O young wife? This is not the right way!" Simoa said: "Never fear, it can be managed thus. Since I have been in your daughters' service I have acquired great reserves of strength and your first wife has taught me how men go about it when they want to satisfy their desires with other men, by turning the body around and hence also changing the sex." The cadi said: 'What is that you are saying?" Simoa said: "Be quiet. From now on there is no call for you to speak."

Simoa pulled down the cadi's trousers. The cadi groaned. Simoa lifted the cadi into a kneeling position. The cadi groaned. Simoa squatted down behind the cadi. Simoa ravished the cadi. The cadi groaned. Simoa rested awhile. Then he began again. The cadi groaned. Simoa continued with this work until it was day. Then he dressed himself, took the cadi's gold, and said: "Farewell, O cadi, and thank your wife from me for her advice which I commend to any man who happens to have nothing better to do." The cadi groaned. Simoa ben Abid went out of the house with the gold that he had taken and left the town.

Simoa ben Abid went along the road. Presently he came upon some shepherds. Simoa said to the shepherds: "Listen, O shepherds! If anyone comes searching for me and asks if you have seen anybody pass this way, tell them that 'Hätu ben Hätu ikari cadi thewa itith!'" The shepherds laughed and said: "Very well, we will say that 'Hätu ben Hätu, who has lain with the cadi and his seven daughters, has passed this way!'" Simoa ben Abid continued on his way.

Meanwhile the people of the town came looking for the cadi. At last they found him on his bed. His trousers were lowered and he was bound hand and foot. The cadi groaned. The people untied the cadi. The cadi sent horsemen after Simoa ben Abid with orders to catch him and bring him back. The horsemen set out.

After a while the horsemen came upon some shepherds. They asked the shepherds: "Have you seen anybody pass this way?" The shepherds said: "Yes, we did see someone hurrying along this road. It was Hätu ben Hätu, who had lain with the cadi and his seven daughters. This person was wearing women's clothing." The horsemen said: "Hold your tongues! You are to say nothing to anyone about this person having lain with the cadi and his seven daughters! Should the cadi hear that you have gossiped, he will be very angry and will punish you." The horsemen returned to the town.

The horsemen went back and said to the cadi: "We were riding along the road and came upon some shepherds. They told us of a person dressed in women's clothing who had passed that way. They said it was Hätu ben Hätu, who had lain with the cadi and his seven daughters." The cadi was angry and said: "Hold your tongues and say nothing to anyone about this. And now be off with you!" The cadi called his wife and said: "What did the young woman do when she was with my seven daughters?" The cadi's wife said: "I do not know. I will ask them." The cadi's wife went. The cadi's wife spoke to her seven daughters. The cadi's wife returned to the cadi and said: "The young woman has made your seven daughters pregnant." The cadi grew angry. The cadi's wife said:.

"Why are you angry? Did you not too satisfy your desires with this person? Every one of you had your joy of him except for me, although I was the one who gave him the advice to which all of the rest of you owe so much pleasure. How ungrateful you men are!" And the cadi's wife walked angrily out of the room.

The cadi's wife went to her chamber and locked herself in. The cadi's wife wept and said to herself: "I told this person everything! I was the first to excite this person's desires! I knew what joys this person would be able to give. I coveted those joys. Yet they were withheld from me, and from me alone!"

Simoa ben Abid continued on his way. Simoa ben Abid said to himself: "The cadi's seven daughters were very beautiful and I am the stronger for having served them. Nor are the delights afforded by the cadi's bed to be despised. His wife advised me well. I give thanks to the cadi's wife. She has opened up a new life for me. Simoa is no longer the Simoa of old. Simoa has become a different Simoa. Simoa will now try out everything that the cadi's wife suggested."

Simoa came to a town. Simoa bought men's garments. He took off his women's garments. Next, Simoa bought a she-ass. Simoa mounted the she-ass and rode out of the town. When he had ridden some distance he said to himself: "This donkey has communicated an agreeable warmth to my person." Simoa dismounted. Simoa went to the donkey's hindquarters. Simoa said: "Now I shall see whether the donkey is as pleasing as a cadi's daughter or as serviceable as a cadi!" Simoa lowered his trousers and began to take his pleasure with the donkey. Everyone who came along the road could see Simoa making love with the donkey.

A man and his pretty wife came riding by on a mule. The pretty wife looked at Simoa and said to her husband: "What is that man doing with the she-ass?" The man shouted to Simoa: "Are you not ashamed to couple with a donkey out here in the road under the noses of all of the people? Are there not enough women for you?" Simoa went on with what he was doing. He shouted back: "You can say what you like, but I would have you know that this poor beast is suffering from luetha sickness and that I am now with much difficulty administering its medicine." Simoa continued with his work. Seated on their mule, the husband and wife went on their way. The wife could not forget Simoa. She kept repeating: "What a handsome man! What a fortunate donkey! What a handsome man! What a fortunate donkey!"

And as the man and his wife rode into the next village, the wife kept on repeating: "What a handsome man! What a fortunate donkey! What a handsome man! What a fortunate donkey!" Just as they were passing the mosque the woman suddenly screamed and fell of the mule's back. Her husband cried: "What is it? What ails you?" The wife said: "I can go no farther. I am suffering from an attack of luetha sickness. Hurry, hurry, find something to cure me!" The husband said: "How can I find something to cure you when I do not know what should be done about luetha sickness? The wife cried: "You must help me! You must help me! How is it that you cannot help? Other men know what to do!"

The husband said: "Wait a moment! Something has just occurred to me. I will go back and fetch the man who was giving medicine to his donkey just now on the road." The wife said: "Yes. Do that. Offer him gold. Pay him well. But make sure that he comes soon to help me in the same way we saw him helping his donkey." The husband hurried back along the road. He met Simoa riding towards him on his she-ass. He said to Simoa: "My wife has just suffered an attack of luetha. Come and help her!" Simoa said: "What is this? Just now you were reviling me, and now you come asking me for help!" The man said: "I beseech you to come. I will pay you with gold." Simoa accompanied the man to the place where the woman was lying.

Simoa got off his donkey. Simoa examined the woman's affected part. Simoa said: "Something has got to be done here, and it must be thoroughly done!" Simoa said to the husband: "I shall squat down here while you sit behind me grasping my buttocks firmly with your hands. Then I will draw your wife towards me and introduce the medicine into the affected parts." Simoa squatted down. The man supported Simoa's buttocks with his hands. Simoa drew the wife towards him. He said to the wife: "Lay your head on the ground, rest your back on my knees and twine your legs around my shoulders. Then I shall be able to introduce the medicine quickly and thoroughly."

The wife did as she had been told. The husband supported Simoa's buttocks with his hands. With powerful strokes, Simoa drove the medicine into the affected parts of the wife. The wife groaned: "Ah, that is good! Thrust it in! Thrust it in! Go in further! Ah, how good it is! That is the best kind of medicine! Ah, if only you, O husband, possessed such skill! There now. That is enough for today. Thank you! Thank you! Now, O husband, give the kind doctor a gold piece." Simoa continued on his way.

Simoa came to another town. He sold his she-ass and was about to continue on his way when he saw an oil vendor. The oil vendor was driving a donkey in front of him. On either flank the donkey was carrying two bags of oil. Simoa went up to the oil vendor and said: "Show me your oil and tell me what it costs." The oil vendor opened one of the left hand bags of oil and said: "That oil costs twelve copper pieces." He closed the bag and opened one on the donkey's right flank, saying: "This oil costs fourteen copper pieces." Simoa said: "And how much is the oil in the two rear bags?"

Opening both rear bags, the oil vendor said: "This is the best oil. That on the left costs sixteen copper pieces, and that on the right costs eighteen." Both of the vendor's hands were busy holding up the bags of oil that he had opened. Simoa went up behind him and pulled down his trousers, saying: "Unless you keep quite still you will lose all of your best oil!" The oil vendor yelled: "What are you doing? The oil at the back here is running out!" Simoa said: "Very well, I will stop up the hole but keep still."

Simoa stopped up the oil vendor's hole. Simoa said: "Wait! Very soon now the spigot will be properly driven home!" The oil vendor groaned. Simoa went on driving in the spigot. Simoa said: "Not very much oil can run out of this hole now!" The oil vendor groaned and said: "Leave me alone!" Simoa said: "Atphithiph ababuthiph mulesh (ularph) achiroa rassemäil!"[1] The oil vendor was forced to stand still until Simoa had completed his work. Then Simoa said: "That will stop the oil from flowing out for the time being. Now I can take the spigot out again. And you, O oil vendor, can close your oil bags and pull up your trousers!" Simoa ben Abid went on his way.

Simoa ben Abid came to another town. He bought blue, red and white paint. He used the colors to paint his member. The tip he painted blue, the middle part red, while the base right up to his belly, he painted white. Then he went to the market place, having removed his nether garments so that all could see his gaily painted member. Some women said to Simoa: "Fie upon you! Are you not ashamed to go around like that, exhibiting yourself to everyone?" Simoa said: "Why should I be ashamed? That is the way God made me. God gives the priest his wisdom and he is allowed to exhibit it everywhere. God gives the smith his skill and he is allowed to exhibit and use it where he likes. God gave me a member with a blue tip with which to engender herdsmen, a red center part which, if I use that as well, will engender caids[2], and a white base so that I can know how far to penetrate in order to engender cadis."

The women looked at the gaily painted member, The women saw that Simoa was comely. The women said: "On what occasion do you engender herdsmen, caids, and cadis?" Simoa said: "I do it professionally. In return for one gold piece, I use only the tip, thus engendering a herdsman. For two gold pieces, I use the red part, thus engendering a caid. For three gold pieces I use the white base as well thus engendering a cadi. In addition, of course, I also have to be given food of exceptional quality."

Among the women was the mother-in-law of the oil vendor whom Simoa had so effectively stoppered in the previous town. Presently the oil vendor's mother-in-law approached Simoa and said to him: "I have a young and very beautiful daughter. She is married to an oil vendor.

[1] Keep your oil and yet lose none of your profits.
[2] Village headmen.

But my daughter is indeed unfortunate, for her husband has been unable to make her a mother. Will you help my daughter? From what I have seen and heard so far, this is something of which you are fully capable." Simoa said: "I am willing to help you. We have only to agree the price." The oil vendor's mother-in-law said: "The price will depend on how much my daughter can stand."

The oil vendor's mother-in-law took Simoa to her daughter, the oil vendor's wife. The oil vendor's wife said: "Perhaps you will be kind enough to engender a son for me. It will not be too easy, for my husband says that while his iron is too soft, my wood is too hard." Simoa said: "We can only try. I split open the cadi's seven daughters. No doubt I can also break down your gateway to paradise. Lie down and we will see." The oil vendor's wife said: "First let me have a look at your nail." Simoa showed her his gaily painted member. The young wife of the oil vendor cried: "Ah, how strong and handsome you are! Quick! Break down my gateway!"

The oil vendor's young wife lay down. Simoa squatted in front of her and placed one of her legs around his flanks. The young wife cried: "It is hurting!" Simoa said: "That is unfortunate for you! For it means that I cannot even give you a son who will be a herdsman!" The young wife said: "Yes. Go on! I can stand it. Give me a son!" Simoa gave a strong thrust. The young wife gave a scream of pain. Simoa said: "What a pity! Now I cannot give you a caid." The young wife said: "Yes, yes! I can still stand it. Go right in as far as the caid!" Simoa drove his nail a little further into the young wife. The young wife screamed. Simoa said: "This wood is true oak. There is small chance here of a cadi." The young wife cried: "Yes, yes, yes! In with it!" She thrust her buttocks violently towards him crying: "In with the cadi!" Simoa drove in his nail right up to the head.

The oil vendor's young wife gave Simoa three gold pieces and said: "Come again soon. Today I am tired. But the pain has gone and already I feel a desire to make advance arrangements for yet another cadi."

Simoa ben Abid went to the market place and bought a little lamb. He still had some paint left and he used it to paint the lamb. The red, white, and blue lamb was very pretty to look at. He tied a bell round its neck. He fed the lamb. The gaily painted lamb followed him everywhere he went.

Simoa ben Abid went for a walk outside the town gates with his gaily painted lamb. He met a woman with a very pretty daughter. The daughter said to her mother: "Look at that pretty lamb trotting behind that handsome man." "Oh my mother, will you buy me the lamb?" The mother went up to Simoa and said: "I want to buy the gaily painted lamb for my daughter. How much do you want for the gaily painted lamb?" Simoa said: "Neither gold nor house nor fold will buy my gaily painted lamb." The woman said: "What then are you asking in return for the lamb?" Simoa said: "In return for my lamb I ask for an enjoyable encounter."

The mother went back to her daughter and said: "Neither gold, nor house nor fold will buy his lamb. He will only sell it in return for an enjoyable encounter. The man, let me tell you, is very strong and handsome." The daughter cried: "Ah, mother! Go and lie with him. It will only take a few minutes, and then we shall have the lamb. And you yourself said that the man is very handsome." The mother said: "I shall do this so that you can have your lamb!" The mother went back to Simoa.

The mother approached Simoa. She said to Simoa: "Very well. I will give you your enjoyable encounter. Simoa said: "Lie down!" The mother lay down. Simoa had his will of her. Simoa got up again. Simoa took a needle and thread out of his pocket. The mother said: "What are you going to do?" Simoa said: "The encounter was not enjoyable because you are too big. To get my due I will have to make it smaller." The mother leaped up in alarm. The mother said: "Wait! I will send you my daughter!" The mother went hurrying back to her daughter.

The mother said to her daughter: "O daughter, the man is strong and handsome. But I was too big to give him an enjoyable encounter. Go to him. You will find it a pleasurable way of acquiring the lamb." The daughter said: "I am willing." The daughter went to Simoa. The daughter said: "What do you want me to do?" Simoa said: "Lie down!" Simoa had his will of the daughter.

Simoa stood up. Simoa drew out a sharp razor. The daughter was alarmed. The daughter asked: "What are you going to do?" Simoa said: "You are too small. If I am to get my due, I shall have to open it up a little more." The daughter leaped to her feet. The daughter ran away as fast as her legs could carry her.

Simoa was left with the gaily painted lamb.

Simoa ben Abid sold the lamb. Then he set out again and came to another town. Simoa asked the people: "Who owns this town?" The people said: "It belongs to an Agellid. He is a very clever judge. The Agellid has two very beautiful daughters. Neither of them is yet married." Simoa asked the way to the Agellid's house. Simoa sat down below the windows of the Agellid's daughters. Simoa went on sitting in the same place for three days on end. The Agellid's elder daughter saw Simoa sitting below the window. She saw that he was very handsome. She saw that he remained sitting in the same place. Again and again the Agellid's elder daughter was drawn to the window. Each time Simoa seemed to her more handsome than before. On the third day the Agellid's elder daughter looked out of the window yet again. She saw Simoa. She called out to Simoa: "What is your name?" Simoa answered: "Twelve-times-a-night!" The Agellid's elder daughter said: "You are called Twelve-times-a-night?" Simoa said: "Yes, that is what I am called." The Agellid's daughter said: "And can you really do it?" Are you ready to wager one hundred gold pieces with me? I will wager that you cannot do it twelve times." Simoa said: "Yes. I am willing to make the wager. Show me your hundred gold pieces." The Agellid's daughter showed him the hundred gold pieces and said: "Now I have laid out the hundred gold pieces. Tonight I will let my hair down from this window. Then you can climb up it and so get into my room. By tomorrow morning one or the other of us will have won the hundred gold pieces." Simoa said: "So be it."

That night the Agellid's elder daughter let her hair down out of the window. Simoa climbed up the hair. The daughter looked at Simoa. She saw that he was strong and handsome. She embraced him. She drew him with her onto the bed. Simoa began his task. Time and again

Simoa did what he had to do. When daylight came he had eleven bouts behind him, but when he embarked on the twelfth the Agellid's daughter began to bleed. Simoa got up. The Agellid's daughter said: "You failed to do it twelve times. The hundred gold pieces are mine." Simoa said: "It was not my fault that you began to bleed. But tomorrow I shall put the case before your father the Agellid. He can decide which of us two must pay one hundred gold pieces to the other." In alarm the Agellid's elder daughter exclaimed: "You must not do that! My father would kill us both!" Simoa said: "Have no fear! Your father will decide the case without knowing the true circumstances."

The following day the Agellid was sitting in judgment. Simoa appeared before him and said: "O Agellid, I have a case for you to decide. It concerns a dispute between two friends. One of the friends wagered that he could eat twelve oranges one after the other. The other wagered that his friend could not do this. The eater of the oranges was provided with the fruit by his friend. He ate eleven of the oranges but when he came to cut open the twelfth he found that it contained nothing but blood. Which of the two friends deserved to win the hundred gold pieces they had wagered?"

The Agellid said: "The eater of the oranges deserves to win the hundred gold pieces. The friend had no right to give him an orange filled with blood. For no man can eat blood."

When evening came, the Agellid's elder daughter again let down her hair from the window. Simoa climbed up it. He entered the room of the Agellid's daughter. Beside the Agellid's elder daughter stood her younger sister. The Agellid's elder daughter said: "My father has already told me how he decided the dispute we had yesterday and I know that I must give you the hundred gold pieces. Here they are. Take them. But now you must give me an opportunity to win back the hundred gold pieces again. I therefore propose another wager. I wager that you will not be able to sleep for a whole night between me and my sister without taking both of us. Do you agree to my proposal?" Simoa said: "You are both very beautiful girls. Nevertheless I am prepared to wager that, unless you

279

ravish me, I can lie between you for one whole night without taking either of you." The Agellid's two daughters removed their clothes and lay down on the bed. Simoa removed his outer garment but retained his trousers, beneath which he had finally secured his member with a piece of cord. Then he lay down between the Agellid's two daughters.

The Agellid's two daughters lay down on either side of Simoa. They took his hands and placed them on their breasts. Simoa did not stir. They placed Simoa's hands on their legs. Simoa did not stir. They wrapped their arms round Simoa's legs. Simoa did not stir. They twined their legs around Simoa's legs. Simoa did not stir. They lay writhing on top of Simoa and pummeled him. Simoa did not stir. They undid Simoa's trousers and pulled them down. Simoa did not stir. They kissed Simoa. Simoa did not stir. They untied the cord that bound Simoa's member.

At that Simoa sprang up and took first one girl and then the other. The Agellid's elder daughter said: "You have lost the wager, for you have not been able to sleep between us for one whole night without taking either of us. You must give me back my hundred gold pieces." But Simoa said: "You ravished me, and therefore you owe me a further hundred gold pieces. But let us not argue. Tomorrow I shall ask your father, the Agellid, which of us should have the hundred gold pieces."

The following day the Agellid was sitting in judgment. Simoa appeared before him and said: "O Agellid, a friend of mine wagered one hundred gold pieces that my horse would be unable to stand for a whole day with a basket of barley on his right and a basket of corn on his left without eating any of the barley or the corn. It was understood that neither of us would be allowed actively to intervene. I agreed to the terms of the wager. Having tethered my horse's head to the manger, I set a basket of barley to the right of him and a basket of corn to his left. From morning until evening my horse stood there without eating a mouthful of either the barley or the corn. But during the evening my friend cut the rope with which my horse was tethered. Now tell me, O Agellid, which of us two must pay the hundred gold pieces to the other?" The Agellid said: "Your friend must pay the hundred gold pieces, for he actively intervened by cutting the rope that tethered the horse." Simoa said: "I thank you, O Agellid."

That evening the Agellid's elder daughter again gave Simoa a hundred gold pieces.

Simon ben Abid was now rich. Having packed up his gold he left the town and continued on his way. Simoa intended to make for another town. But when he was passing through a small village, he saw a young girl standing by the well. So lovely was she that Simoa said to himself: "I have already known many beautiful girls and women, but I have never yet seen one so beautiful as this girl. If I can succeed in having her, and if I find that she is no cleverer than I am, then I will give up my wandering life, marry her, and settle down in this village." Simoa went up to the girl, but the girl refused to take any notice of him. Simoa said to himself: "I shall have to find some special way of winning over this girl."

One day when the beautiful girl was going to the well, Simoa ben Abid followed her. He went and stood near her, in the sunshine. He lowered his trousers and thrust out his posterior so that the hot sunlight shone straight down on it. The beautiful girl watched what Simoa was doing. The beautiful girl said: "Fie upon you! You have no more decency than a dog!" Simoa said: "Say what you will it may well be that your customs here are different. But where I come from it is very hot in summer and very cold in winter. Where I come from you are in danger of freezing to death during the winter if you fail to collect enough warmth during the summer. All I am doing now is to collect warmth in my posterior against the winter cold. And if you are sensible you will do the same. I have already collected half the warmth that I need." The beautiful girl said: "How clever you are! Here it is cold in winter too. So I am going to collect warmth in the same way as you. Then the beautiful girl bared her posterior also. She came to stand beside Simoa and adopted the same posture so that the sun shone full on her buttocks.

Presently the beautiful girl said to Simoa: "Do you really feel as though you have collected a lot of warmth in your posterior? It does not seem to me that I have collected any at all." Simoa said: "Already I have an abundant supply. But it is not the same with women. We men have only one hole at the back through which warmth can enter, and once it is there it is there for good. But unfortunately for you women, you have two openings, and as soon as you have succeeded in collecting warmth in the back opening, it escapes through the front one. For this reason you have to get someone to stop up the front opening for you. Then the warmth you have collected will not be able to escape so easily." The beautiful girl said: "But who is going to stop up my front opening for me?" Simoa said: "I will be glad to do so if that is what you wish." The beautiful girl said: "I beg you to do it! Stop up my front entrance so that the warmth cannot escape!"

Simoa turned to face the girl. Simoa said: "Here is the stopper. Now part your thighs a little so that I can make it fit properly." The girl parted her thighs a little. Simoa pushed the stopper into the passage by which the warmth was seeking to escape. The beautiful girl groaned and sighed. The beautiful girl said: "Oh, this is good. Go on stoppering it. This is good. But the warmth is not coming from behind! Now I can feel it. Now it is coming. Now the warmth is inside me! Oh, there is much warmth inside me. But the warmth has not come from behind. The warmth came from in front."

Simoa said: "O beautiful girl, no doubt that is because we were standing up while I put in the stopper. If you agree, we will try putting the stopper into your front opening in a sitting position. Then you will have an even greater sensation of warmth." The girl said: "That will suit me very well." Simoa squatted down on the ground. Raising the beautiful girl's legs and resting them on his shoulders, he once again closed her front entrance with strokes even more vigorous than before. The beautiful girl groaned: "Ah, what warmth! Ah! What a stopper! Push the warmth right in. Push it really far back. Oh, now I can feel the warmth far back inside me! But my posterior is still cold."

Simoa said: "O beautiful girl, if your posterior is still cold, that is no doubt because this is still not the best

position. If you like we can try it in yet another way."
The girl said: "I am willing. The more I think about
how cold the winter is, the more afraid I become of not
being able to collect enough warmth before the cold
weather sets in." Simoa said: "Then kneel down. I will
see if I can stop up this insatiable opening from behind."
The beautiful girl knelt down, propping herself up on
her elbows. Simoa bent over her from behind and pressed
his spigot firmly into the opening. With a powerful thrust
of the buttocks, he drove the spigot forward so that it
penetrated far into the beautiful girl. The girl groaned
and sighed: "Go on driving it in! Drive the spigot in
well! Further! Further! Oh, now it is nearly up to my
heart! Oh, what warmth! Oh, now I really am warm,
now my posterior is warm as well. It must be because
your belly has been rubbing against it. But this time it is
my stomach that is cold. Oh Simoa, the more I think
about it, the more afraid I grow of the winter cold. Is
there any other way of capturing warmth?"

Simoa said: "O beautiful girl, certainly there are other
ways of capturing it. But the very best way to collect
warmth is to carry on this business in bed, because then
there is a warm blanket on which to rest your posterior
when you have finished. But that is possible only when
two people are married and live together in one house.
Your wishes where the winter is concerned are the same
as mine. Our wishes can best be fulfilled by the two of us
together. For I have already known many beautiful
women and girls, but not one of them has meant to me
what you mean. God has made people different from
each other, women as well as men. Not everyone is suited
to everyone else. But you and I, O my beautiful girl, we
are suited to one another and therefore we will be able
to give one another plenty of warmth and many children.
Tell me what you think about the matter." The beautiful
girl laughed and said: "How clever you are, Simoa! I
agree. You go on giving me your warmth and I will give
you children in return."

Simoa ben Abid and the beautiful young girl went
back to the village. Simoa ben Abid married the young
girl. He never resumed his wandering life but remained

with her and begot four girls and three boys, the youngest of whom is known by the name of Nsäni.

Simoa ben Abid was much travelled and widely experienced. But at last he was content to remain with this his one wife. He had found something which God bestows only upon very few, a woman who was wholly suited to him. May God grant that you are all as fortunate as he. But God will bestow such good fortune only upon those who pursue it zealously and experience much, as did Simoa ben Abid, that man of many parts.